PROBABILITY THEORY

with Applications to Econometrics and Decision-Making

SAUL H. HYMANS

Assistant Professor of Economics
The University of Michigan

Prentice-Hall, Inc., Englewood Cliffs, N.J.

Library of Congress Catalog Card No.: 67-24021

Printed in the United States of America

Current Printing (last digit):

10 9 8 7 6 5 4 3 2 1

PRENTICE-HALL INTERNATIONAL, INC., *London*
PRENTICE-HALL OF AUSTRALIA, PTY. LTD., *Sidney*
PRENTICE-HALL OF CANADA, LTD., *Toronto*
PRENTICE-HALL OF INDIA PRIVATE LTD., *New Delhi*
PRENTICE-HALL OF JAPAN, INC., *Tokyo*

TO MY PARENTS

PREFACE

This book is intended primarily for the use of juniors, seniors, and first year graduate students in economics and business administration. Such students generally face the requirement of a semester course in basic quantitative methods, and it is that course to which this book is aimed.

There is somewhat more material here than can adequately be covered in a semester, yet, in comparison with many other texts, a substantial amount of "standard" material has been excluded. There is, for example, no treatment of index numbers, decomposition of time series, t-tests, or F-tests. Instead, there is a rather complete development of probability theory from first principles through probability distributions, expected value operators, sums of random variables, and convergence of distributions. The basic inductive method is the theory of parameter estimation for both small and large samples, including a Bayesian approach to small sample estimation. Throughout the book attempts are made to relate the material being developed to applications which are meaningful to students of economics and business administration. This is true first with respect to illustrative problems and exercises. In addition, three main applications are developed in considerable detail, namely, Quality Control, Econometrics, and Firm Decision-Making under Uncertainty, which together comprise about one-third of the text.

There are three prime reasons for the book's major concentration on probability theory to the exclusion of more "standard" topics.

1. Probability theory turns out to be a single unifying thread for all the applications presented.
2. A student who has been through a thorough treatment of probability, random variables, estimation, and so on is well equipped to read about specific hypothesis tests, times series decomposition, index numbers, and special distributions by himself.
3. One can never be sure what, if any, further quantitative training the student will acquire. The first course should open the way to many subsequent directions of study and should provide the most useful background for the terminal student.

The third point is perhaps the most basic and requires some elaboration. It is the author's feeling that a one semester course in quantitative methods simply cannot hope to provide the level of training which is adequate for quantitative research. Pushing all such topics as t-tests, contingency tables, regressions, time series, index numbers, analysis of variance, and control charts into the basic course leaves the student with vague recollections of "catch-phrases," but little more. On the other hand, an approach which develops in depth a small number of applied topics, all as logical extensions of one underlying frame of reference, can have the benefit of reinforcement so that both the applications and the underlying rationale remain with the student. In this way the terminal student acquires the ability to judge the research of others, and to avoid the pitfalls which are all too common in basic quantitative application, even though he himself is not prepared to undertake complex quantitative research. Further, the probability approach allows the nonterminal student to continue his training in any of the myriad directions available: classical statistics, operations research, econometrics, decision-theory, and so on.

Finally, a few words about the applied topics selected for special emphasis. Quality Control is not only important in its own right, but is a natural vehicle for developing the methodology of statistical testing. Errors in testing and evaluation of test procedures are discussed through the use of Operating Characteristic Curves. Beyond Quality Control, it has seemed to the author that the major contributions to quantitative techniques in economics and business administration have been made in the areas of Econometrics, and Operations Research. In the last two chapters of the book, the student is given the opportunity to delve quite deeply into these methods of analysis. Whether or not the student continues his quantitative training, these are the topics which he will run across quite often in both empirical and theoretical quantitative literature. It is hoped that this book will impart sufficient understanding of these areas to make such literature somewhat comprehensible to the student.

All the probability theory presented here is based on Set Theory and high school algebra. The latter is assumed as part of the reader's background. The necessary Set Theory is presented in Chapter 1, and no calculus is used anywhere in the book. Calculus, of course, is another indispensable ingredient needed to read the quantitative literature, but that the reader will have to acquire elsewhere. The author has not felt seriously enough constrained anywhere in the book to justify a calculus prerequisite. Those topics which could only have been treated well by calculus methods simply have not been included. Such topics, however, are not much missed at the level of this book, despite their being indispensable in more advanced treatments.

A good deal of the teaching in this book is by example. This is true particularly when the example does not give a misleading view of the general theory and, instead, contributes to an understanding of the latter. Forty-five illustrative examples are worked out in the body of the text. More than one hundred eighty problems are available as end of chapter exercises. The majority of the exercises deal specifically with the textual material, but many are used to extend the applications and even to develop further theoretical results.

SAUL H. HYMANS

ACKNOWLEDGMENTS

This is a textbook and, with possibly one or two exceptions, the only thing "new" in these pages is in the realm of pedagogical approach. I therefore owe a truly immeasurable debt both to the many outstanding professors who conveyed to me the essence and importance of quantitative analysis, and to the many students at the Universities of California and Michigan who put up with my own attempts to convey knowledge. Space and memory preclude my naming all of them, but I cannot refrain from giving special thanks to Professor Frederick Mosteller, my first teacher in this area, and a gentleman unsurpassed in the art of teaching the substance and excitement of Probability and Statistics.

Past and present colleagues have contributed much in lengthy discussion and in the reading of early drafts. I benefited from many hours of discussion with Eugene N. Savin at the time when my own ideas on pedagogy were only beginning to crystallize. My good friend and colleague, Professor Harold T. Shapiro, read several parts of the manuscript. His critical appraisal, especially of Chapter 8, resulted in substantial improvements in content and presentation.

My research assistant, Mr. Gregory V. Jump, was a constant source of penetrating criticism. The end of chapter problems are largely his and the extent to which they complement and extend the text is ample evidence of his unique contribution to the book.

I also wish to thank Professor Edward L. Wallace of the School of Business Administration, State University of New York, and Professor Lawrence R. Klein of the Department of Economics, University of Pennsylvania, for their helpful comments.

Throughout the writing of this book, my wife Eileen continually supplied a very welcome understanding and encouragement. If Chapter 2 accomplishes its purpose, much of the credit is really hers.

Finally, I must express my gratitude to the Secretarial Staff of the Department of Economics of the University of Michigan. A manuscript such as this one surely tries the patience and stamina of the typist, and I must have been an ogre.

SAUL H. HYMANS

CONTENTS

4 RANDOM VARIABLES AND PROBABILITY DISTRIBUTIONS 73

5 THE BINOMIAL RANDOM VARIABLE (Analysis of a Dichotomy) 116

6 THE CONVERGING BINOMIAL 149

7 CLASSICAL ESTIMATION THEORY 175

1 ELEMENTS OF SET THEORY

1.1 Introduction

If this book had been written in the mid-1980's rather than the mid-1960's, this chapter would undoubtedly be quite unnecessary. In its place would stand merely a glossary of set-theory symbols, the purpose of which would be to assure a common understanding between author and reader. The subject of set theory is so basic to advancement in mathematics (as well as to advanced mathematics) that it is a cornerstone of the so-called *new math* now being taught in most grammar schools in the United States. Our subsequent work will show quite clearly that set theory is the most natural vehicle for the study of probability theory.

The present chapter is complete only in the sense of providing sufficient material for the needs of this book. While this will permit a substantial excursion into theoretical and applied probability, it represents little more than a minimal introduction to the rich subject of set theory.

1.2 First Principles

Before giving a precise definition of the term *set*, let us begin by thinking of a set as a collection of "things" grouped together according to some common characteristic(s). We can think of the following:

(i) The set of students in a classroom.
(ii) The set of people in a classroom (that is, the students plus the instructor).
(iii) The set of seats in a grandstand.
(iv) The set of words on page 80 of this book.
(v) The set of red or yellow flowers in a garden.
(vi) The set of possible outcomes which can result if a die (plural: dice) is thrown.

and many others. While the examples above bring the notion of a set down to a concrete and intuitive level, the following example illustrates the need for some care in defining a set. "The set of men who are about 30 years of age" presents some difficulty because it is not quite clear what defines membership in the set. Is a 28 year old man "about 30" or not? "The set of men whose ages are from 28 to 32 years inclusive" presents no such difficulty, however. This further specification makes it perfectly clear that a 28 year old man is — for the purpose at hand — to be considered "about 30."

From now on, we shall think of a set as a *well-defined collection*, the modifier *well-defined* indicating a total lack of ambiguity with respect to the condition(s) defining membership in the set. Finally, we shall agree that sets contain no "duplicate members"; that is, the set of letters in the word *tree* is a set composed of three letters, namely "t," "r," and "e."

We summarize in the following definition:

DEFINITION. A *set* is a well-defined collection of distinct objects.[1] Any object which is a member of a set is called an *element* of the set. A set is generally labeled by a capital letter, such as S.

If x is some object which is a member of the set S, we write

$$x \in S,$$

which is read *x is an element of the set S* or *x belongs to the set S* or *x is in the set S*. The symbol $\in$ is referred to as an *inclusion* symbol. To denote that some object y is not a member of the set S, we write

$$y \notin S.$$

A given set S is a *finite set* if the total number of its elements is some positive number or zero; otherwise it is an *infinite set*.

[1]The word *object* is used quite loosely and can stand for numbers, letters, people, animals, geometrical shapes, natural phenomena, ideas, blades of grass, and so on.

A special finite set is a *null* or *empty* set, that is, a set with no members. The label for a null set is $\varnothing$ (pronounced *fie* as in *pie*). Before long it will become quite apparent why we should be concerned with sets devoid of elements; for the moment, let us simply present an example of an empty set. The set of girls in a given college class is a perfectly proper finite set. The set will be empty, however, if the class in question happens to be a men's gym class or an R.O.T.C. class.[2]

1.3 Specifying a Set

Suppose we wish to specify the set S of all possible outcomes which can result if a die is thrown. One way to specify the set is simply to list all the elements of the set within "curly braces":

$$S = \{1, 2, 3, 4, 5, 6\}.$$

The possible outcomes when a die is thrown are the integers from one through six which therefore comprise, or are the elements of, the set of possible outcomes.

Specifying a set by listing all its elements is convenient only when the set contains a fairly small number of elements.[3] It is not possible when the set contains an infinite number of elements or no elements at all. It is therefore quite useful to be able to specify a set by means of a defining property. In the case of rolling a die, we may write

$$S = \{x \mid x \text{ is an integer from one to six inclusive}\},$$

which is read *S is the set of all x such that x is an integer from one to six inclusive.* The correspondences may be shown in the following diagram:

[2]Note the need to distinguish between "the set of girls" in the class and "the number of girls" in the class. The number of girls is zero; the set of girls is empty or null since it contains no members.

[3]When there is no danger of confusion, a fairly large set such as the set of positive even numbers less than 100 might be specified as

$$\{2, 4, 6, 8, 10, 12, \ldots 96, 98\}.$$

Although it is far from satisfactory, an infinite set such as the set of *all* positive even numbers is sometimes specified as

$$\{2, 4, 6, 8, 10, 12, \ldots\}.$$

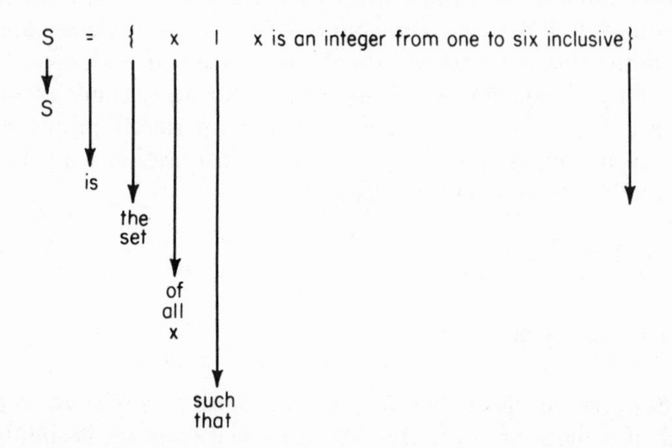

The same set may also be defined slightly more compactly as

$$S = \{x \mid x \text{ is an integer and } 1 \leq x \leq 6\}.$$

The lower case x plays no role except as a symbol for an element of S. We could just as well use y, s, Δ, or any other symbol. While the vertical line is a common symbol for *such that* in specifying a set, a colon is also frequently used; hence

$$S = \{x \mid x \text{ is an integer and } 1 \leq x \leq 6\}$$

and

$$= \{s : s \text{ is an integer and } 1 \leq s \leq 6\}.$$

EXAMPLE 1.3.1. Specify the following sets by means of a defining property:

(a) The set of all numbers greater than three.
(b) The set of all numbers from zero to one inclusive.
(c) The set of all male, high school graduates.

Solution:

(a) $S = \{x \mid x > 3\}$.

(b) $T = \{t \mid 0 \leq t \leq 1\}$.

(c) Let A = the set of all males,

B = the set of all high school graduates, and

U = the set of all male, high school graduates.

Then

$$U = \{y \mid y \in A \text{ and } y \in B\}.$$

Note that U is simply the set of all elements which are simultaneously members of both A and B.

It is often useful to represent a set by means of a *Venn diagram.* The latter is simply a plane figure, the shape of which is quite arbitrary. All the elements of the set are then considered to be points contained within the boundary of the figure. If T is a set, $y \in T$, and $z \notin T$; this can be conveniently represented by the following Venn diagram.

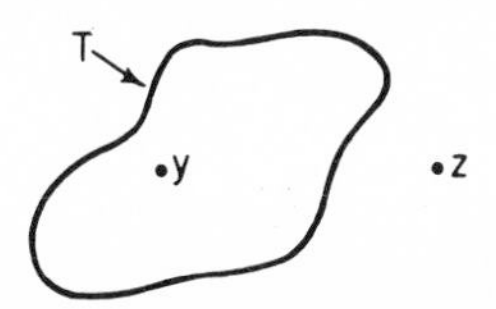

EXAMPLE 1.3.2. Represent the set of all male, high school graduates by means of a Venn diagram.

Solution: Recalling from Example 1.3.1(c) that the desired set is composed of all elements which are simultaneously members of

A = the set of all males and

B = the set of all high school graduates,

we can proceed as follows: Represent A and B by different, but overlapping figures (A is the circle, B the rectangle).

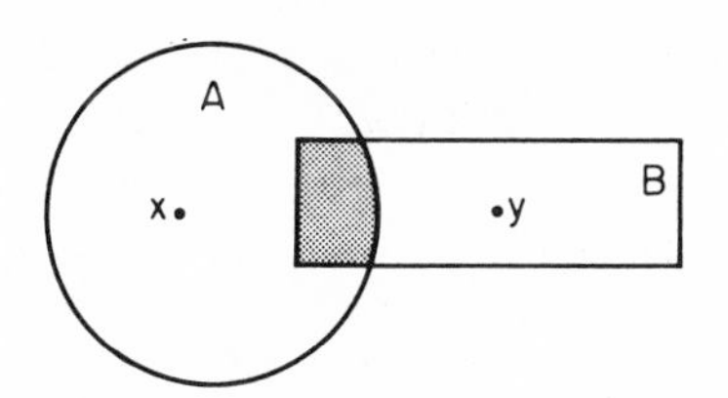

If the circle contains all elements of the set A, while the rectangle contains all elements of the set B, then the shaded portion common to both figures must contain all elements which are simultaneously members of both sets. Thus an element such as $x \in A$ must be a male who did *not* graduate from high school, while an element such as $y \in B$ must be a *female,* high school graduate. An element in the shaded region would be a male who graduated from high school; hence the shaded region represents the desired set.

1.4 Equality, Equivalence, and Subsets

In this section we present three notions which will permit us to develop useful relations between sets.

Two sets A and B are said to be *equal*, denoted $A = B$, if and only if they have exactly the same elements.

EXAMPLE 1.4.1. Three brothers, Tom, Dick, and Harry, received grades of A, B, and B respectively in an English literature course. In mathematics their respective grades were B, B, and A. Is the set of grades received in English equal to the set of grades received in mathematics? (Solution is left to the reader.)

Two sets A and B are said to be *equivalent* if and only if they are one-to-one matching. One-to-one matching means nothing more than the ability to assign to each element of A its own unique "partner" or "counterpart" in the set B, then to do the same for the elements of B. As an example, consider

$$A = \{q, 3, *\} \quad \text{and} \quad B = \{1, 5, 7, 9\}.$$

Each element of A can be assigned a unique counterpart in B; for example,

$$q \rightarrow 5 \quad (q \in A \text{ assigned } 5 \in B)$$

$$3 \rightarrow 1 \quad (3 \in A \text{ assigned } 1 \in B)$$

$$* \rightarrow 9 \quad (* \in A \text{ assigned } 9 \in B).$$

Given the assignment above, it is clear that it will not be possible to assign each element of B its own counterpart in A. The sets so specified are clearly not equivalent.

From the preceding discussion, the reader might wonder why equivalence is not defined in terms of two sets having the same number of elements. It is clear, in fact, that any two sets which *do* have the same number of elements must be one-to-one matching and therefore equivalent. On the other hand, consider the set of positive natural numbers,

$$\mathcal{R} = \{1, 2, 3, 4, \ldots\},$$

and the set of positive even numbers,

$$E = \{2, 4, 6, 8, \ldots\},$$

each of which is an infinite set. Since each natural number in $\mathcal{R}$ can be associated with a number twice as large in E, and since each even number in E can be associated with a number half as large in $\mathcal{R}$, it is clear that the sets $\mathcal{R}$ and E are one-to-one matching and therefore equivalent. If equivalence had been defined in terms of sets having the same number of elements. $\mathcal{R}$ and E could not have been shown to be equivalent due to the obvious impossibility of stating how many elements each set contains.[4]

The set A is said to be a *subset* of the set B, denoted $A \subset B$, if every element of the set A is also an element of the set B. The symbol $\subset$ is read *is a subset of* and is an inclusion symbol. It is useful to distinguish between the statements

(i) $a \in B$,

and

(ii) $A \subset B$.

Statement (i) indicates that a is an element contained in the set B. Statement (ii) indicates that A is a set with all its elements contained in the set B. A statement equivalent in meaning to (i) would be

(iii) $\{a\} \subset B$.

In the latter case the element a has been formed into a one-element set $\{a\}$ which is then a subset of the set B.

Taking $A = \{1, 2\}$ and $B = \{1, 2, 3, 4, 5\}$, it is clear that $A \subset B$. This can be represented by the following Venn diagram.

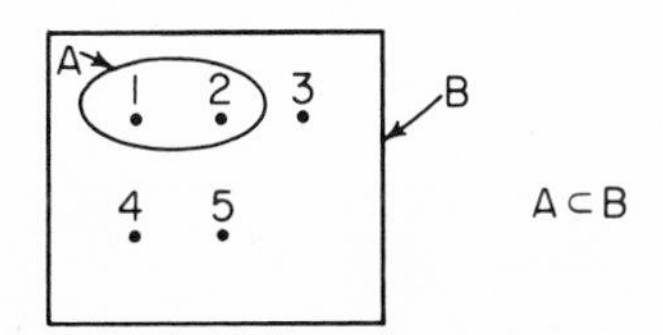

Set equality can be defined in terms of subsets, for if $A \subset B$ and $B \subset A$, then A and B must have precisely the same elements. We may therefore state that if $A \subset B$ and $B \subset A$, it must be that $A = B$.

Using the definition of a subset, it is easily shown that if A is any set whatever, $\varnothing \subset A$; that is, a null set is a subset of all sets. If $\varnothing \subset A$ were not true, then $\varnothing$ would have to contain some element not in A. But $\varnothing$ has no elements; hence $\varnothing \subset A$. Further, it can be shown that there is only one null set; that is, we should refer to "the" null set rather than "a" null set. To show that the null set is unique, suppose that $\varnothing$ and θ are both null sets. Since $\varnothing$ has no elements not in θ,

$$\varnothing \subset \theta$$

[4]Note that all the elements of the set E are contained in the set $\mathcal{R}$, while $\mathcal{R}$ contains elements not contained in E. The two sets are therefore unequal. They are, however, one-to-one matching even though $\mathcal{R}$ seems, in some sense, to be a "bigger" set. This is one of the many seeming paradoxes associated with the arithmetic of infinities.

and similarly

$$\theta \subset \varnothing,$$

but this means

$$\varnothing = \theta,$$

which establishes the uniqueness of the null set.

Intimately connected with the notion of a subset is that of the *power set,* for which we present the following definition.

DEFINITION. Let A be a set with a finite number of elements. The set of all subsets of A is called the power set of A and is denoted $\mathcal{P}_A$. As an example, consider $A = \{3, 5, t\}$. The subsets of A are the sets

$$\varnothing, \{3\}, \{5\}, \{t\}, \{3, 5\}, \{3, t\}, \{5, t\}, \text{ and } A \text{ itself.}$$

Hence

$$\mathcal{P}_A = \{\varnothing, \{3\}, \{5\}, \{t\}, \{3, 5\}, \{3, t\}, \{5, t\}, A\}.$$

Note that the power set is defined as a set whose elements are also sets. In this connection it is therefore proper to write $\{5, t\} \in \mathcal{P}_A$.

It is frequently of interest to know how many elements are contained in a power set; that is, how many subsets can be formed from a given finite set. We state the following theorem.

THEOREM. If A is a finite set with n elements, it has 2^n subsets, or — what is the same thing — $\mathcal{P}_A$ has 2^n elements.

This theorem is proved in Section 1.4 of the appendix. We may note, however, that the theorem holds for the case $A = \{3, 5, t\}$ discussed above. A simple count will show that we found eight subsets in all (including $\varnothing$ and A itself) and in fact $2^3 = 8$.

1.5 Set Operations and the Algebra of Sets

In presenting the basic set operations, we require a frame of reference known as the *universal set,* denoted $\mathcal{U}$. Henceforth all sets are considered to be subsets of the set $\mathcal{U}$; the importance of the universal set will become apparent as we proceed.

The three basic operations are *intersection, union,* and *complement,* which are defined as follows (A, B, etc., are all subsets of $\mathcal{U}$):

Intersection. The intersection of A and B is defined as the set of all elements of $\mathcal{U}$ which belong to *both* A and B. The following Venn diagrams illustrate this.

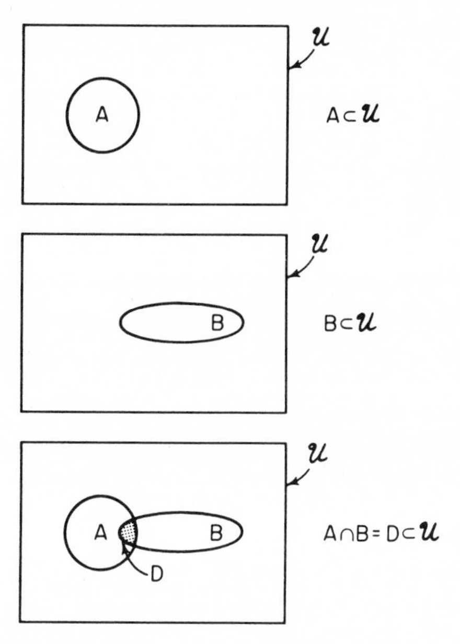

The set D is the shaded subset of $\mathcal{U}$, which is the intersection of A and B; that is, D contains all elements of $\mathcal{U}$ which are simultaneously in A and B.

The intersection of A and B is denoted

$$A \cap B,$$

which is read *A intersect B*. Calling D the intersection, we note

$$D = A \cap B = \{x \mid x \in A \text{ and simultaneously } x \in B\}.$$

The sets A and B are said to be *disjoint* or *mutually exclusive* if no element of $\mathcal{U}$ can belong to both A and B. In this case

$$A \cap B = \varnothing.$$

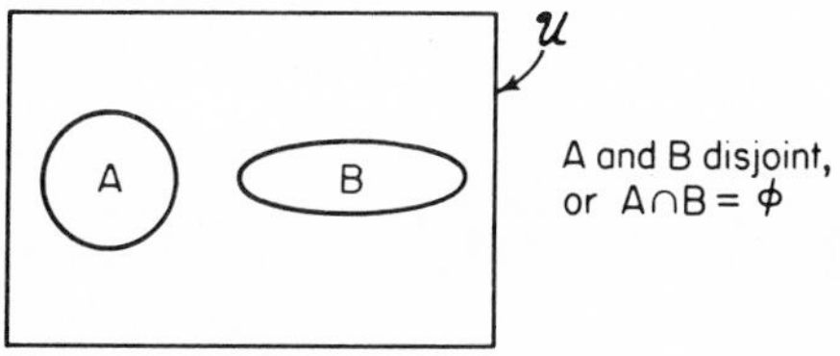

A and B disjoint,
or $A \cap B = \phi$

Union. The union of the sets A and B is the set of all elements of $\mathcal{U}$ which belong either to A or B (or to both).

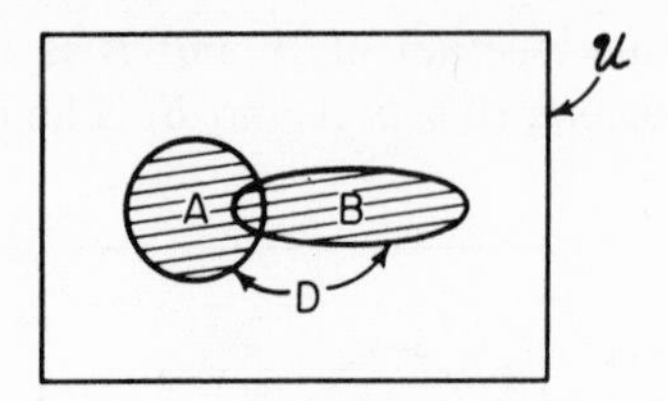

In the Venn diagram above, the shaded area is the set D, which contains all elements of $\mathcal{U}$ which are either in A or B. We write

$$D = A \cup B,$$

where $A \cup B$ is read A *union* B. More fully,

$$D = A \cup B = \{x \mid x \in A \text{ or } x \in B \text{ or } x \in (A \cap B)\}.$$

If A and B are disjoint, the definition of their union is unchanged, but there are no elements in their intersection. In this case, a Venn diagram would show the union as two disjoint shaded regions.

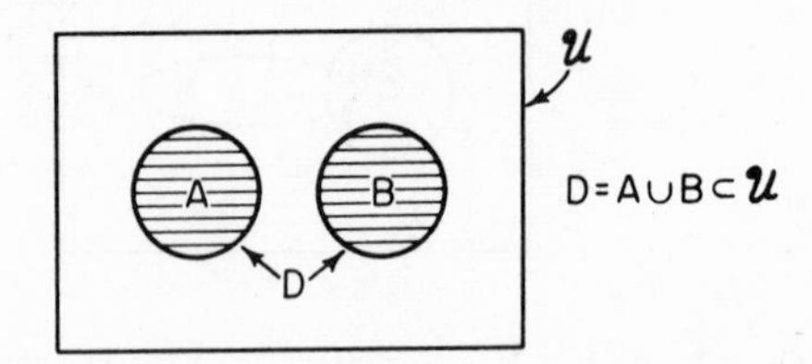

Complement. The complement of the set A is the set of all elements of $\mathcal{U}$ which are not in A.

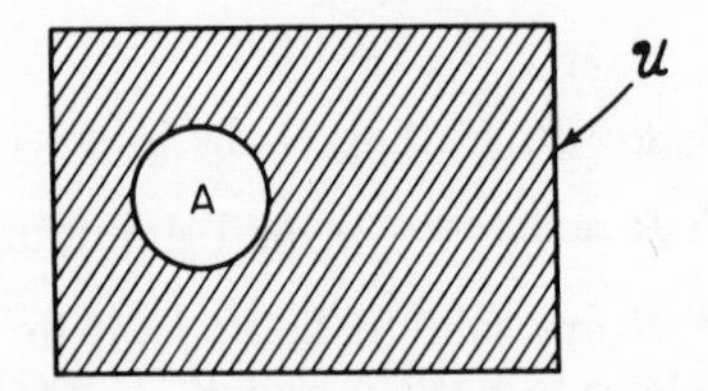

The shaded region in the diagram above is the set (subset of $\mathcal{U}$) which contains no elements of A.

The complement of A, say D, is denoted

$$D = A^c,$$

where A^c is read A *complement.* More fully,

$$D = A^c = \{x \mid x \notin A\}.$$[5]

[5]In the case of the complement it is particularly crucial that care be taken to make the universal set explicitly known.

EXAMPLE 1.5.1. Let $A = \{x \mid 0 < x \leq 60\}$

$$B = \{x \mid x > 0\}$$

$$D = \{x \mid x > 50\}.$$

Then

(a) $A \cap B = \{x \mid x \in A \text{ and } x \in B\}$

$= A.$ (why?)

(b) $A \cup B = B.$ (why?)

(c) $A \cup D = B.$ (why?)

(d) $A \cap D = \{x \mid 50 < x \leq 60\}.$ (why?)

(e) $(A \cup B) \cap (A \cap B) = A.$

Comment on (e):

$(A \cup B) \cap (A \cap B)$

$= B \cap (A \cap B)$ [from (b)]

$= B \cap A$ [from (a)]

$= A \cap B$ (why?)

$= A.$

(f) Regarding B as the universal set, $D^c = \{x \mid 0 < x \leq 50\}.$ (why?)

(g) Regarding D as the universal set, $B^c = \emptyset.$ (why?)

The notion of *partitioning* is extremely useful in probability theory. We present the following definition.

DEFINITION. The sets $S_1, S_2, \ldots, S_n$ are said to partition (or form a partition of) the set S if

(a) $S_i \subset S \quad (i = 1, 2, \ldots, n).$

(b) $S_i \cap S_j = \emptyset \quad (i, j = 1, 2, \ldots, n \text{ and } i \neq j).$

and

(c) $S_1 \cup S_2 \cup S_3 \cup \ldots \cup S_n = S.$[6]

[6]An expression such as $S_1 \cup S_2 \cup S_3 \cup S_4$ is sometimes written $\bigcup_{i=1}^{4} S_i$, so that (c) could be written $\bigcup_{i=1}^{n} S_i = S$. Similarly an expression such as $S_1 \cap S_2 \cap S_3 \cap S_4$ can be abbreviated as $\bigcap_{i=1}^{4} S_i$.

In other words, a group of disjoint subsets partition the set which is their union. The following Venn diagram illustrates this.

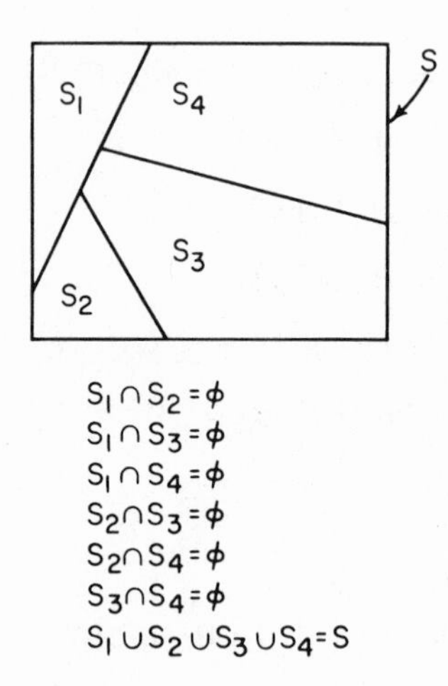

Therefore: S_1, S_2, S_3, and S_4 partition S.

The basic algebraic laws of set theory follow from our previous definitions. The first set of laws to be presented is sufficiently obvious so that no proofs will be given.

I. **(a)** $A \cup \varnothing = A$.

(b) $A \cap \varnothing = \varnothing$.

(c) $A \cup \mathcal{U} = \mathcal{U}$.

(d) $A \cap \mathcal{U} = A$.

(e) $A \cup A = A$.

(f) $A \cap A = A$.

(g) $A \cup A^c = \mathcal{U}$.

(h) $A \cap A^c = \varnothing$.

(i) $(A^c)^c = A$.

(j) $A \cup B = B \cup A$.
(k) $A \cap B = B \cap A$.
} Commutative laws

Any of the laws listed under I which are not immediately obvious will quickly become so via the aid of a Venn diagram. The following algebraic laws are far less obvious and we shall present some of their proofs.

II. **(a)** $(A \cup B)^c = A^c \cap B^c.$ } De Morgan's laws
(b) $(A \cap B)^c = A^c \cup B^c.$

Proof of II(a): Let $x \in (A \cup B)^c$ (see the following Venn diagram).

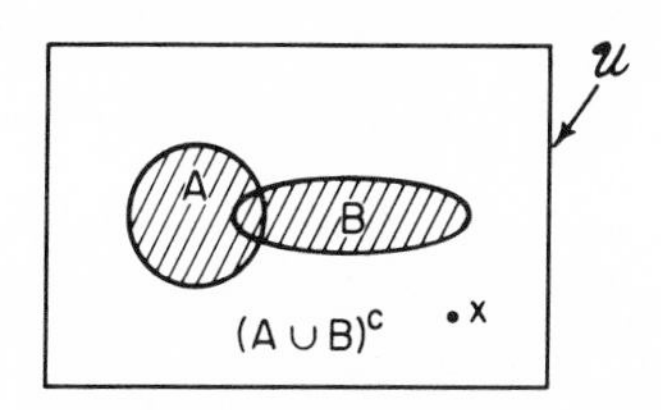

$$x \in (A \cup B)^c \Rightarrow x \notin A \quad \text{and} \quad x \notin B.$$[7]

$$x \notin A \Rightarrow x \in A^c.$$

$$x \notin B \Rightarrow x \in B^c.$$

$$x \in A^c \quad \text{and} \quad x \in B^c \Rightarrow x \in (A^c \cap B^c).$$

Hence

$$x \in (A \cup B)^c \Rightarrow x \in (A^c \cap B^c).$$

Therefore

$$(A \cup B)^c \subset (A^c \cap B^c). \qquad *$$

Let

$$y \in (A^c \cap B^c).$$

Then

$$y \in A^c \quad \text{and} \quad y \in B^c.$$

$$y \in A^c \Rightarrow y \notin A.$$

$$y \in B^c \Rightarrow y \notin B.$$

$$y \notin A \quad \text{and} \quad y \notin B \Rightarrow y \notin (A \cup B).$$

$$y \notin (A \cup B) \Rightarrow y \in (A \cup B)^c.$$

Hence

$$y \in (A^c \cap B^c) \Rightarrow y \in (A \cup B)^c.$$

Therefore

$$(A^c \cap B^c) \subset (A \cup B)^c. \qquad **$$

But

$$* \text{ and } ** \Rightarrow (A \cup B)^c = (A^c \cap B^c). \qquad \text{Q.E.D.}$$

[7]The symbol $\Rightarrow$ should be read *imply* or *implies*. Thus, for example, $a > 2 \Rightarrow 2a > 2$ is read *a being greater than* 2 *implies that* 2a *is greater than* 2.

III. **(a)** $A \cup (B \cup C) = (A \cup B) \cup C.$
(b) $A \cap (B \cap C) = (A \cap B) \cap C.$ } Associative laws

Proof of III(b): Let $x \in A$ and $x \in (B \cap C)$ so that

$$x \in [A \cap (B \cap C)].$$

$$x \in (B \cap C) \Rightarrow x \in B \quad \text{and} \quad x \in C.$$

$$x \in A \quad \text{and} \quad x \in B \Rightarrow x \in (A \cap B).$$

$$x \in (A \cap B) \quad \text{and} \quad x \in C \Rightarrow x \in [(A \cap B) \cap C].$$

Hence

$$x \in [A \cap (B \cap C)] \Rightarrow x \in [(A \cap B) \cap C].$$

Therefore

$$[A \cap (B \cap C)] \subset [(A \cap B) \cap C]. \qquad *$$

By a symmetrical argument (left to the reader), it is easily shown that

$$[(A \cap B) \cap C] \subset [A \cap (B \cap C)]. \qquad **$$

But

$$* \text{ and } ** \Rightarrow A \cap (B \cap C) = (A \cap B) \cap C. \qquad \text{Q.E.D.}$$

IV. **(a)** $A \cup (B \cap C) = (A \cup B) \cap (A \cup C).$
(b) $A \cap (B \cup C) = (A \cap B) \cup (A \cap C).$ } Distributive laws

Proof of IV(a): Let $x \in [A \cup (B \cap C)]$.

Then

$$x \in A \quad \text{or} \quad x \in (B \cap C).$$

(a) Suppose $x \in A$:

$$x \in A \Rightarrow x \in (A \cup B) \quad \text{and} \quad x \in (A \cup C).$$

$$x \in (A \cup B) \quad \text{and} \quad x \in (A \cup C) \Rightarrow x \in [(A \cup B) \cap (A \cup C)].$$

(b) Suppose $x \in (B \cap C)$:

$$x \in (B \cap C) \Rightarrow x \in B \quad \text{and} \quad x \in C.$$

$$x \in B \Rightarrow x \in (A \cup B).$$

$$x \in C \Rightarrow x \in (A \cup C).$$

$$x \in (A \cup B) \quad \text{and} \quad x \in (A \cup C) \Rightarrow x \in [(A \cup B) \cap (A \cup C)].$$

Hence,

$$x \in [A \cup (B \cap C)] \Rightarrow x \in [(A \cup B) \cap (A \cup C)].$$

Therefore

$$[A \cup (B \cap C)] \subset [(A \cup B) \cap (A \cup C)]. \qquad *$$

Let

$$y \in [(A \cup B) \cap (A \cup C)].$$

$$y \in [(A \cup B) \cap (A \cup C)] \Rightarrow y \in (A \cup B) \quad \text{and} \quad y \in (A \cup C).$$

$$y \in (A \cup B) \quad \text{and} \quad y \in (A \cup C) \Rightarrow$$

(i) $y \in A$, or

(ii) $y \in A$ and $y \in C$, or

(iii) $y \in B$ and $y \in C$ (see the following Venn diagram).

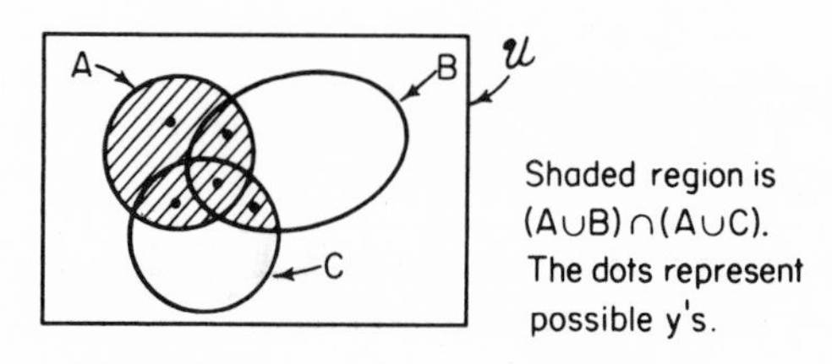

(i) $y \in A \Rightarrow y \in [A \cup (B \cap C)]$.

(ii) $y \in A$ and $y \in C \Rightarrow y \in [A \cup (B \cap C)]$, the condition $y \in C$ being irrelevant.

(iii) $y \in B$ and $y \in C \Rightarrow y \in (B \cap C)$.

$$y \in (B \cap C) \Rightarrow y \in [A \cup (B \cap C)].$$

Hence,

$$y \in [(A \cup B) \cap (A \cup C)] \Rightarrow y \in [A \cup (B \cap C)].$$

Therefore

$$[(A \cup B) \cap (A \cup C)] \subset [A \cup (B \cap C)]. \qquad **$$

But

$$* \text{ and } ** \Rightarrow A \cup (B \cap C) = (A \cup B) \cap (A \cup C). \qquad \text{Q.E.D.}$$

It has often been noted that null set, union, and intersection are analogous, respectively, to zero, addition, and multiplication in ordinary algebra. The reader might go back and substitute 0, $+$, and $\times$ for $\varnothing$, $\cup$, and $\cap$ in all the laws of set algebra (excepting I(c), I(d), I(g), I(h), and I(i) for obvious reasons) and see which continue to hold as ordinary algebraic laws (show that I(e), I(f), and IV(a) fail).

EXAMPLE 1.5.2. Using the algebraic laws presented above, show that

(a) $(A^c \cap B^c)^c = A \cup B$.

(b) $A \cap B = \varnothing \Rightarrow (A \cap D) \cap (B \cap D) = \varnothing$.

Solution to (a): According to II(a),

$$(A^c \cap B^c)^c = (A^c)^c \cup (B^c)^c.$$

By I(i),

$$(A^c)^c = A \quad \text{and} \quad (B^c)^c = B;$$

Therefore

$$(A^c \cap B^c)^c = A \cup B. \qquad \text{Q.E.D.}$$

Solution to (b): Let $A \cap D = E$,

then by III(b),

$$(A \cap D) \cap (B \cap D) = E \cap (B \cap D) = (E \cap B) \cap D.$$

Now by I(k)

$$A \cap D = D \cap A.$$

Therefore

$$E \cap B = (A \cap D) \cap B = (D \cap A) \cap B = D \cap (A \cap B) = D \cap \varnothing,$$

since

$$A \cap B = \varnothing.$$

Consequently,

$$\begin{aligned}(A \cap D) \cap (B \cap D) &= (E \cap B) \cap D.\\ &= (D \cap \varnothing) \cap D.\\ &= (\varnothing \cap D) \cap D, && \text{by I(k).}\\ &= \varnothing \cap (D \cap D), && \text{by III(b).}\\ &= \varnothing \cap (D), && \text{by I(f).}\\ &= \varnothing && \text{by I(b).} \qquad \text{Q.E.D.}\end{aligned}$$

The following Venn diagram corresponds to (b).

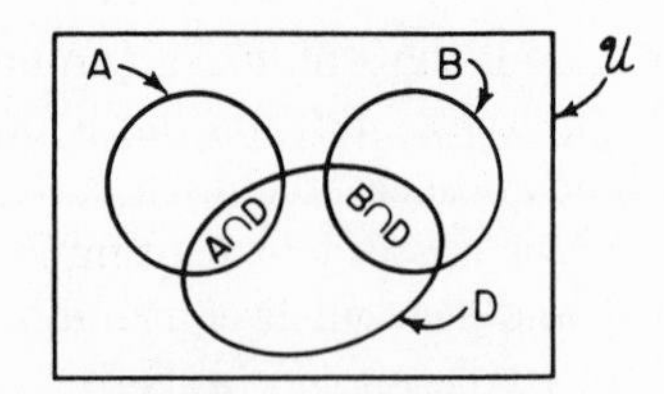

1.6 Cartesian Product Sets

It will be seen in Chapter 3 that most complex problems in probabilistic analysis can be reduced to manageable proportions by the use of Cartesian product sets. Since the latter is merely a set of ordered pairs (or triples, etc.), we first present the following definition.

DEFINITION. A pair of objects in which one object is said to be the first and the other (not necessarily distinct) the second is said to be an *ordered pair*.

As an example, the following two sets are equal because they contain the same elements: $\{5, 7\} = \{7, 5\}$. The following two ordered pairs, however, are unequal: $(5, 7) \neq (7, 5)$. In other words, the ordered pair (a, b) is equal to the ordered pair (c, d) if and only if $a = c$ and $b = d$.

To illustrate further the distinction between sets and ordered pairs, consider the following. To pass the freshmen requirement in English composition, College I requires a student to take two courses and obtain an average of at least C. A student in College I is therefore interested in the *set* of grades he obtains in the two courses; the set of grades {D, B} is sufficient to pass freshman English. In College II the requirement is an average of at least C in the two courses and a grade of at least C in the first course. A student in College II is therefore interested in the ordered pair (x, y), where x is the grade in the first course and y is the grade in the second course. Whereas (D, B) is as good as (B, D) to a student in College I, (D, B) is failing and (B, D) is passing in College II. Finally, note that if grades of C had been obtained in both courses, a student in College I would have obtained {C} as his set of grades, while a student in College II would have obtained (C, C) as his ordered pair of grades.

The Cartesian product set may now be defined as follows.

DEFINITION. Let $A = \{a_1, a_2, \ldots, a_m\}$ and

$$B = \{b_1, b_2, \ldots, b_n\}$$

The set of all ordered pairs (a, b) such that $a \in A$ and $b \in B$ is the Cartesian product of A and B. The Cartesian product is denoted $A \times B$, which is read *A cross B*. Formally,

$$A \times B = \{(a, b) \mid a \in A \quad \text{and} \quad b \in B\}.$$

We note that there are mn ordered pairs in $A \times B$; by the definition of an ordered pair $A \times B \neq B \times A$ unless A and B are equal.

EXAMPLE 1.6.1. Let $A = \{1, 2, 3\}$ and $B = \{q, t\}$. Write out the sets $A \times B$ and $B \times A$.

Solution:

$$\begin{aligned} A \times B &= \{(a, b) \mid a \in A \quad \text{and} \quad b \in B\} \\ &= \{(1, q), (1, t), (2, q), (2, t), (3, q), (3, t)\}. \end{aligned}$$

Any reordering of the ordered pairs themselves is still $A \times B$; that is,

$$A \times B = \{(1, q), (2, q), (3, q), (1, t), (2, t), (3, t)\}.$$

The important point is that within any ordered pair of $A \times B$ the element of A appears first. On the other hand,

$$B \times A = \{(b, a) \mid b \in B \quad \text{and} \quad a \in A\}$$
$$= \{(q, 1), (q, 2), (q, 3), (t, 1), (t, 2), (t, 3)\}.$$

Given three sets A, B, D, the Cartesian product set $A \times B \times D$ would be defined as

$$A \times B \times D = \{(a, b, d) \mid a \in A, b \in B, \quad \text{and} \quad d \in D\},$$

where (a, b, d) is known as an *ordered triple*. If the sets A, B, and D contain l, m, and n members respectively, the set $A \times B \times D$ contains $(l\, m\, n)$ ordered triples.

The following theorem is crucial in the probabilistic application of Cartesian product sets.

THEOREM 2. Let $A \times B$ be a Cartesian product set. The ordered pair (a, b) can be written as the following set theoretic intersection:

$$(a, b) = (\{a\} \times B) \cap (A \times \{b\}).$$

Proof: Let $A = \{a_1, a_2, \ldots, a_m\}$,

$B = \{b_1, b_2, \ldots, b_n\}$,

and, without loss of generality, let the a and b of the Theorem be a_1 and b_1 respectively. Then

$$\{a\} \times B = \{(a, b) \mid a = a_1 \quad \text{and} \quad b \in B\}$$
$$= \{(a_1, b_1), (a_1, b_2), (a_1, b_3), \ldots, (a_1, b_n)\}$$

and

$$A \times \{b\} = \{(a, b) \mid a \in A \quad \text{and} \quad b = b_1\}$$
$$= \{(a_1, b_1), (a_2, b_1), (a_3, b_1), \ldots, (a_m, b_1)\}.$$

From the above, it is perfectly obvious that

$$(a_1, b_1) = (\{a_1\} \times B) \cap (A \times \{b_1\}). \qquad \text{Q.E.D.}$$

PROBLEMS

1-1. Give verbal equivalents of the following:

(a) $S = \{1, 2, 3, \ldots, 9, 10\}$.

(b) $S = \{1, 3, 5, 7, 9, \ldots\}$.

(c) $S = \{1, 4, 9, 25, 36, 49, \ldots\}$.

(d) $S = \{x \mid -1 \leq x \leq 1\}$.

(e) $S = \{a, b, c, \ldots, y, z\}$.

1-2. Specify the following sets in symbolic notation:

(a) All men taller than 6 feet.
(b) The product of zero and all positive real numbers.
(c) All numbers which are simultaneously members of S in Problem 1(a), and S in Problem 1(b).
(d) The proportion of persons in the United States who purchased new refrigerators in 1960, and the proportion who purchased new refrigerators in 1961.

1-3. Represent the sets specified in Problem 2 by means of Venn diagrams.

1-4. If two sets A and B are equal, must they also be equivalent? Why?

1-5. Determine whether set A equals set B in each of the following:

(a) $A = \{X \mid X^2 - 4X + 4 = 0\}$, $B = \{X \mid X - 2 = 0\}$.

(b) $A = \{X \mid 2X^2 + 5X - 12 = 0\}$,

$B = \{X \mid 2X^3 + 5X^2 - 12X = 0\}$.

(c) $B =$ the power set of A.

1-6. Show that the sets A and B are equivalent, whereas A and C are not equivalent sets, when

$$A = \{X \mid X \text{ is a positive natural number}\},$$

$$B = \{X^2 \mid X \text{ is a positive natural number}\},$$

$$C = \{X \mid X^2 = a \text{ and } a \text{ is a positive natural number}\}.$$

1-7. Tom, Dick, and Harry take an exam. Let P denote the set of those who pass the exam and let $T = \{X \mid X = P \text{ for all possible } P\}$. What is T and how many elements does it contain?

1-8. Illustrate each of the following set-theoretic statements with a Venn diagram and give its verbal equivalent. (Lower-case letters denote elements and capital letters denote sets.)

(a) $a \in A$.

(b) $a \notin B$.

(c) $D \subset A$.

(d) $b \in (A \cup B)$.

(e) $b \in (A \cap B)$.

(f) $C = A \cup B$.

(g) $F = A \cap B$.

(h) $A \cap E = \varnothing$.

(i) $a \in A^c$.

1-9. Let $A = \{X \mid 12 < X \leq 55\}$,

$B = \{X \mid X \text{ is a positive natural number}\}$,

$C = \{X \mid X > 0\}$.

What are the following?

(a) $A \cup B$.

(b) $A \cup C$.

(c) $B \cup C$.

(d) $A \cap B$.

(e) $A \cap C$.

(f) $B \cap C$.

(g) $(A \cup C) \cap (A \cap C)$.

(h) $(B \cup C) \cap (A \cup B)$.

(i) $A^c \cap C$.

1-10. There are four major blood types — A, B, AB, and O. A person can accept blood only from another person with the same type or type O — with the exception that a person with type AB can receive from anyone. Suppose 50% of the persons in a community of 500 have type O blood, 10% have type AB, and half the remainder have type A. Let O denote the set of persons in this community who have type O blood; let A denote the set with type A blood, etc. Suppose a person from a nearby community requires a blood transfusion. What is the set of all possible blood donors and how many persons are in the set if the person in need of the transfusion has

(a) Type A blood?
(b) Type B blood?
(c) Type AB blood?
(d) Type O blood?

1-11. Let $S = \bigcup_{i=1}^{10} S_i$ and

$$S_i = \{X \mid X = y + i,\ y \in \{0, 10, 20, 30\}\}.$$

What is S? Do the S_i partition S?

1-12. Consider the following hypotheses:

(a) All economists smoke.
(b) All smokers are vain.

Use any appropriate set-theoretic symbols to prove that, if the hypotheses are true, the logical conclusion (all economists must be vain) must also be true.

1-13. Prove $(A \cap B)^c = A^c \cup B^c$ (De Morgan's law, p. 13).

1-14. Prove $A \cup (B \cup C) = (A \cup B) \cup C$ (associative law, p. 14).

1-15. Prove $A \cap (B \cup C) = (A \cap B) \cup (A \cap C)$ (distributive law, p. 14).

1-16. Let $\mathcal{U}$ be the set of all people and

M = the set of all males,

A = the set of all Americans,

E = the set of all Europeans,

W = the set of all wealthy people,

I = the set of all intelligent people,

H = the set of all handsome people.

Using only the set-theoretic symbols $=$, $\neq$, $\cap$, $\cup$, and symbols for subsets of $\mathcal{U}$, express each of the following statements in set-theoretic notation:

Hint: A statement such as *some Americans are intelligent* means that the intersection of A and I is not empty and is expressed as $A \cap I \neq \emptyset$.

(a) All Americans are wealthy.
(b) Some Europeans are intelligent.
(c) Only Americans are wealthy.
(d) No Europeans are intelligent.
(e) Non-Americans are neither intelligent nor handsome.
(f) Some intelligent Europeans are handsome.
(g) If a person is wealthy, then that person is handsome.
(h) A person is handsome if and only if he is European.
(i) All wealthy persons are either Americans or Europeans.

1-17. Prove that if $A \subset B$, then $B^c \subset A^c$.

1-18. In a class of 200 students let

M = the set of all male students,

B = the set of blond students,

E = the set of blue-eyed students.

There are 110 students in set M, 70 students in set B, and 85 students in set E. Of the male students, 30 have blond hair and 45 have blue eyes. Of the female students 60% who have blue eyes also have blond hair. Answer the following questions and specify the appropriate set in each case:

(a) How many students are neither male nor have blond hair?
(b) How many students are either male or have blue eyes and blond hair?
(c) How many students are female and have either blond hair or blue eyes?

1-19. A, B, and C partition a universal set $\mathcal{U}$. Arrange the following sets in sequential order so that each set in the sequence is a subset of the following set: $(A \cup B)$, $(A \cap B)$, $\varnothing$, $\varnothing^c$, $(A \cup B \cup C)$, C^c, B, and $\mathcal{U}$.

1-20. Prove $A^c \cap (B \cap C)^c = A \cup B^c \cup C^c$.

1-21. Prove that $A \times B \subset C \times D$ if $A \subset C$ and $B \subset D$.

1-22. Let x and y be the coordinates of a point in a plane relative to a set of rectangular coordinates. Express the following sets and illustrate each geometrically:

(a) $\{(x, y) \mid x - y = 0\}$.

(b) $\{(x, y) \mid x + 2y = 0\}$.

(c) $\{(x, y) \mid x + y = 3 \text{ and } 2x - y = 6\}$.

(d) $\{(x, y) \mid 4x - 5y = 0 \text{ and } 3x + 2y = 4\}$.

1-23. Consider a rectangle with sides $OX = 20$ and $OY = 10$. Let A denote the set of all points along OX with each point being identified by its distance from point O and let B denote the set of all points

along OY with each point being identified by its distance from point O. Also let

$$A' = \{x \mid 0 \leq x \leq 20\},$$

$$B' = \{y \mid 0 \leq y \leq 10\}.$$

Why is it not true that $A = A'$ and $B = B'$? *Hint:* Consider $A \cap B$ and $A' \cap B'$.

What interpretation is given to the elements of $A \times B$?

1-24. Prove

(a) $A \times (B \cap C) = (A \times B) \cap (A \times C)$.

(b) $A \times (B \cup C) = (A \times B) \cup (A \times C)$.

2 A PREVIEW OF PROBABILITY THEORY

2.1 Introduction

Economic decisions always involve a confrontation of benefits and costs. Since decisions are generally made *before the fact*, the relevant benefits and costs are often conjectural and the ultimate decision is in the nature of a gamble. Frequently the bits of information gained from experience and study make it possible to control or predict or guard against the odds when decisions must be made long before the facts are known.

As we proceed to develop the notions of probability theory, its intimate relation to decision-making will (hopefully) become apparent. We begin with an example.

2.2 Smoked Salmon: An Ordering Problem

Sliced smoked salmon is highly perishable and remains "fresh" for only 3 days. Ike's problem as the dairy manager in a supermarket is to decide how much smoked salmon should be ordered for delivery to his department on Mondays and Thursdays. The Monday order is used for early week sales and the Thursday order has to handle the weekend demand. Ike pays $1.50 per pound for smoked salmon and sells it, sliced, for $2.40 per pound. Since Ike generally sells a minimum of 100 pounds of salmon per week and has often sold as much as 150 pounds in a week, he considers this commodity to have the largest profit potential in the dairy department. The substantial potential, however, has gone largely unfulfilled because Ike has not been able to determine any particular pattern in the fluctuations which he experiences in the demand for smoked salmon. Frequently, for example, he prepares on Thursday with 120 pounds of salmon only to find 40 pounds unsold by Saturday night. Overstocking thus leads to a substantial reduction in the profits which can be realized on actual sales. In the example above, the sale of 80 pounds results in a profit of $72 which is reduced to $12 by the cost of the 40 pounds of excess stock.[1] On other occasions Ike finds that he has sold out by early Saturday and is forced to forego substantial profits the rest of the day.

Experience has taught Ike that there is little to gain in trying to outguess the fluctuations of demand. Instead, he decides to try the following experiment. From now on he will place "safe" order levels of 70 and 90 pounds for Mondays and Thursdays respectively. Then by watching the demand very carefully, he will attempt to decide whether or not it is worthwhile to change his ordering levels. His observations over the next 6 months lead to the following important conclusions concerning late-week sales. Although Ike cannot predict how much salmon will be demanded between Thursday and Saturday of a given week, he finds that in three out of four such periods there is demand for at least 100 pounds.[2] Regarding even higher levels of demand, Ike's experience indicates that at least 110 pounds could be sold between Thursday and Saturday in 2 out of 4 weeks. Ike then lists the following consequences of increasing his Thursday order to 100 pounds.

1. Additional order (from 90 to 100): 10 pounds.
2. Additional cost: 10 × $1.50 = $15.
3. Additional revenue: 10 × $2.40 = $24 if the extra 10 pounds can be sold, that is, if the total demand amounts to at least 100 pounds.

Ike concludes that over a typical 4 week period he can expect to earn an additional $24 three times, hence a weekly average of $18 [(3 × $24)/4] in additional revenue. Since the additional cost is only $15 per week, Ike decides tentatively to increase his Thursday order to 100 pounds. The decision is tentative only in the sense that Ike wishes to go further and

[1](80 lbs × $2.40) − (80 lbs × $1.50) = $72.
40 lbs × $1.50 = $60.

[2]This is not to say that Ike knows in *which* 3 out of 4 weeks he can sell at least 100 pounds, merely that if he stocked 100 pounds he would be sold out by Saturday night 3 out of 4 weeks *on the average*.

consider the possibility of another 10 pound increase which would bring the order to 110 pounds. In this case,

1. Additional order (from 100 to 110): 10 pounds.
2. Additional cost: $10 \times \$1.50 = \$15$.
3. Additional revenue: $10 \times \$2.40 = \$24$ if the extra 10 pounds can be sold, that is, if the total demand amounts to at least 110 pounds.

This time Ike decides that an additional $15 expenditure would not be justified since the extra revenue would amount to only $12 per week on the average, that is, $24 with a frequency of only 50%. Ike therefore rejects the second 10 pound increase and settles on a Thursday order of 100 pounds.[3]

Early week sales are in general a good deal smaller than those on the weekend. Ike notices that by stocking 70 pounds on Mondays he winds up half the time with at least 5 pounds unsold. If he reduces his Monday order from 70 to 65 pounds, he will save $7.50 weekly in purchasing costs while foregoing on the average only $6 per week in revenue, that is, 5 pounds at $2.40 per pound with a 50% frequency. The decision is therefore made to reduce the Monday order to 65 pounds.[4]

2.3 The Language of Probability

The smoked salmon problem contains, in simplified form, many of the basic elements which will concern us throughout the book. We shall find that some of the most important aspects of the application of probability theory were already present in the situation treated above. It is convenient, as we proceed, to use standard terminology to refer to those concepts which will recur continually in our study. Let us develop the

[3]The reader might note the following. Ike has apparently made his decision somewhat conservatively. Increasing his order level from 100 to 110 pounds would lead to additional weekly revenue of $12 on the average from the sale of the *entire* 10 *pound increment*. This is clearly not enough by itself to justify a $15 increase in purchasing cost. In deciding against this increment, however, Ike has clearly neglected the possibility of gaining revenue from selling only part of the added 10 pounds. Another element that Ike has neglected is that there might be a serious loss of future customers if he is out of stock too frequently. These important qualifications are *not* inherent in the techniques to be treated in this book; rather they result from the fact that this is just the beginning of Chapter 2.

[4]The reader might try and discover why it would not have been worthwhile to consider increasing the Monday order beyond 70 pounds.

terminology with reference to the concrete problem we have already discussed.

We used the word *experiment* to describe Ike's careful study of the quantity of salmon demanded between Thursday and Saturday. The particular characteristics of this experiment were that Ike could never predict in advance how much would be demanded and that the experiment could be repeated;[5] in fact, Ike repeated it every week for 6 months. An experiment with these characteristics is said to be a *random experiment.*

Although Ike could not predict the outcome of the random experiment in advance, he could specify a *set* which would contain the final outcome. If, for example, Ike had 10 regular customers, each of whom placed standing orders for 2 pounds of salmon, then the set

$$\mathcal{S} = \{x \mid x \geq 20\}$$

would surely contain the final outcome (or *realization*) of the experiment. A set which can be specified in advance of the experiment and contains all possible outcomes of the experiment, and hence the final outcome, is referred to as a *sample space.*[6]

In general the outcome of a random experiment can *vary* from trial to trial as the experiment is repeated. Ike may experience demand for 100 pounds of salmon between Thursday and Saturday of this week and only 55 pounds in the same period next week. We therefore refer to the outcome of a random experiment as a *random variable.*[7] Thus the number of pounds of smoked salmon demanded between Thursday and Saturday is a random variable. Several more examples will help to sharpen the concept.

[5]Repetition (or replication) of an experiment means performing it again under identical circumstances. The classic example is flipping a coin. For Ike's purpose the circumstances may be considered identical if relative prices, the pattern of consumer tastes, and other factors affecting the demand for salmon remained approximately constant over his observation period.

[6]We say "a" sample space because a set such as $\{x \mid x \geq 0\}$ would also contain all possible outcomes of the experiment. The subset $\{x \mid 0 \leq x < 20\}$ would in a sense be redundant since the outcome must be at least 20, but we shall see that this is of no consequence.

[7]Strictly, we limit the term random variable to apply to the outcome of a random experiment so defined that its sample space is a set of real numbers. If we think of flipping a coin once and recording the outcome as heads (H) or tails (T), we have the 2-element sample space, $\{H, T\}$. In this case, we would not refer to the outcome as a random variable. On the other hand, by redefining the random experiment so that we flip a coin once and count the number of heads, we obtain the sample space $\{0, 1\}$. *Zero* refers to no heads (that is, the occurrence of tails), *one* refers to one head, and these are the only possibilities in a single coin flip. In this case the sample space is a set of real numbers and we would refer to the outcome as a random variable.

(i) Take a brand new light bulb, turn it on, leave it on until it burns out, and note its life to the nearest half hour. This random experiment has associated with it the sample space

$$\mathcal{S} = \{0, \tfrac{1}{2}, 1, 1\tfrac{1}{2}, 2, 2\tfrac{1}{2}, 3, \ldots\},$$

which is a set of real numbers. The outcome of the random experiment — the life of a light bulb — is a random variable.

(ii) The drive-in teller of a local bank is busiest between 2 and 3 P.M. on Friday. Each Friday at 2:30 a bank employee records the length of the queue (the number of cars waiting to be serviced). The sample space is

$$\mathcal{S} = \{0, 1, 2, 3, \ldots\},$$

which is a set of real numbers. Queue length is thus a random variable.

(iii) Each month a research agency samples 50 families in a large metropolitan area and inquires whether they intend to purchase any consumer durables in the coming 3 months. The agency then records the number replying affirmatively. The sample space contains 51 real numbers,

$$\mathcal{S} = \{0, 1, 2, 3, \ldots, 50\}.$$

The random variable is the number intending to purchase durables.[8]

The notion of a random variable is so basic to probability, both in theory and application, that it is absolutely essential that we understand it. The examples above should make it perfectly clear that we have all been aware of random variables from the moment we realized that the same actions performed twice under the same conditions do not always lead to the same results. One final example: Suppose I live in a state in which the minimum

[8]Here another comment on replication is called for. The number intending to purchase durables depends on many things: the distribution of income in the community, the state of the business cycle, the rate of purchase of durables in the past, etc. If we think of the replications as the successive monthly surveys, it is clear that conditions determining buying intentions will not have remained constant. We would *not* therefore be repeating the experiment. On the other hand, in a given month we could conceive of sampling one group of 50 families, then a second group of 50, then a third group, and so on, and this would indeed be repeating the experiment. The important point, then, is that the number (out of 50) intending to purchase as of January is a random variable. The number intending to purchase as of February is also a random variable, but quite possibly a different random variable than that of the previous month.

voting age is 21. I am either old enough to vote or I am not. If you ask whether I am old enough to vote, you are not performing a random experiment. Indeed, you may not be able to predict the outcome with certainty in advance, but that is only because you do not know my age. Once you learn my age, the outcome is certain in all future *replications*. On the other hand, suppose you wish to distribute political leaflets on a busy street corner in my neighborhood. You are then interested in knowing what proportion of those who pass the street corner are of voting age. Here you would be unable to predict the outcome with certainty in advance even if you knew the age and address of every citizen in town. You still would not know which individuals would pass the corner at what time. Here is the element of randomness. If you stood at the corner every Friday between 8 and 10 A.M., you would not be surprised to find 20% of voting age the first week, 18 the second week, 30 the third week, and so on. It is thus clear that the proportion of voting-age people who pass the corner between 8 and 10 A.M. on Fridays is a random variable.[9]

When there is no danger of confusion, we use a capital letter such as X as a label for a random variable. Suppose $\mathcal{S}$ is a sample space for the random experiment which produces the random variable X. The most basic property connecting X and $\mathcal{S}$ is

$$X \in \mathcal{S}.$$

This is true by definition and simply means that X is an element of $\mathcal{S}$. Before performing the experiment it is not known *which* element of $\mathcal{S}$ will result, but one of them must. This is the only certainty connected with the situation in advance. Certainty is expressed by a probability of unity. We thus say that *the probability that X is an element of $\mathcal{S}$ is equal to one.* More succinctly,

$$\text{Prob } (X \in \mathcal{S}) = 1,$$

which is read precisely as the statement in italics above. Impossibility is expressed by a probability of zero; hence

$$\text{Prob } (X \notin \mathcal{S}) = 0,$$

which is read *the probability that X is not an element of $\mathcal{S}$ is equal to zero.*

In the example of the research agency investigating the intention to buy consumer durables, the random variable X is the number intending to purchase durables and the sample space is the set $\mathcal{S} = \{0, 1, 2, \ldots, 50\}$. Thus,

$$\text{Prob } [X \in \{0, 1, 2, \ldots, 50\}] = 1,$$

[9]Define the corresponding random experiment and sample space.

which means it is certain that X will be either 0, or 1, or 2, or 3, or 4, and so on out to 50. Further,

$$\text{Prob}\ (X = 51) = 0,$$

since only 50 families are to be sampled; that is,

$$51 \notin \mathcal{S}.$$

Let $S_1 = \{0, 1, 2,\}$; clearly $S_1 \subset \mathcal{S}$. Any subset of a sample space is referred to as an *event*. Obviously it is neither certain nor impossible for X to be an element of S_1. This situation, logically enough, is represented by a probability greater than zero, but less than one. The more nearly certain the event is to happen, the closer its probability is to unity. If we define the event $S_2 = \{0, 1, 2, 3\}$, it should be intuitively clear that

$$\text{Prob}\ (X \in S_2) > \text{Prob}\ (X \in S_1).$$

Finally, we tie in the notion of the power set[10] in the case of a finite sample space such as that relating to the consumer durables survey. In this case the sample space $\mathcal{S}$ contains 51 elements. Any subset is an event. The total number of possible events is therefore 2^{51}, the number of subsets in the power set. Fifty-one of these events are one-element subsets, namely the elements of $\mathcal{S}$. The latter are referred to as *elementary events*.[11] The null set, which by convention is a subset of $\mathcal{S}$, a member of the power set, and an event, has probability zero. $X \in \varnothing$ means that "nothing happens" when the experiment is performed. Since this is an impossibility,

$$P(X \in \varnothing) = 0.$$

PROBLEMS

2-1. Consider the experiment "toss a fair die once and record its outcome." Is this a *random* experiment? Why? What is the sample space of the experiment?

[10]See Chapter 1, p. 8.

[11]The final outcome (or realization) of the random experiment is one of the elementary events of the sample space. Nonetheless, it is useful to think in terms of all the events in the power set because there are times when the elementary events themselves are not the prime concern of the decision-maker. Suppose, for example, that the decision to initiate an advertising campaign hinges on whether or not at least 40% of the families in the metropolitan area intend to buy durables in the next 3 months. Then the events of prime interest are the subsets $S_3 = \{0, 1, 2, \ldots, 19\}$ and $S_4 = \{20, 21, 22, \ldots, 50\}$. It really matters very little whether the realization is the elementary event 32 as opposed to, say, 36. What is of prime importance is whether $X \in S_3$ or $X \in S_4$.

2-2. Let X denote the number of families (in a sample of 100) with annual incomes below $3,000. Is X a random variable? Why? Suppose one such sample yields 12 families with incomes below $3,000. Is 12 a random variable? If not, what is it?

2-3. Let $\mathcal{S}_1$ denote the sample space for the experiment "toss a fair die once and record its outcome." Let $\mathcal{S}_2$ denote the sample space for the experiment "toss a fair die twice and record the *ordered* outcome." In set-theoretic notation, what is $\mathcal{S}_2$? What random experiment has the sample space $\mathcal{S}_3 = \{x \mid x = a + b \text{ and } (a, b) \in \mathcal{S}_2\}$?

2-4. A farmer has a 40 acre section of land which is suitable for growing crops only if rainfall is heavy during the growing season. The farmer is contemplating planting a crop of field corn on this 40 acres at a total cost of $1,600. He sells field corn at $1.15 per bushel and can expect this 40 acres to yield 2,480 bushels if rainfall is heavy but only 1,120 bushels otherwise. Annual records covering the past 90 years indicate that there is a 40% chance of heavy rainfall during the upcoming growing season. Should he plant the 40 acres? What profit can he expect to make if he does plant?

2-5. In Problem 2-4, what constitutes the random experiment and what is its sample space? In order to answer the question of whether the farmer should or should not plant, you had to transform this sample space so that the outcome of the experiment in question is a random variable. How was this done?

3 PROBABILITY THEORY FOR FINITE SAMPLE SPACES

3.1 Introduction

Consider an experiment with outcome called X, such that

(i) Outcome X cannot be predicted with certainty prior to the performance of the experiment.
(ii) $\mathcal{S}$, a set containing all possible outcomes, is known prior to the performance of the experiment.
(iii) Replication of the experiment is conceivable.[1]

Then,

(i) The experiment is called a *random experiment.*
(ii) The set $\mathcal{S}$ is called a *sample space.*
(iii) $X \in \mathcal{S}$.
(iv) If the elements of $\mathcal{S}$ are real numbers, X is called a *random variable.*

As an example, it is easily seen that rolling a six-sided die meets *all* these conditions:

[1]We stress again that replication (that is, repetition under the same conditions) need not be undertaken. Indeed, in some cases replication is not feasible, but it must be conceivable. The requirement that we be able to conceive of repeating the experiment precludes statements about the probability that "Bacon really wrote the works of Shakespeare" and other such inherently unique events.

(i) The outcome X is unknown prior to rolling the die.
(ii) The set of all possible outcomes is known,

$$\mathcal{S} = \{1, 2, 3, 4, 5, 6\} = \text{sample space.}$$

(iii) Replication is conceivable.
(iv) Clearly $X \in \mathcal{S}$, since $\mathcal{S}$ contains all possible values of X.
(v) The elements of $\mathcal{S}$ are real numbers; hence X is a random variable.

Any subset of $\mathcal{S}$ is called an *event;* in particular the elements of the sample space are referred to as *elementary events.* In the die example the subset $\{2, 4, 6\}$ is an event; namely the event that an even number results when the die is rolled.

Up to this point the definitions have been perfectly general. However, from here to the end of this chapter we shall restrict attention to the special case of finite sample spaces, that is, to random experiments having a finite number of possible outcomes.

A *probability* is a number assigned to an event. We have already noted that impossibility is represented by a probability of zero, while certainty is represented by a probability of one. In general, probabilities are restricted to the range from zero to one inclusive; the more nearly certain an event is to happen, the closer its probability is to one.

Suppose S is an event ($S \subset \mathcal{S}$) and contains only the elements x_1, x_2, and x_3.[2] The probability of the event S is written Prob $(X \in S)$, and often it is abbreviated further to merely $P(S)$. For the record,

$$P(S) = \text{Prob } (X \in S) = \text{Prob } (X \in \{x_1, x_2, x_3\})$$

$$= \text{Prob } (X = x_1 \quad \text{or} \quad X = x_2 \quad \text{or} \quad X = x_3).$$

3.2 Probability Axioms

In this section we state three *axioms*[3] which will form the basic foundation of all finite sample space probability theory. In fact, only one of the axioms will be new to us.

Consider a random experiment with sample space $\mathcal{S}$, associated random variable X, and any events (subsets of $\mathcal{S}$) S_1 and S_2.

[2] $\mathcal{S}$ contains x_1, x_2, x_3, and more.

[3] An *axiom* is a statement which we take to be true without proof. A basic axiom of Euclidean geometry, for example, is that parallel lines never meet.

AXIOM 1.

$$0 \le P(S_1) \le 1.$$

Axiom 1 is merely a restatement of the principle that probabilities are restricted to the range from zero to one inclusive.[4]

AXIOM 2.

$$P(\mathcal{S}) = \text{Prob}\ (X \in \mathcal{S}) = 1.$$

Axiom 2 states that since it is certain that X will be an element of $\mathcal{S}$, the probability associated with $\mathcal{S}$ is unity.

AXIOM 3. Let $(S_1 \cap S_2) = \varnothing$, then

$$\begin{aligned} P(S_1 \cup S_2) &= \text{Prob}\ [X \in (S_1 \cup S_2)] = \text{Prob}\ (X \in S_1 \quad \text{or} \quad X \in S_2) \\ &= \text{Prob}\ (X \in S_1) + \text{Prob}\ (X \in S_2). \end{aligned}$$

Axiom 3 is concerned with the union of disjoint events. Stated simply, it means that if S_1 and S_2 *cannot both occur simultaneously*, then the probability that *one or the other* occurs is the sum of their individual probabilities. Axiom 3 is pictured in the following Venn diagram. Clearly, S_1 and S_2 are disjoint so that if $X \in S_1$, it must be that $X \notin S_2$ and vice versa. The

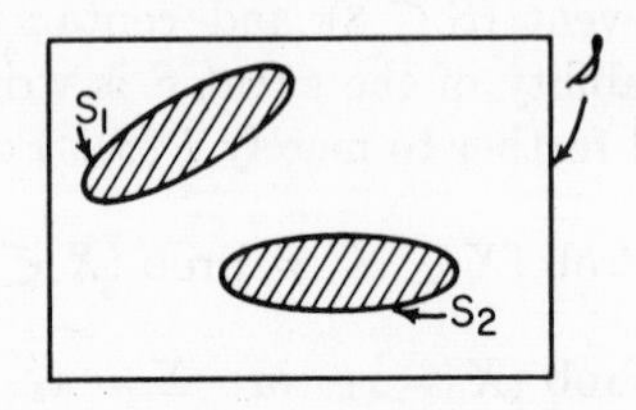

union of S_1 and S_2 is composed of the shaded areas in $\mathcal{S}$. The probability of being in the union — in either S_1 or S_2 — is just the probability of being in S_1 plus the probability of being in S_2.

EXAMPLE 3.2.1. Consider again the die experiment with sample space $\mathcal{S} = \{1, 2, 3, 4, 5, 6\}$ and events $S_1 = \{1, 3, 5\}$, $S_2 = \{2, 4, 6\}$, and $S_3 = \{5, 6\}$. Then $S_1 \cap S_3 = \{5\} \ne \varnothing$ and $S_2 \cap S_3 = \{6\} \ne \varnothing$. It is clear that S_1 and S_3 can occur simultaneously. If the die shows 5, then S_1 and S_3 have both occurred since $5 \in S_1$ and $5 \in S_3$. Similarly, the occur-

[4]The colloquialism that something has for example a "50-50 chance" of occurring would be stated technically as having a probability of $\frac{1}{2}$. Similarly, a "10% chance" or a "1-in-10 chance" becomes a probability of $\frac{1}{10}$.

rence of a 6 means S_2 and S_3 have both occurred. S_1 and S_2, however, are disjoint (S_1 contains only odd numbers, S_2 only even numbers) so that one or the other can occur, but not both.[5] Here Axiom 3 applies and

$$\text{Prob}\,[X \in (S_1 \cup S_2)] = \text{Prob}\,(X \in S_1 \quad \text{or} \quad X \in S_2)$$
$$= \text{Prob}\,(X \in S_1) + \text{Prob}\,(X \in S_2).$$

We note further that $S_1 \cup S_2 = \mathcal{S}$. Since $P(\mathcal{S}) = 1$, we should have

$$\text{Prob}\,[X \in (S_1 \cup S_2)] = \text{Prob}\,(X \in \mathcal{S}) = 1.$$

In words, S_1 is the event that the die shows an odd number, while S_2 is the event that the die shows an even number. These are the only possibilities; hence it is *certain* that one or the other (that is, the union) must occur. We also note that

$$S_2 = S_1^c,$$

where S_1^c refers to the complement of S_1 with respect to $\mathcal{S}$. It is clear that S_1 and S_2 ($= S_1^c$) partition $\mathcal{S}$.

Finally, let us regard a die as "fair" if it favors no number over any others — that is, in many replications of the die experiment each number would tend to occur as often as any other. In this case we would say that the sample space contains *equally likely elementary events*. An implication of this is that the events S_1 and S_2 would have equal probability; the die would as likely produce an odd number as an even number. Since then

$$P(S_1) = P(S_2), \quad \text{and} \quad P(S_1 \cup S_2) = P(S_1) + P(S_2) = 1,$$

it must be that

$$P(S_1) = P(S_2) = \tfrac{1}{2}.$$

If, on the other hand, the die were not fair ("loaded"), it might be that even numbers were more nearly certain to occur than with a fair die. If the "degree of loading" were such that $P(S_2) = \frac{2}{3}$, then Axiom 3 would imply that $P(S_1) = \frac{1}{3}$ since the sum must still be unity.[6]

The strength of the axioms will become apparent as we proceed now to the theorems which endow probability theory with its great potential for application.

[5]Disjoint subsets are often referred to as *mutually exclusive events* since the occurrence of either one precludes simultaneous occurrence of the other.

[6]The case of S_2 having probability $\frac{2}{3}$ and S_1 having probability $\frac{1}{3}$ is easily interpreted. An even number is twice as likely as an odd number. Alternatively, after many replications, there would tend to be twice as many even as odd realizations.

3.3 Probability Theorems, I

In the development of the theorems we shall employ the following notation.

Sample space: $\mathcal{S} = \{x_1, x_2, x_3, \ldots, x_T\}$.

Subsets (events): S, S_1, S_2, S_3, etc.

Elementary events: $x_1, x_2, x_3, \ldots, x_T$.

THEOREM 1. If $S = \varnothing$, $P(S) = 0$.

Proof:

(a) Since $S = \varnothing$, $\mathcal{S} \cup S = \mathcal{S}$; hence

$$P(\mathcal{S} \cup S) = P(\mathcal{S}). \tag{3.1}$$

(b) Since $S = \varnothing$, $\mathcal{S} \cap S = \varnothing$ and we can apply Axiom 3 to write

$$P(\mathcal{S} \cup S) = P(\mathcal{S}) + P(S). \tag{3.2}$$

(c) Combining (3.1) and (3.2),

$$P(\mathcal{S} \cup S) = P(\mathcal{S})$$

$$P(\mathcal{S} \cup S) = P(\mathcal{S}) + P(S).$$

Therefore

$$P(\mathcal{S}) = P(\mathcal{S}) + P(S)$$

$$P(\mathcal{S}) - P(\mathcal{S}) = P(S)$$

$$0 = P(S).$$

Q.E.D.

Comment: We have noted before that the null set is an impossible event and therefore has probability zero. Note, however, that this did not appear as one of the three axioms. We now see that the *impossibility of the null event* is indeed a logical consequence of the axioms.

THEOREM 2. If $S = \{x_1, x_2, x_3, \ldots, x_m\}$ with $m \leq T$,

$$P(S) = P(x_1) + P(x_2) + P(x_3) + \ldots + P(x_m)$$

$$= \sum_{i=1}^{m} P(x_i).$$

Proof:

(a) Let $S_1 = \{x_1\}$ and $S_2 = \{x_2, x_3, \ldots, x_m\}$. Clearly,

$$S_1 \cup S_2 = S \quad \text{and} \quad S_1 \cap S_2 = \varnothing. \tag{3.3}$$

(b) Since S_1 and S_2 are disjoint (mutually exclusive), we can apply Axiom 3 to write

$$P(S) = P(S_1 \cup S_2) = P(S_1) + P(S_2) \tag{3.4}$$

but,

$$P(S_1) = P(x_1);^7$$

hence by substituting in (3.4),

$$P(S) = P(x_1) + P(S_2). \tag{3.5}$$

(c) Let $S_3 = \{x_2\}$ and $S_4 = \{x_3, x_4, \ldots, x_m\}$. Clearly

$$S_3 \cup S_4 = S_2 \quad \text{and} \quad S_3 \cap S_4 = \varnothing. \tag{3.6}$$

Hence by Axiom 3,

$$P(S_2) = P(S_3 \cup S_4) = P(S_3) + P(S_4) \tag{3.7}$$

but,

$$P(S_3) = P(x_2);$$

hence by substituting in (3.7),

$$P(S_2) = P(x_2) + P(S_4). \tag{3.8}$$

(d) Now substitute (3.8) into (3.5) to obtain

$$P(S) = P(x_1) + P(x_2) + P(S_4). \tag{3.9}$$

(e) By now the pattern should be clear. We define $S_4 = S_5 \cup S_6$ where $S_5 = \{x_3\}$ and $S_6 = \{x_4, x_5, \ldots, x_m\}$ and arrive at

$$P(S) = P(x_1) + P(x_2) + P(x_3) + P(S_6). \tag{3.10}$$

Since there are only a finite number m of elementary events in S, we carry out $(m - 1)$ such steps and arrive at[8]

$$P(S) = P(x_1) + P(x_2) + P(x_3) + P(x_4) + \ldots + P(x_m). \qquad \text{Q.E.D.}$$

Comment: This theorem is extremely important. It implies that once the probability of each of the elementary events is known, the probabilities of all other events are uniquely determined. This follows from the fact that any event (subset) can be written as a set of elementary events.

[7]Suppose X is the random variable associated with $\mathcal{S}$. Then $P(S_1) = P(x_1)$ is just shorthand for $P(X \in S_1) = P(X = x_1)$, since $S_1 = \{x_1\}$.

[8]Some may recognize that this can be considered essentially a "proof by induction."

EXAMPLE 3.3.1. A random experiment can result in any one of n different, equally likely outcomes, $x_1, x_2, \ldots, x_n$. Hence $\mathcal{S} = \{x_1, x_2, \ldots, x_n\}$. Let $S_1 = \{x_1, x_2, x_3\}$, $S_2 = \{x_8, x_{10}\}$, and $S_3 = \{x_3, x_5, x_7\}$. What is the probability of

(a) x_1?
(b) The event S_1?
(c) The event $S_1 \cup S_2$?
(d) The event $S_1 \cup S_3$?

Solution:

(a) Obviously, $P(\mathcal{S}) = 1$. Applying Theorem 2 to the event $\mathcal{S}$,

$$P\,(\mathcal{S}) = 1 = \sum_{i=1}^{n} P\,(x_i).$$

But each elementary event has the same probability, say p, so that

$$1 = \sum_{i=1}^{n} p = np.$$

Therefore

$$p = \frac{1}{n}.$$

Thus $1/n$ is the probability of each of the n equally likely outcomes, and therefore

$$P(x_1) = \frac{1}{n}.$$

(b) By Theorem 2 and part (a),

$$\begin{aligned} P(S_1) &= P(x_1) + P(x_2) + P(x_3) \\ &= \frac{1}{n} + \frac{1}{n} + \frac{1}{n} \\ &= \frac{3}{n}. \end{aligned}$$

(c) There are several ways to approach this problem. Probably the simplest is to note that $S_1 \cap S_2 = \varnothing$, so that by Axiom 3,

$$P(S_1 \cup S_2) = P(S_1) + P(S_2).$$

Now in part (b) we found $P(S_1) = 3/n$, and the reader should be able to show similarly that $P(S_2) = 2/n$.

Therefore

$$P(S_1 \cup S_2) = \frac{3}{n} + \frac{2}{n} = \frac{5}{n}.$$

(d) Since $S_1 \cap S_3 = \{x_3\} \neq \emptyset$, Axiom 3 will not apply. However,

$$S_1 \cup S_3 = \{x_1, x_2, x_3, x_5, x_7\}.$$

Applying Theorem 2 and part (a),

$$\begin{aligned} P(S_1 \cup S_3) &= P(x_1) + P(x_2) + P(x_3) + P(x_5) + P(x_7) \\ &= \frac{1}{n} + \frac{1}{n} + \frac{1}{n} + \frac{1}{n} + \frac{1}{n} \\ &= \frac{5}{n}. \end{aligned}$$

Note that part (c) could have been done in precisely the same way by writing $S_1 \cup S_2 = \{x_1, x_2, x_3, x_8, x_9\}$.

THEOREM 3. (General Addition Theorem).

$$P(S_1 \cup S_2) = P(S_1) + P(S_2) - P(S_1 \cap S_2).$$

Comment: The power of Theorem 3 is in the case where S_1 and S_2 are *not* disjoint. For if they are disjoint, $S_1 \cap S_2 = \emptyset$, and by Theorem 1 $P(S_1 \cap S_2) = 0$ so that we are back to Axiom 3. We use the following Venn diagram to aid in the proof.

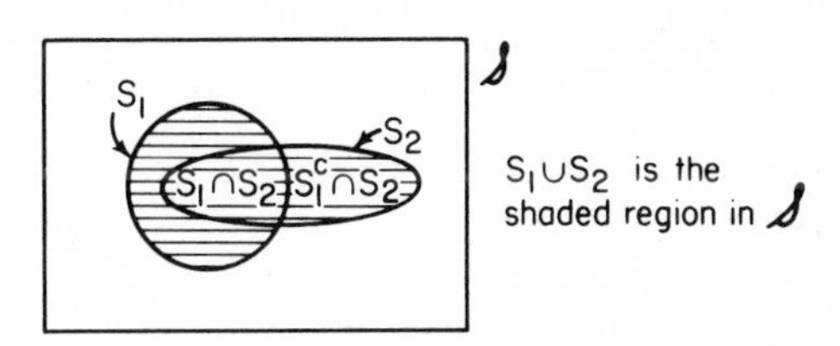

Proof:

(a) $S_1 \cup S_2 = S_2 \cup (S_1^c \cap S_2)$

and

$$S_1 \cap (S_1^c \cap S_2) = \emptyset. \tag{3.11}$$

(b) Apply Axiom 3 to the union of the disjoint events S_1 and $(S_1^c \cap S_2)$:

$$\begin{aligned} P(S_1 \cup S_2) &= P[S_1 \cup (S_1^c \cap S_2)] \\ &= P(S_1) + P(S_1^c \cap S_2). \end{aligned} \tag{3.12}$$

(c) $S_2 = (S_1 \cap S_2) \cup (S_1^c \cap S_2)$

and

$$(S_1 \cap S_2) \cap (S_1^c \cap S_2) = \emptyset. \tag{3.13}$$

(d) Apply Axiom 3 to the union of the disjoint events $(S_1 \cap S_2)$ and $(S_1^c \cap S_2)$:

$$P(S_2) = P[(S_1 \cap S_2) \cup (S_1^c \cap S_2)],$$

$$P(S_2) = P(S_1 \cap S_2) + P(S_1^c \cap S_2),$$

$$P(S_1^c \cap S_2) = P(S_2) - P(S_1 \cap S_2). \tag{3.14}$$

(e) To complete the proof, substitute the expression for $P(S_1^c \cap S_2)$ given by (3.14) into (3.12):

$$P(S_1 \cup S_2) = P(S_1) + P(S_1^c \cap S_2)$$

$$= P(S_1) + P(S_2) - P(S_1 \cap S_2). \qquad \text{Q.E.D.}$$

Comment: Stop to think what is actually being done if S_1 and S_2 are *not* disjoint and we merely add their separate probabilities. It should be clear from the Venn diagram that $P(S_2)$ includes $P(S_1 \cap S_2)$. Further, $P(S_1)$ also includes $P(S_1 \cap S_2)$. If we add $P(S_1)$ and $P(S_2)$, we are therefore including $P(S_1 \cap S_2)$ twice. Theorem 3 thus states that one obtains the probability of the union of S_1 and S_2 by first adding their separate probabilities and then subtracting the probability of their intersection to compensate for the inherent "double counting."

EXAMPLE 3.3.2. One card is to be dealt from a well-shuffled bridge deck of 52 cards. What is the probability that the card dealt is

(a) An ace of hearts?
(b) An ace?
(c) A red king?
(d) A red card or a king?

Solution: The natural sample space for this experiment is the set of 52 cards comprising the elementary events, all of which are obviously equally likely.

(a) There is only 1 elementary event out of 52 which is an ace of hearts; therefore

$$P(\text{ace of hearts}) = \tfrac{1}{52}.$$

(b) Letting A_c, A_d, A_h, and A_s stand for ace of clubs, diamonds, hearts, and spades respectively, we form the subset

$$S_1 = \{A_c, A_d, A_h, A_s\}.$$

The subset S_1 clearly corresponds to the event, an ace. Using Theorem 2,

$$P(\text{an ace}) = P(S_1) = \tfrac{1}{52} + \tfrac{1}{52} + \tfrac{1}{52} + \tfrac{1}{52} = \tfrac{4}{52} = \tfrac{1}{13}.$$

(c) Let $S_2 = \{K_d, K_h\}$, where K_d and K_h are the kings of diamonds and hearts respectively, that is, the red kings.

$$P(S_2) = \tfrac{1}{52} + \tfrac{1}{52} = \tfrac{1}{26}\,.$$

(d) Let S_3 denote the event, a red card, and S_4, a king. It is clear that $P(S_3) = \frac{1}{2}$, while $P(S_4) = \frac{1}{13}$ by analogy with (b). Here we are interested in the event, a red card or a king, which is $(S_3 \cup S_4)$. In general,

$$P(S_3 \cup S_4) = P(S_3) + P(S_4) - P(S_3 \cap S_4).$$

But the event $(S_3 \cap S_4)$ is just the event, red king, which appeared in (c), thus $(S_3 \cap S_4) = S_2$.

Therefore

$$P(S_3 \cap S_4) = P(S_2) = \tfrac{1}{26},$$

and

$$P\,(S_3 \cup S_4) = \tfrac{1}{2} + \tfrac{1}{13} - \tfrac{1}{26} = \tfrac{7}{13}.$$[9]

EXAMPLE 3.3.3. The bottles in a wine cellar contain either dry red, sweet red, or dry white wine or quinine water. All the bottles are of the same size and made of dark glass, which not only protects the contents but makes it impossible to identify the contents visually. A flood in the cellar has washed all labels from the bottles and the owner's records only indicate that 20% of the bottles contain dry wine, 60% contain red wine, and 25% contain quinine water. If a bottle is chosen at random, what is the probability that it contains

(a) Wine?
(b) Dry red wine?
(c) Sweet wine?
(d) White wine?

Solution: Suppose we consider the bottles themselves as the elementary events. A subset of the bottles contains dry red wines and this subset will be denoted by DR. Similarly, SR is the subset of sweet red wines, DW is the subset of dry white wines, and Q is the subset of bottles containing quinine water.

(a) Since 25% of the bottles contain quinine water, 75% must contain wine. Thus, $P(\text{wine}) = 0.75$. We note that the event wine may be written

$$\text{wine} = (DR \cup SR \cup DW).$$

[9]This problem can be done perhaps a bit more easily — but without illustrating Theorem 3 as well — by noting that the event, a red card or a king, is made up of all red cards (which include the red kings) plus the two black kings; hence a total of 26 + 2 = 28 cards. The probability is then simply $\frac{28}{52} = \frac{7}{13}$.

(b) The owner's records indicate probabilities for the events dry and red, which events may be written[10]

$$\text{dry} = (DR \cup DW),$$

and

$$\text{red} = (DR \cup SR).$$

Then, according to the records,

$$P(DR \cup DW) = 0.20,$$

and

$$P(DR \cup SR) = 0.60.$$

We are here interested in dry red and we notice that

$$DR = (DR \cup DW) \cap (DR \cup SR),$$

while

$$\text{wine} = (DR \cup DW) \cup (DR \cup SR).$$

Now applying Theorem 3,

$$P(\text{wine}) = P(DR \cup DW) + P(DR \cup SR) - P(DR),$$

$$0.75 = 0.20 + 0.60 - P(DR).$$

Therefore

$$P(DR) = 0.05.$$

(d) White wine is the event DW since the only white wine is dry white. We already know $P(DR \cup DW) = 0.20$ and clearly $(DR \cap DW) = \varnothing$ since no wine can be both dry red and dry white. It must then be, by Axiom 3, that

$$P(DR \cup DW) = P(DR) + P(DW),$$

$$0.20 = 0.05 + P(DW).$$

Therefore

$$P(DW) = 0.15.$$

[10]This illustrates two invaluable aids in doing probability problems. 1. Always translate the verbal conditions of the problem into precise probability statements. 2. When trying to determine the probability of some event, be sure you understand the event and ask yourself "how can this event occur;" this will aid you in stating the event in precise set-theoretic terms.

THEOREM 4. (Mutually Exclusive Events). Suppose S_1, S_2, and S_3 are mutually disjoint; that is, they partition the subset which is their union. Then

$$P(S_1 \cup S_2 \cup S_3) = P(S_1) + P(S_2) + P(S_3).$$

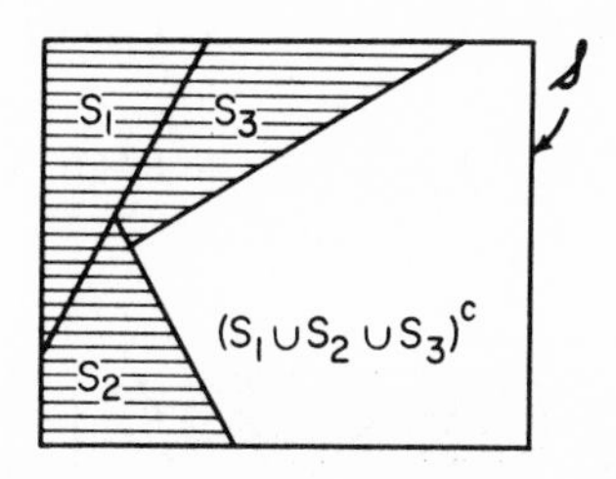

Proof:

(a) $(S_1 \cup S_2) \cap S_3 = \varnothing$, hence

$$P[(S_1 \cup S_2) \cup S_3] = P(S_1 \cup S_2) + P(S_3). \tag{3.15}$$

(b) But $S_1 \cap S_2 = \varnothing$, so that

$$P(S_1 \cup S_2) = P(S_1) + P(S_2). \tag{3.16}$$

(c) Now substitute the expression in (3.16) into (3.15):

$$P[(S_1 \cup S_2) \cup S_3] = P(S_1 \cup S_2 \cup S_3)$$
$$= P(S_1) + P(S_2) + P(S_3). \quad \text{Q.E.D.}$$

Comment: It is clear that this theorem can be extended to any finite number of mutually disjoint subsets of $\mathcal{S}$.

THEOREM 5.

$$P(S^c) = 1 - P(S).$$

Proof is left to the reader.

EXAMPLE 3.3.4. S and V are subsets of the sample space $\mathcal{S}$. The probabilities $P(S)$, $P(V)$, and $P(S \cap V)$ are known. Find expressions in terms of these known probabilities for the following:

(a) $P[(S \cup V)^c]$.
(b) $P(S^c \cup V^c)$.
(c) $P(S^c \cap V^c)$.
(d) $P(S^c \cap V)$.
(e) $P(S^c \cup V)$.

Solution: In this problem we illustrate again the extent to which Venn diagrams may provide immeasurable aid in "seeing" the problem to be solved.

(a) By Theorem 5,

$$P[(S \cup V)^c] = 1 - P(S \cup V);$$

hence

$$P[(S \cup V)^c] = 1 - [P(S) + P(V) - P(S \cap V)].$$

(b)

$S^c \cup V^c$ is therefore all the shaded portion of $\mathcal{S}$. The only part of $\mathcal{S}$ which is *not* shaded is $S \cap V$; that is, any element $x \in (S \cap V)$ is neither in S^c nor V^c. Any $x \notin (S \cap V)$ must be in S^c or V^c or both. We have, then, that

$$(S^c \cup V^c) = (S \cap V)^c,$$

which implies

$$P(S^c \cup V^c) = P(S \cap V)^c$$
$$= 1 - P(S \cap V).$$

(c) From the Venn diagram in (b), we determine that $S^c \cap V^c$ is the crosshatched portion of $\mathcal{S}$. The part of $\mathcal{S}$ which is *not* crosshatched is $S \cup V$; hence

$$S^c \cap V^c = (S \cup V)^c.$$

The answer to (c) is therefore the same as that to (a).

(d) V can clearly be expressed as follows:

$$V = (S \cap V) \cup (S^c \cap V),$$

while

$$(S \cap V) \cap (S^c \cap V) = \varnothing.$$

Therefore

$$P(V) = P(S \cap V) + P(S^c \cap V),$$

or

$$P(S^c \cap V) = P(V) - P(S \cap V).$$

(e) $P(S^c \cup V) = P(S^c) + P(V) - P(S^c \cap V)$.

Using the expression for $P(S^c \cap V)$ derived in (d) and applying Theorem 5 to $P(S^c)$,

$$\begin{aligned} P(S^c \cup V) &= [1 - P(S)] + P(V) - [P(V) - P(S \cap V)] \\ &= 1 - P(S) + P(S \cap V).^{11} \end{aligned}$$

3.4 Cartesian Products and Compound Experiments

We shall introduce the notion of the *compound experiment* by means of an example. The following table indicates the (hypothetical) age–sex distribution of employees in a large company.

Age	Sex		Total
	B_1: Male	B_2: Female	
A_1: under 34 years	2,100	900	3,000
A_2: 34–54 years	4,200	1,800	6,000
A_3: at least 55 years	700	300	1,000
Total	7,000	3,000	10,000

Consider the following random experiments.

EXPERIMENT E_1. Select an employee randomly, record his[12] age, and return him to the group.

EXPERIMENT E_2. Select an employee randomly, record his sex, and return him to the group.

EXPERIMENT $E_1 \times E_2$. Select an employee randomly, record his age *and* sex, and return him to the group.

[11]An alternative solution would be to notice that

$$S^c \cup V = S^c \cup (S \cap V),$$

while

$$S^c \cap (S \cap V) = \varnothing.$$

The desired result then follows from Axiom 3 and Theorem 5.

[12]*His* is a possessive pronoun referring to the antecedent *employee* and is not meant to indicate sex.

Experiments E_1 and E_2 are random experiments of the type we have considered all along. Let us note that A_1, A_2, and A_3 are mutually disjoint events whose union is a sample space $\mathcal{S}_1$ for the experiment E_1. Similarly, the union of the disjoint events B_1 and B_2 is a sample space $\mathcal{S}_2$ for the experiment E_2. We can specify a sample space for the *compound experiment* $E_1 \times E_2$ in the manner of a Cartesian product as follows.

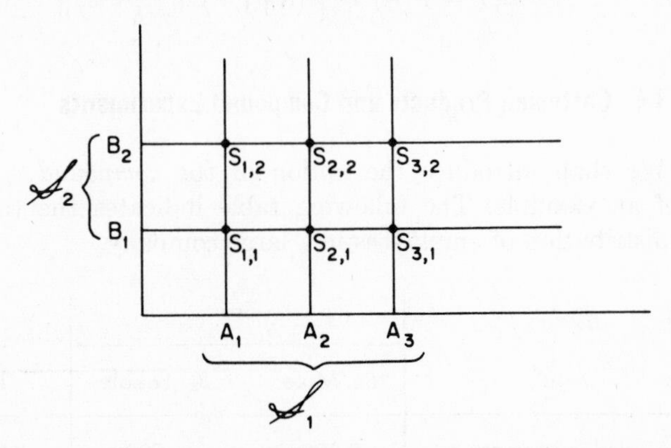

The point $S_{1,1}$ in the figure above represents the occurrence of *both* A_1 *and* B_1, that is, a male under 34 years of age. $\{S_{1,1}\}$[13] is thus an event in the compound experiment $E_1 \times E_2$.

We wish now to show that any event such as $\{S_{1,1}\}$ in the compound experiment can be written as an intersection in the set-theoretic sense. The Cartesian product $A_1 \times \mathcal{S}_2$ can be represented as a set:

$$A_1 \times \mathcal{S}_2 = \{S_{1,1}, S_{1,2}\}.$$

Similarly,

$$B_1 \times \mathcal{S}_1 = \{S_{1,1}, S_{2,1}, S_{3,1}\}.$$

Then,

$$(A_1 \times \mathcal{S}_2) \cap (B_1 \times \mathcal{S}_1) = \{S_{1,1}\}.$$

Ultimately, we are interested in the probability of such an intersection, but

$$\begin{aligned} P(A_1 \times \mathcal{S}_2) &= P[\{S_{1,1}, S_{1,2}\}] \\ &= P[\{S_{1,1}\} \cup \{S_{1,2}\}] \\ &= P(\text{male or female under 34}) \\ &= P(A_1). \end{aligned}$$

[13] $\{S_{1,1}\}$ is the set composed of the point $S_{1,1}$ in the Cartesian product space $\mathcal{S}_1 \times \mathcal{S}_2$.

Thus the probability of the Cartesian product of *an event* from E_1 with the *entire set of events* from E_2 is just the probability of the event from E_1. This is a perfectly general result although we have illustrated it only for a specific case. Since the $\mathcal{S}_2$ in the expression $(A_1 \times \mathcal{S}_2)$ plays no part in determining $P(A_1 \times \mathcal{S}_2)$ and similarly the $\mathcal{S}_1$ plays no part in determining $P(B_1 \times \mathcal{S}_1)$, we shall henceforth abbreviate an expression such as

$$(A_1 \times \mathcal{S}_2) \cap (B_1 \times \mathcal{S}_1) = \{S_{1,1}\}$$

to simply

$$(A_1 \cap B_1) = \{S_{1,1}\}$$

whenever there is no danger of confusion.

In the sense just discussed, it is clear that the intersection of any event from E_1 with any event from E_2 results in a set of ordered pairs, which is an event from $E_1 \times E_2$. Thus, for example, $A_3 \cap B_1 = \{S_{3,1}\} = \{$a male at least 55 years of age$\}$, which is an $E_1 \times E_2$ event. Further, if we start with any elementary event from $E_1 \times E_2$, we can represent it as an element of the intersection of an event from E_1 with an event from E_2. A 35 year old female, say, would be a member of the set $A_2 \cap B_2$, which is the set $\{S_{2,2}\}$. These considerations lead to the following

DEFINITION. Let E_1 be a random experiment with sample space partitioned by the events $A_1, A_2, A_3, \ldots, A_m$. Let E_2 be a random experiment with sample space partitioned by the events $B_1, B_2, B_3, \ldots, B_n$. Let E be another random experiment with sample space (a set of ordered pairs) denoted by $\mathcal{S}$. If

$$\text{(a)}\quad \left.\begin{array}{l} (A_1 \cap B_1) \subset \mathcal{S}, \\ (A_1 \cap B_2) \subset \mathcal{S}, \\ \quad\cdot \\ \quad\cdot \\ \quad\cdot \\ (A_1 \cap B_n) \subset \mathcal{S}, \\ (A_2 \cap B_1) \subset \mathcal{S}, \\ \quad\cdot \\ \quad\cdot \\ \quad\cdot \\ (A_m \cap B_n) \subset \mathcal{S}, \end{array}\right\} \begin{array}{c} m \cdot n \\ \text{statements} \end{array}$$

and

(b) $x \in \mathcal{S}$ implies that x is an element of one of the intersections in (a) above,

then E is a *compound experiment* with respect to E_1 and E_2, and the mn intersections in (a) partition $\mathcal{S}$. To denote E as a *compound experiment*, we write $E = E_1 \times E_2$.

EXAMPLE 3.4.1. An experimenter rolls a die, tosses a coin, and records both results. A sample space for this experiment is a set of ordered pairs:

$$\mathcal{S} = \{(a, b) \mid a \in \{1, 2, 3, 4, 5, 6\} \quad \text{and} \quad b \in \{\text{H}, \text{T}\}\}.$$

Represent this experiment as a compound experiment with respect to the die roll and coin toss.

Solution: First let us write out $\mathcal{S}$ in detail:

$$\mathcal{S} = \begin{Bmatrix} (1, \text{H}), (2, \text{H}), (3, \text{H}), (4, \text{H}), (5, \text{H}), (6, \text{H}), \\ (1, \text{T}), (2, \text{T}), (3, \text{T}), (4, \text{T}), (5, \text{T}), (6, \text{T}) \end{Bmatrix}.$$

The A's of the definition are the one-element sets $\{1\}, \{2\}, \{3\}, \{4\}, \{5\}, \{6\}$; the B's are $\{\text{H}\}$, and $\{\text{T}\}$.

A typical intersection is, say, $\{2\} \cap \{\text{T}\}$ which represents the set of all ordered pairs which are 2 on the die roll and tails on the coin toss. There is only one such element:

$$\{2\} \cap \{\text{T}\} = \{(2, \text{T})\} \subset \mathcal{S}.$$

Now consider any elementary event in $\mathcal{S}$, say (5, H). $(5, \text{H}) \in \{(5, \text{H})\}$, and $\{(5, \text{H})\}$ is the set of all ordered pairs which are 5 on the die roll and heads on the coin toss, so that $\{(5, \text{H})\} = \{5\} \cap \{\text{H}\}$. Thus $(5, \text{H}) \in \{5\} \cap \{\text{H}\}$; indeed it is the only element.

EXAMPLE 3.4.2. This example considers an experiment which is compound with respect to three (simple) experiments.

A retailer stocks 50 different items in his store. As a first step toward gaining more knowledge about the nature of his clientele, he decides to note for every tenth buying customer the following three characteristics:

(a) Sex.
(b) Number of different items purchased.
(c) Approximate age.

Calling the retailer's experiment E, with sample space $\mathcal{S}$, define three (simple) experiments E_1, E_2, and E_3 such that $E = E_1 \times E_2 \times E_3$.

Solution: Let E_1 be the experiment *note customer's sex* with sample space $\{M, F\}$. Let E_2 be the experiment *count number of different items purchased* with sample space $\{1, 2, 3, \ldots, 50\}$. Let E_3 be the experiment *note customer's age*. Since there is an approximation involved in the latter, let us represent the sample space for E_3 in terms of the partitioning events

A_1: under 20 years of age.
A_2: 20–34 inclusive.
A_3: 35–50 inclusive.
A_4: over 50.

A typical triple intersection would be $\{M\} \cap \{2\} \cap A_2$, which represents a male judged to be between 20 and 34 years of age buying two items. Fifteen elementary events of the E experiment, namely

$$
\begin{array}{l}
(M, 2, 20) \\
(M, 2, 21) \\
(M, 2, 22) \\
\quad \cdot \\
\quad \cdot \\
\quad \cdot \\
(M, 2, 34)
\end{array}
$$

comprise this triple intersection. Indeed, then $\{M\} \cap \{2\} \cap A_2 \subset \mathcal{S}$.

Now consider any elementary event of the E experiment, say, a woman judged to be 45 buying six items. This event is represented by the ordered triple $(F, 6, 45)$. Clearly $(F, 6, 45) \in \{F\} \cap \{6\} \cap A_3$.

Many experiments which are of practical importance often seem to be somewhat complicated to analyze probabilistically. Frequently, however, such experiments can be viewed as compounds of several simple experiments and this device greatly facilitates the analysis. The key element then reduces to the problem of making probability statements about intersections of events from the simple experiments. The latter aspect will be treated fully in the next section. Here let us select — in simplified form — a reasonably common problem which can be viewed in terms of a compound experiment.

The purchasing agent of a manufacturing corporation receives electrical transformers in lots of 50 from a supplier. As the lot arrives, the agent must decide whether to accept it, in which case the transformers are installed as integral components of a manufactured item, or to reject it as a possibly defective lot. To this end, the agent chooses 3 transformers at random from the 50, hooks each up to a bell system, and tests whether the transformer enables the bell to ring. The agent's decision to accept or reject the lot of 50 depends on what happens with the sample of 3. The agent is clearly performing a random experiment and the outcome of interest is *how many transformers work*. Put another way, *the number of transformers which work* is a random variable X with associated sample space $\mathcal{S}$:

$$X \in \mathcal{S} = \{0, 1, 2, 3\}.$$

If the lot contains no defective transformers, then the experiment will produce 3 as the realization of X; if all the transformers are defective, X will take on the value zero. In general, the probability that X will take on any particular value in $\mathcal{S}$ will depend on how many defectives are present in the lot. The assignment of probabilities to the elements of $\mathcal{S}$ is most easily made by considering that the agent is performing an experiment which is compound relative to three simple experiments as follows:

E_1: Choose a transformer from the lot of 50 and test whether it is good (g_1) or defective (d_1).
E_2: Choose a transformer from the remaining 49 and test whether it is good (g_2) or defective (d_2).
E_3: Choose a transformer from the remaining 48 and test whether it is good (g_3) or defective (d_3).

Viewed this way, the agent's experiment is $E_1 \times E_2 \times E_3$ and produces results which are ordered triples. If, for example, the first transformer sampled is defective and the next two ring the bell, the realized ordered triple will be (d_1, g_2, g_3). Another way of looking at this is clearly

$$\{(d_1, g_2, g_3)\} = \{d_1\} \cap \{g_2\} \cap \{g_3\},$$

so that the probability of observing the event above is simply the probability of a triple intersection,

$$P[\{d_1\} \cap \{g_2\} \cap \{g_3\}].$$

Now let us return to the problem as viewed by the purchasing agent, who is interested in *how many* transformers work, not in *which* ones work. The event we considered above corresponded to *two transformers work*, but so also do the events (g_1, d_2, g_3) and (g_1, g_2, d_3). The probability of each of the latter is again the probability of a triple intersection. Finally, since these three ordered triples comprise the event $X = 2$, we appeal to Theorem 2 to obtain[14]

$$P(X = 2) = P[\{d_1\} \cap \{g_2\} \cap \{g_3\}] + P[\{g_1\} \cap \{d_2\} \cap \{g_3\}] + P[\{g_1\} \cap \{g_2\} \cap \{d_3\}].$$

The next set of theorems will be concerned specifically with probabilities of intersections of events.

3.5 Probability Theorems, II

DEFINITION. Two events, S_1 and S_2, are said to be *stochastically independent*[15] events if and only if $P(S_1 \cap S_2) = P(S_1) \cdot P(S_2)$.

[14] Review Footnote 10.

[15] Other terms used are *statistically independent, independent in a probability sense,* and simply *independent.* The word "stochastic" derives from the Greek "stochos" meaning "guess."

Comment: In normal usage, independence conveys the meaning of somehow "having nothing to do with each other." If interpreted correctly, this same idea carries over to stochastic independence. We shall see that stochastic independence means that the occurrence or nonoccurrence of S_1 has no effect on the probability of occurrence of S_2 and vice versa. In other words, if you had to bet on S_2, you would pay nothing to learn whether or not S_1 had already occurred, since S_1 has no effect on the probability of S_2.

A few words may be in order as a reminder about *if and only if*. The *if* part: if $P(S_1 \cap S_2) = P(S_1)P(S_2)$, then S_1 and S_2 are stochastically independent. The *only if* part: if S_1 and S_2 are stochastically independent, then $P(S_1 \cap S_2) = P(S_1)P(S_2)$.

THEOREM 6. If $S_1 \cap S_2 = \emptyset$, and $P(S_1) > 0$ and $P(S_2) > 0$, then S_1 and S_2 are *not* stochastically independent events.

Proof: There are only two possibilities:

(a) S_1 and S_2 are independent, or
(b) S_1 and S_2 are not independent.

Assume (a) is true, then $P(S_1 \cap S_2) = P(S_1)\,P(S_2) > 0$, since $P(S_1) > 0$ and $P(S_2) > 0$. But $S_1 \cap S_2 = \emptyset$, so that, by Theorem 1, $P(S_1 \cap S_2) = 0$.

Hence the assumption that S_1 and S_2 are independent leads to a contradiction, and it must then be that S_1 and S_2 are *not* independent. Q.E.D.

Comment: This theorem is important in pointing out that disjoint does *not* mean stochastic independence. Indeed, Theorem 6 states that *disjoint* events are stochastically *dependent.* Suppose $S_1 \cap S_2 = \emptyset$, and $P\,(S_1) = \frac{1}{3}$ and $P(S_2) = \frac{1}{4}$. These probabilities, of course, apply when a random experiment is about to be conducted, that is, when the only certainty is that the result must be an element of the sample space. Now suppose *additional* information is available, namely that S_1 has occurred. It is clear that S_2 cannot also have occurred since $S_1 \cap S_2 = \emptyset$; hence Prob (S_2 occurs given that S_1 is known to have occurred) $= 0$. Lack of independence: the occurrence of S_1 has affected the probability of occurrence of S_2. Suppose, however, that $S_1 \cap S_2 \neq \emptyset$. Then if S_1 has occurred, S_2 might still occur.

These remarks lead naturally to consideration of *conditional probability.*

DEFINITION. The probability of S_1 *conditional* on S_2 is denoted

$$P(S_1 \mid S_2),$$

and is read *the probability of* S_1 *given* S_2 or *the probability of* S_1 *given the occurrence of* S_2. The conditional probability is defined by

$$P(S_1 \mid S_2) = \frac{P(S_1 \cap S_2)}{P(S_2)},$$

provided $P(S_2) \neq 0$. If $P(S_2) = 0$, no probability conditional on S_2 is defined.

A Venn diagram will aid in interpreting conditional probability.

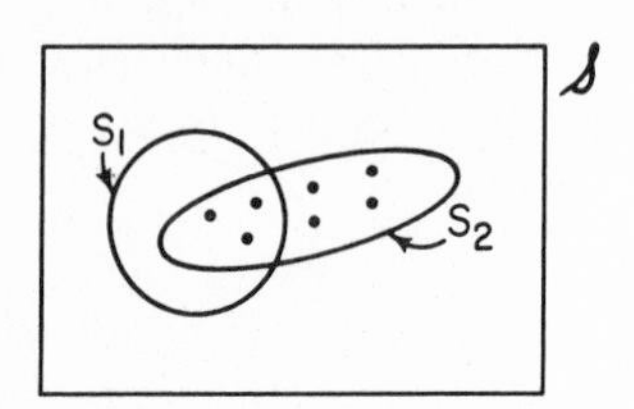

Suppose $S_1 \cap S_2 = \{x_1, x_2, x_3\}$ and $S_2 = \{x_1, x_2, x_3, x_4, x_5, x_6, x_7\}$. If it is known that S_2 has occurred, then one of the elements $x_1, x_2, \ldots, x_7$ must have occurred. If X is the random variable involved, it must be that $X \in S_2$, and S_2 now has the properties of a sample space. We must therefore assign new probabilities to the elements of S_2 such that the sum of the new probabilities is unity, reflecting the certainty of occurrence of S_2. Denote the original probability of x_i by p_i. We have

$$\sum_{i=1}^{7} p_i = P(S_2) < 1.$$

Now we wish to assign new probabilities to the x_i, say p_i^*, such that

$$\sum_{i=1}^{7} p_i^* = 1.$$

These p_i^* will have the following meaning relative to the p_i: p_i is the (absolute) probability that the random experiment results in x_i; p_i^* is the (conditional) probability that the experiment results in x_i when it is known that one of the elements of S_2 must occur. Clearly p_i^* should be greater than p_i because in defining the former we eliminate from the sample space all elements which are not in S_2. In a very real sense there is now more probability to be distributed to the elements of S_2 than there was formerly.

There is another condition which, logically, we should like the p_i^* to satisfy. If x_7 had been twice as likely as x_3 when we had no prior information ($p_7 = 2p_3$), we should certainly expect x_7 to continue to be twice as likely as x_3 under the additional condition that one of the elements of S_2 must occur. Hence we should require $p_7^* = 2p_3^*$. In general, this condition will be satisfied if we have $p_i^* = kp_i$, where k is a constant, for all i — that is, if the p_i^* are all proportional to the p_i.

Putting this all together, we want

$$\sum_{i=1}^{7} p_i^* = 1 \tag{3.17}$$

subject to

$$p_i^* = kp_i \quad (i = 1, 2, \ldots, 7). \tag{3.18}$$

We already have

$$\sum_{i=1}^{7} p_i = P(S_2) < 1. \tag{3.19}$$

Now sum both sides of (3.18):

$$\sum_{i=1}^{7} p_i^* = \sum_{i=1}^{7} kp_i = k \sum_{i=1}^{7} p_i. \tag{3.20}$$

Substitute from (3.19) into (3.20):

$$\sum_{i=1}^{7} p_i^* = kP(S_2). \tag{3.21}$$

Substitute from (3.17) into (3.21):

$$1 = kP(S_2).$$

Therefore

$$k = \frac{1}{P(S_2)} \tag{3.22}$$

Thus, all conditions are satisfied if we take as the revised (conditional) probabilities

$$p_i^* = kp_i = \frac{p_i}{P(S_2)} \quad (i = 1, 2, \ldots, 7).$$

For example, if p_3 is the (absolute) probability of x_3 when it is known only that one of the elements of $\mathcal{S}$ must occur, $p_3/P(S_2)$ is the conditional probability of x_3 given that an element of S_2 must occur.

Now suppose we wish the probability of S_1 given S_2. If $X \in S_2$, the only way for S_1 to occur is to have $X \in (S_1 \cap S_2)$. Appealing to Theorem 2, then, we want to add the probabilities associated with the elements of $S_1 \cap S_2$. Here we are interested in the revised (conditional) probabilities since we are applying the restriction that $X \in S_2$. Thus,

$$\begin{aligned} P(S_1 \mid S_2) = p_1^* + p_2^* + p_3^* &= \frac{p_1}{P(S_2)} + \frac{p_2}{P(S_2)} + \frac{p_3}{P(S_2)} \\ &= \frac{p_1 + p_2 + p_3}{P(S_2)} \\ &= \frac{P(S_1 \cap S_2)}{P(S_2)}, \end{aligned}$$

which is the rule defining the conditional probability of S_1 given S_2.

It is also true that

$$P(S_2 \mid S_1) = \frac{P(S_2 \cap S_1)}{P(S_1)} = \frac{P(S_1 \cap S_2)}{P(S_1)}$$

since $(S_2 \cap S_1) = (S_1 \cap S_2)$. Using these results, we can write $P(S_1 \cap S_2)$ in two equivalent ways:

$$P(S_1 \cap S_2) = P(S_1) \cdot P(S_2 \mid S_1),$$

and

$$P(S_1 \cap S_2) = P(S_2) \cdot P(S_1 \mid S_2).$$

These two results are referred to as the *general multiplication rule* (sometimes the *compound probability theorem*) and follow directly from the definition of conditional probability.

Since the development of conditional probability made no restrictions regarding dependence or independence, the general multiplication rule for the probability of an intersection always holds. Recall, however, that in the case of stochastic independence of S_1 and S_2, $P(S_1 \cap S_2) = P(S_1)P(S_2)$. This implies that in the case of independence

$$P(S_2) = P(S_2 \mid S_1) \quad \text{and} \quad P(S_1) = P(S_1 \mid S_2);$$

that is, the occurrence of S_1 has no effect on the probability of occurrence of S_2 and vice versa. This also indicates that stochastic independence is a symmetrical relation: If S_1 is independent of S_2, then S_2 is independent of S_1.

THEOREM 7. Stochastic independence of S_1 and S_2 implies stochastic independence of

(a) S_1 and S_2^c.
(b) S_2 and S_1^c.
(c) S_1^c and S_2^c.

We shall prove (a) only, leaving (b) and (c) for the reader.

Proof:

(a) By the general multiplication rule,

$$P(S_1 \cap S_2^c) = P(S_1)P(S_2^c \mid S_1) \tag{3.23}$$

(b) Now let us work on the term $P(S_2^c \mid S_1)$ with the aid of a Venn diagram.

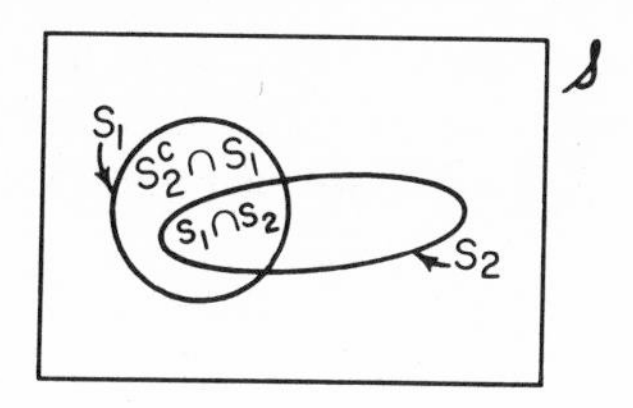

The condition that S_1 occurs implies that either $S_1 \cap S_2$ occurs or $S_2^c \cap S_1$ occurs. Therefore

$$P(S_1 \cap S_2 \mid S_1) + P(S_2^c \cap S_1 \mid S_1) = 1. \tag{3.24}$$

But $P(S_1 \cap S_2 \mid S_1) = P(S_2 \mid S_1)$, since if S_1 must occur, $S_1 \cap S_2$ is the only way S_2 can occur.

Similarly, $P(S_2^c \cap S_1 \mid S_1) = P(S_2^c \mid S_1)$, since if S_1 must occur, $S_2^c \cap S_1$ is the only way S_2^c can occur. Using the latter two results, (3.24) becomes

$$P(S_2 \mid S_1) + P(S_2^c \mid S_1) = 1,$$

or

$$P(S_2^c \mid S_1) = 1 - P(S_2 \mid S_1). \tag{3.25}$$

(c) By independence of S_2 and S_1, (3.25) becomes

$$P(S_2^c \mid S_1) = 1 - P(S_2). \tag{3.26}$$

(d) Then by Theorem 5, which states $1 - P(S_2) = P(S_2^c)$, (3.26) becomes

$$P(S_2^c \mid S_1) = P(S_2^c). \tag{3.27}$$

(e) Substituting (3.27) into (3.23),

$$P(S_1 \cap S_2^c) = P(S_1) \cdot P(S_2^c). \qquad \text{Q.E.D.}$$

EXAMPLE 3.5.1. A machine produces a ball bearing, the diameter of which is of critical importance. Under normal circumstances the machine produces ball bearings of incorrect size only 3% of the time. Periodically, the production supervisor chooses two ball bearings at random from the latest production run and determines how many are of the correct size.

Assuming the machinery is operating properly, what probabilities would you assign to finding zero, one, and two ball bearings of correct size?

Solution: First we must realize the meaning of the statement "Under normal circumstances the machine produces ball bearings of incorrect size only 3% of the time." This signifies that there is a probability of 0.03 that a randomly chosen ball bearing will be of incorrect size *if* the machine is operating properly.

Next, translating the supervisor's problem into technical terms, we have a random variable X equal to the number of ball bearings of correct size. The possible values of X when two parts are sampled comprise a sample space $\mathcal{S}$:

$$X \in \mathcal{S} = \{0, 1, 2\}.$$

We recognize that this sample space results from a compound experiment $E_1 \times E_2$, where E_1 is sampling and testing one ball bearing and E_2 is a replication of E_1.[16] Viewed in this way, a sample space for E_1 may be taken as $\mathcal{S}_1 = \{g_1, d_1\}$, where g_1 stands for a good ball bearing on the first trial and d_1 stands for a defective on the first trial. For experiment E_2, we have $\mathcal{S}_2 = \{g_2, d_2\}$. $E_1 \times E_2$ then produces a set of ordered pairs as a sample space:

$$\{(g_1, g_2), (g_1, d_2), (d_1, g_2), (d_1, d_2)\}.$$

We calculate the probability of a pair such as (d_1, d_2) as follows:

$$P(d_1, d_2) = P[\{d_1\} \cap \{d_2\}].$$

Applying the general multiplication rule,

$$P[\{d_1\} \cap \{d_2\}] = P(\{d_1\})\, P(\{d_2\} \mid \{d_1\}).$$

Since by assumption the machine is operating properly, any part chosen has a probability 0.03 of being the wrong size regardless of what has happened to any previously chosen part. As a result, the events $\{d_1\}$ and $\{d_2\}$ are stochastically independent; that is, the first part's being defective has no effect on the probability of a defective on the second trial — indeed, *whatever* occurs on the first trial has no effect on any probabilities connected with the second trial. We have, then, *stochastically independent trials.* Consequently,

$$\begin{aligned} P(\{d_1\})P(\{d_2\} \mid \{d_1\}) &= P(\{d_1\})P(\{d_2\}) \\ &= (0.03)(0.03) = 0.0009. \end{aligned}$$

Since the probability of a defective on any trial is 0.03, the probability of a ball bearing of correct size must be 0.97; hence

$$\begin{aligned} P(d_1, g_2) &= P(\{d_1\})P(\{g_2\}) \\ &= (0.03)(0.97) = 0.0291, \\ P(g_1, d_2) &= P(\{g_1\})P(\{d_2\}) \\ &= (0.97)(0.03) = 0.0291, \end{aligned}$$

[16]The replications of an experiment are frequently referred to as *trials;* thus E_1 and E_2 may be referred to as two trials of the same experiment.

$$\begin{aligned} P(g_1, g_2) &= P(\{g_1\})P(\{g_2\}) \\ &= (0.97)(0.97) = 0.9409. \end{aligned}$$

The two events (d_1, g_2) and (g_1, d_2) comprise the event one ball bearing of correct size; hence

$$P(X = 2) = P(d_1, g_2) + P(g_1, d_2) = 0.0291 + 0.0291 = 0.0582.$$

We can put the results together in the form of a set D as follows: Let $D = \{(x, y) \mid x \in \mathcal{S}, \text{ and } y = P(x)\}$. We thus summarize via a set of ordered pairs in which the first element of a pair is one of the possible values of X and the second element is its probability. In this case:

$$D = \{(0, 0.0009), (1, 0.0582), (2, 0.9409)\}.$$[17]

As a check on our arithmetic, we note that $0.0009 + 0.0582 + 0.9409 = 1.0000$. This must be the case since the elementary events 0, 1, and 2 comprise an entire sample space.

The example above illustrates the theoretical and practical importance of compound experiments, stochastic independence, etc. The concept of independence is not, fortunately, limited to two events or two experiments. We turn now to the concept of stochastic independence of three events, from which the generalization to any finite number of events is perfectly straightforward.

It might be conjectured that the simple product rule

$$P(S_1 \cap S_2 \cap S_3) = P(S_1)P(S_2)P(S_3)$$

would be sufficient to define stochastic independence of three events. The natural requirement that if the events S_1, S_2, and S_3 are independent, then any pair of them such as S_2 and S_3 should also be independent will show that the conjecture above leaves something to be desired. Consider, for example, the following three events defined with respect to the roll of a fair die:

S_1: an even number.
S_2: a number greater than 2.
S_3: a number divisible (without remainder) by either 3 or 5.

Clearly,

$$S_1 = \{2, 4, 6\} \quad \text{and} \quad P(S_1) = \tfrac{1}{2},$$

$$S_2 = \{3, 4, 5, 6\} \quad \text{and} \quad P(S_2) = \tfrac{2}{3},$$

$$S_3 = \{3, 5, 6\} \quad \text{and} \quad P(S_3) = \tfrac{1}{2}.$$

[17]When all the elements of a finite sample space are paired with their probabilities, we have what is known as a *probability distribution*. The set D is therefore a representation of a probability distribution.

Now, $S_1 \cap S_2 \cap S_3 = \{6\}$; hence $P(S_1 \cap S_2 \cap S_3) = \frac{1}{6}$, while $P(S_1)P(S_2)$ $P(S_3) = (\frac{1}{2})(\frac{2}{3})(\frac{1}{2}) = \frac{1}{6}$. On our conjectured definition, then, these three events would seem to be independent. If we consider S_1 and S_2 alone, $S_1 \cap S_2 = \{4, 6\}$ so that $P(S_1 \cap S_2) = \frac{1}{3}$ and indeed $P(S_1)P(S_2) = \frac{1}{3}$. However, $S_1 \cap S_3 = \{6\}$ so that $P(S_1 \cap S_3) = \frac{1}{6}$, while $P(S_1)P(S_3)$ $= (\frac{1}{2})(\frac{1}{2}) = \frac{1}{4}$. Further, $P(S_2 \cap S_3) = P(\{3, 5, 6\}) = \frac{1}{2}$, while $P(S_2)P(S_3)$ $= \frac{1}{3}$. Thus, *independence* of S_1, S_2, and S_3 in the sense only of the product rule for the triple intersection implies in this case independence of S_1 and S_2, but not S_1 and S_3 or S_2 and S_3.

Suppose on the other hand that we begin by requiring independence for all possible pairs out of three events and then see whether this implies the product rule for the triple intersection. Consider the experiment of choosing a number at random from among the numbers 1, 2, . . . , 9. In this case each digit has probability $\frac{1}{9}$ of being chosen. Now define the following three events:

S_1: a number divisible (without remainder) by 3.
S_2: a number greater than 6.
S_3: a number which is either odd or a perfect square.

Clearly,

$$S_1 = \{3, 6, 9\} \quad \text{and} \quad P(S_1) = \tfrac{1}{3},$$

$$S_2 = \{7, 8, 9\} \quad \text{and} \quad P(S_2) = \tfrac{1}{3}.$$

To determine S_3, we note that the odd numbers are 1, 3, 5, 7, 9 and the perfect squares are 1, 4, 9. Thus,

$$S_3 = \{1, 3, 4, 5, 7, 9\} \quad \text{and} \quad P(S_3) = \tfrac{2}{3}.$$

That all pairs contain independent events is shown as follows:

(i) $S_1 \cap S_2 = \{9\}$. Hence $P(S_1 \cap S_2) = \frac{1}{9}$, while
$P(S_1)P(S_2) = (\frac{1}{3})(\frac{1}{3}) = \frac{1}{9}$.

(ii) $S_1 \cap S_3 = \{3, 9\}$. Hence $P(S_1 \cap S_3) = \frac{2}{9}$, while
$P(S_1)P(S_3) = (\frac{1}{3})(\frac{2}{3}) = \frac{2}{9}$.

(iii) $S_2 \cap S_3 = \{7, 9\}$. Hence $P(S_2 \cap S_3) = \frac{2}{9}$, while
$P(S_2)P(S_3) = (\frac{1}{3})(\frac{2}{3}) = \frac{2}{9}$.

Turning to all three events together, however,

$$S_1 \cap S_2 \cap S_3 = \{9\}; \text{hence } P(S_1 \cap S_2 \cap S_3) = \tfrac{1}{9}. \text{ But}$$
$$P(S_1)P(S_2)P(S_3) = (\tfrac{1}{3})(\tfrac{1}{3})(\tfrac{2}{3}) = (\tfrac{2}{27}) \neq \tfrac{1}{9}.$$

Finally, then, the two examples above lead to the following *acceptable* definition of independence for three events.

DEFINITION. Three events S_1, S_2, and S_3 are said to be stochastically independent if and only if the following two conditions are satisfied:

(a) $P(S_1 \cap S_2 \cap S_3) = P(S_1)P(S_2)P(S_3)$.

(b) All events are stochastically independent in pairs.

We remark here that independence of S_1, S_2, and S_3 implies independence of such events as

(i) S_1 and $(S_2 \cap S_3)$.
(ii) S_1^c and $(S_2 \cap S_3)$.
(iii) S_1 and $(S_2^c \cap S_3)$.
(iv) S_1 and $(S_2 \cup S_3)$, etc.

In other words, any event which depends only on S_1 is stochastically independent of any event which depends only on S_2 and/or S_3. This is a three-event analogue of Theorem 7.

In terms of three events the general multiplication rule becomes

$$\begin{aligned} P(S_1 \cap S_2 \cap S_3) &= P(S_1)P(S_2 \mid S_1)P(S_3 \mid S_1 \cap S_2) \\ &= P(S_1)P(S_3 \mid S_1)P(S_2 \mid S_1 \cap S_3) \\ &= P(S_2)P(S_1 \mid S_2)P(S_3 \mid S_1 \cap S_2) \\ &= P(S_2)P(S_3 \mid S_2)P(S_1 \mid S_2 \cap S_3) \\ &= P(S_3)P(S_1 \mid S_3)P(S_2 \mid S_1 \cap S_3) \\ &= P(S_3)P(S_2 \mid S_3)P(S_1 \mid S_2 \cap S_3). \end{aligned}$$

It is clear that if the three events are stochastically independent, all six forms of the general multiplication rule collapse to

$$P(S_1 \cap S_2 \cap S_3) = P(S_1)P(S_2)P(S_3).$$

Having defined independence for three events, the definition for four events is immediate:

DEFINITION. Four events S_1, S_2, S_3, and S_4 are said to be stochastically independent if and only if the following two conditions are satisfied:

(a) $P(S_1 \cap S_2 \cap S_3 \cap S_4) = P(S_1)P(S_2)P(S_3)P(S_4)$.

(b) All events are stochastically independent in combinations of three (S_1, S_2, S_3 independent; S_1, S_3, S_4 independent; S_1, S_2, S_4 independent; or S_2, S_3, S_4 independent).

In general, once stochastic independence has been defined for $(n - 1)$ events, we have the following definition.

DEFINITION. n events $S_1, S_2, S_3, S_4, \ldots, S_n$ are said to be stochastically independent if and only if the following two conditions are satisfied:

(a) $P(S_1 \cap S_2 \cap S_3 \cap S_4 \cap \ldots \cap S_n)$

$$= P(S_1)P(S_2)P(S_3)P(S_4) \cdots P(S_n).$$

(b) All events are stochastically independent in combinations of $(n - 1)$.

EXAMPLE 3.5.2. The commander of a hypothetical antimissile system issues the following statement: "We have three defense barriers against an enemy missile. The probability of a missile being destroyed at the first barrier is 0.15, at the second barrier 0.35, and at the third barrier 0.50; it is therefore impossible for a missile to penetrate our defenses." Is he correct?

Solution: The commander has apparently added $0.15 + 0.35 + 0.50 = 1.00$ and concluded that it is certain that one of his three defenses will destroy any missile launched against him. We shall see, of course, that this is utterly incorrect. That simply adding the probabilities is totally indefensible is made immediately obvious by considering what would result if the first barrier had a 0.25 probability of destroying a missile. The sum would then be 1.10!

When a missile is launched, it either penetrates all barriers or gets shot down. The experiment of launching a missile and seeing whether or not it is destroyed can be viewed as the experiment $E = E_1 \times E_2 \times E_3$, where

E_1 is the missile being destroyed by or penetrating the first barrier.
E_2 is the missile being destroyed by or penetrating the second barrier.
E_3 is the missile being destroyed by or penetrating the third barrier.

For E_1 we have the sample space $\{d_1, p_1\}$, where d_1 indicates destroyed at first barrier and p_1 indicates penetrated first barrier. Similarly, for E_2 we have $\{d_2, p_2\}$ and for E_3 we have $\{d_3, p_3\}$.

The experiment E results in ordered triples, such as (p_1, p_2, d_3) which indicates that the missile was destroyed at the third barrier after it penetrated the first two. The probability of this event is

$$\begin{aligned} P(p_1, p_2, d_3) &= P(\{p_1\} \cap \{p_2\} \cap \{d_3\}) \\ &= P(\{p_1\})P(\{p_2\} \mid \{p_1\})P(\{d_3\} \mid \{p_1\} \cap \{p_2\}) \\ &= (0.85)(0.65)(0.50) = 0.27625, \end{aligned}$$

since if the first barrier is penetrated, the probability of penetrating the second is 0.65 (1 − 0.35); if the first two are penetrated, the third will destroy the missile with probability 0.50.

Some of the triple intersections (or ordered triples) are clearly impossible events. For example, consider (p_1, d_2, d_3). This event corresponds to being destroyed at both the second and third barriers, but if the missile is destroyed at the second barrier it never reaches the third. This causes no difficulty, however, since

$$\begin{aligned} P(p_1, d_2, d_3) &= P(\{p_1\})P(\{d_2\} \mid \{p_1\})P(\{d_3\} \mid \{p_1\} \cap \{d_2\}) \\ &= (0.85)(0.35)(0) = 0. \end{aligned}$$

That is, given that the missile penetrated the first and was destroyed at the second barrier, the probability that it is also destroyed at the third barrier is zero. This indicates most clearly that the three events are *not* stochastically independent, for $P(\{d_3\} \mid \{p_1\} \cap \{d_2\}) \neq P(\{d_3\})$. Thus the three experiments (or trials) composing the experiment E are themselves dependent.

The event of interest according to the commander's statement is the event that a missile launched against his defenses is destroyed. It is far easier, however, to consider the complementary event that the missile is not destroyed since the latter event is composed of only one ordered triple, namely (p_1, p_2, p_3).

$$\begin{aligned} P(p_1, p_2, p_3) &= P(\{p_1\})P(\{p_2\} \mid \{p_1\})P(\{p_3\} \mid \{p_1\} \cap \{p_2\}) \\ &= (0.85)(0.65)(0.50) = 0.27625. \end{aligned}$$

The probability that a launched missile is destroyed is clearly one minus the probability that it is not destroyed. Hence the probability that any missile launched is destroyed by the defense system is only 1 − 0.27625 = 0.72375, a far cry from certainty!

Note to Chapter 3

The Gapped Sample Space

In Chapter 3 we presented a set of theorems which are of fundamental importance in probability theory. For reasons of mathematical convenience we restricted attention solely to finite sample spaces. It is easy to envision situations in which the finiteness restriction would be inconsistent with a phenomenon to be investigated. Suppose, for example, that we were interested in the number of imperfections (scratches, dents, discolorations, etc.) present on a machine component produced by an assembly line process. The set of possibilities is

$$\mathcal{S} = \{0, 1, 2, \ldots, 1{,}000, 1{,}001, \ldots\},$$

which is an infinite set. One may claim that for practical purposes the sample space can be considered to "stop" at 1,000 since beyond that point it becomes impossible even to distinguish individual imperfections. The objection to this is that 1,000 is perfectly arbitrary; why not stop at 950 or 973 or 1,001? Alternatively, one might claim that it makes sense to stop at 1,000 because the probability of more than 1,000 imperfections is so unlikely as to be negligible. Such an argument, however, presupposes the ability to apply probabilistic analysis to an infinite sample space, which is precisely the point of this note.

Specifically, we wish to state the conditions under which the results of Chapter 3 (and 4) would also apply to infinite sample spaces. Though we can offer no proof here, it turns out that Axioms 1–3 are insufficient to develop our probability theorems in the case of infinite sample spaces. We require

AXIOM 4. Let $\mathcal{S}$ be an infinite sample space with an infinite number of subsets S_1, S_2, S_3, S_4, ... If $S_i \cap S_j = \varnothing$ for all $i \neq j$, and if

$$S = S_1 \cup S_2 \cup S_3 \cup S_4 \cup \ldots,$$

then

$$P(S) = \sum_{i=1}^{\infty} P(S_i).$$

Stated simply, Axiom 4 extends Axiom 3 to the union of an infinite number of disjoint subsets.

Any sample space to which probabilities can be assigned in such a way that Axioms 1–4 hold can be considered a "legitimate" sample space in the sense that all subsequent theorems continue to hold true.

The question now is whether all infinite sample spaces are consistent with Axioms 1–4. The answer is no! We state without proof, however, that the set of all natural numbers

$$\mathcal{R} = \{1, 2, 3, 4, \ldots\}$$

is consistent with our axioms and that in fact any infinite set which is one-to-one matching with the set $\mathcal{R}$ is also consistent with the axioms. Any set which is either finite or one-to-one matching with $\mathcal{R}$ will be referred to as a *gapped* sample space,[18] and all theorems in Chapters 3 and 4 will be considered to apply to gapped sample spaces even though the proofs refer only to the finite case.

In some instances we are interested in phenomena of the following sort. Suppose a new light bulb is known to have a maximum life of 100 hours. The length of life of the light bulb is a random variable, say X, defined on the set

$$\{x \mid 0 \leq x \leq 100\},$$

where the numbers refer to hours (and of course fractions of hours). This set is clearly infinite, but not one-to-one matching with the set $\mathcal{R}$ and clearly not gapped. Nonetheless, we should like to be able to consider a problem of this sort and apply probabilistic analysis to it. For example, we might wish to know the probability that the bulb will last more than 50 hours; that is,

$$P(50 < X \leq 100).$$

Such a question, in fact, provides the key to handling a nongapped sample space. We simply divide the original set into a finite number of intervals, say,

$$\{a, b, c, d \mid 0 \leq a < 25, 25 < b < 50, 50 < c < 75, 75 < d \leq 100\},$$

and apply our analysis to this redefined "finite" sample space.[19] The number of intervals we choose depends of course on our interests in the particular problem.

Random variables defined with respect to gapped sample spaces are termed *discrete* random variables, while those which arise from situations such as that of the light bulb are termed *continuous* random variables. Although most of this book is concerned with discrete random variables, we shall have occasion in Chapter 6 to consider the so-called *normal* random variable, which is continuous.

[18]This is for the obvious reason that there are "gaps" in the sample space. That is, the set

$$\{x \mid 0 < x < 1\}$$

will not do, for it contains *all* numbers between zero and one; there are no "gaps."

[19]Note that we have defined the intervals such that the numbers 25, 50, and 75 are excluded, thereby actually making the sample space gapped. While the original set contained the numbers 25, 50, and 75, nothing has been lost by excluding them since no positive probabilities could have been defined for these individual points. We are able to assign positive probabilities to intervals of positive length, but not to points (which are intervals of length zero).

PROBLEMS

3-1. In October, 1965 an official in the United States space program stated "There is a possibility that the United States will attempt a manned lunar landing by 1968, but not a probability." What do you suppose he meant? How should the statement have been worded?

3-2. If S_1 and S_2 are subsets of a sample space $\mathcal{S}$ such that $P(S_1) + P(S_2) = 1$, is it necessarily true that $S_1 \cap S_2 = \varnothing$? If your answer is yes, explain why. If your answer is no, give a counter example.

3-3. One card is drawn at random from a standard bridge deck of 52 cards. Find the probabilities of the following events by defining subsets (of the sample space) S_1 and S_2 such that $P\{\text{the indicated event}\} = P(S_1) + P(S_2)$.

(a) The card selected is a heart or a spade.
(b) The card selected is a spade or a red card.
(c) The card selected is a king or a queen.
(d) The card selected is a king or a black queen.
(e) The card selected is a face card or an ace.

3-4. A letter of the alphabet is selected at random. Find the probability that the letter selected

(a) Is a vowel.
(b) Precedes u.
(c) Follows n and is a vowel.

3-5. Suppose $A_1, A_2, \ldots, A_5$ partition a sample space. Prove

$$\sum_{i=1}^{5} P(A_i) = 1.$$

3-6. The event D is twice as likely as A, and B is twice as likely as $(A \cup D)$. The events A, B, and D partition a sample space. Find their respective probabilities.

3-7. A card is drawn at random from a standard deck. Let A be the event that the card selected is an ace and S be the event that the card selected is a spade.

(a) Are A and S mutually exclusive?
(b) Find the probability that at least one of the events A and S occurs.

3-8. A state highway department has records which indicate that there are 5.76 automobile accidents per 1,000 vehicle miles after dark. The records also show that, while only 10% of after dark drivers have been drinking, 50% of the after dark accidents involve a driver who has been drinking. Find the probability that a man will safely make the one-mile trip home from an after dark party, given

(a) He has been drinking.
(b) He has not been drinking.

3-9. A card is drawn at random from a standard deck. Find the probability that the card is

(a) A face card and a club.
(b) A face card but not a club.
(c) A club but not a face card.
(d) A face card or a club.
(e) A king or a black face card.

3-10. Let $A = A_1 \cup A_2 \cup A_3 \cup A_4$. Prove

$$P(A) \leq P(A_1) + P(A_2) + P(A_3) + P(A_4).$$

3-11. Prove $P(S^c) = 1 - P(S)$.

3-12. A warehouse contains 100 coats left over from several bargain sales. Due to considerable handling, age, etc., there are no size tags left on the coats. Sketchy inventory records indicate the following:

(a) The only sizes left unsold were 10, short; 10, average; 12, average; and 12, long.
(b) Of the remaining coats 45% are average length, 60% are size 10, and 12% are long.

If a coat is selected at random, what is the probability that it is

(i) Not long?
(ii) 10, short?
(iii) 12, average?

3-13. Let $A = A_1 \cup A_2 \cup A_3$. Prove

$$P(A) = P(A_1) + P(A_2) + P(A_3) - P(A_1 \cap A_2) - P(A_1 \cap A_3)$$
$$- P(A_2 \cap A_3) + P(A_1 \cap A_2 \cap A_3).$$

Can you see how this result and the theorem $P(A_1 \cup A_2) = P(A_1) + P(A_2) - P(A_1 \cap A_2)$ may be generalized to

(a) Four events?
(b) Any finite number of events?

3-14. One card is drawn at random from a standard deck. What is the probability that the card selected is a king or a face card or a heart?

3-15. A large city has three daily newspapers — paper A, paper B, and paper C. A survey of the population yields the following:

(a) Twenty percent of the population reads at least paper A.
(b) Sixteen percent reads at least B.
(c) Fourteen percent reads at least C.
(d) Seventeen percent reads at least two papers and 1.5% reads all three.
(e) Five percent of the population reads at least A and C and the proportion reading at least B and C is twice as large as the proportion reading at least A and B.

If an individual is selected at random from the population of the city, what is the probability that he reads

(i) At least one newspaper?
(ii) Only newspaper A?

3-16. Let A_1, A_2, A_3, A_4 partition the sample space for experiment E_1, and B_1, B_2, B_3 partition the sample space for experiment E_2. Prove that the set of 12 events (A_i, B_j) for $(i = 1, 2, 3, 4)$ and $(j = 1, 2, 3)$ partition the sample space for experiment $E = E_1 \times E_2$.

3-17. Consider the experiment of rolling a die twice and recording the outcome as an ordered pair. What is the sample space $\mathcal{S}$ for this experiment? Is $\mathcal{S}$ the same as the sample space for the experiment of rolling two indistinguishable dice at the same time? Why?

3-18. The following table summarizes the results of 200 repetitions of a compound experiment. Each in a group of 200 households was asked how much his household planned to spend on additions and repairs to their residence during the next year. The responses were categorized into one of the following ($\leq$ \$199, \$200–499, $\geq$ \$500). A year later the same 200 households were asked how much they actually spent on additions and repairs to residence. The responses were again categorized and each household's planned and actual expenditures were compared. It was found that, of the 50 households which planned to spend \$199 or less, 42 actually did while 6 actually spent from \$200 to \$499 and 2 actually spent \$500 or more. These plus the remaining findings are listed in the table.

		Planned expenditures for additions and repairs to residence			
		≤$199	$200–$499	≥$500	Total
Actual expenditures for additions and repairs to residence	≤$199	42	28	22	92
	$200–$499	6	20	14	40
	≥$500	2	12	54	68
	Total	50	60	90	200

Suppose we pick a household at random and determine its planned expenditures on additions and repairs to residence during the next year. Then suppose a year from now we determine the amount that some household actually has spent on additions and repairs. We record the results as an ordered pair corresponding to the expenditure categories listed above.

(a) Let E_1 denote the experiment of determining the household's planned expenditures and E_2 denote the experiment of determining the household's actual expenditures. Write out the sample space and probability associated with each element for the experiments E_1, E_2, and $E_1 \times E_2$. Be sure and make explicit any assumptions involved in your answer.

(b) Find the probability that the household selected at random

(i) Spent what it planned.

(ii) Spent more than planned.

3-19. The following table summarizes the results of 261 repetitions of a compound experiment which compares the past behavior of household income with expected future behavior.

		Income during the past 10 years has				
		Increased	Been constant	Decreased	Fluctuated	Total
Expected income during the next 10 years will	Increase	68	31	22	42	163
	Be constant	10	20	7	12	49
	Decrease	5	7	8	6	26
	Fluctuate	4	3	4	12	23
	Total	87	61	41	72	261

Suppose we choose a household at random and perform the compound experiment E above.

(a) Define two simple experiments E_1 and E_2, complete with sample spaces and (implied) associated probabilities, such that

$$E_1 \times E_2 = E.$$

(b) Find the probability that the household selected at random

(i) Expects future income to rise.
(ii) Expects future income to rise and it rose in the past.
(iii) Expects future income to fluctuate and it fell in the past.
(iv) Expects future income to behave in the same manner as past income.

(c) The households in this sample seem to be generally optimistic concerning future income behavior. Does there appear to be any relation between a household's past and its expectations of the future? Explain.

3-20. In a four-child family, what is the probability that all children are of the same sex? (Assume the sexes are equiprobable at birth.)

3-21. A coin is flipped three times. What is the probability that it lands *heads* exactly once?

3-22. Describe the relationship between the events A and B and express $P(A \cup B)$ under each of the following conditions:

(a) $P(A \cap B) = P(A)P(B)$.

(b) $P(A \cap B) = P(A)$.

(c) $P(A \mid B) = P(A \cap B)$.

Does (c) imply (b)? Explain.

3-23. The probability of a white male, age 60, dying within 1 year is 0.023 and the probability of a white female, age 55, dying within 1 year is 0.008. If a man and his wife are ages 60 and 55 respectively, what is the probability

(a) Neither will die within 1 year?
(b) At least one will die within 1 year?
(c) At least one will live through 1 year?

3-24. Of all men drafted, 45% are physically unfit for military service. Of all draftees, 20% are rejected because of poor eyesight. Given that a draftee was rejected, what is the probability he was rejected because of poor eyesight?

3-25. A boy enjoys throwing rocks at the bell in a church steeple. He has a probability of 0.7 of hitting the bell on any throw. Unfortunately he is hard-of-hearing and has to rely on his little brother to tell him whether he has scored a hit. If his brother tells him the truth 60% of the time, what is the probability that he hit the bell, given that his brother said he did?

3-26. A man tosses a red die and a white die simultaneously. Find the probability that

(a) The white die reads 3, given the red die reads 2.
(b) The results sum to 5, given at least one die reads 3.

3-27. A bag contains three luminous white, five luminous green, four nonluminous white, and six nonluminous green beads. A bead is selected at random. What is the probability that

(a) It is white?
(b) It is luminous green, given it is green?
(c) It is green, given it is luminous?
(d) It is green or luminous?

3-28. Three students — Tom, Dick, and Harry — all want to borrow a book of which the lender has but one copy. The lender says "I am thinking of a number from one to three, inclusive. Tom, you guess first. If you are right you get the book. If you guess wrong, Dick guesses. If Dick guesses wrong, Harry gets the book." Harry protests that the plan is unfair. Is it?

3-29. In Problem 3-28 suppose the lender had said "Each of you submit a guess in writing. No collusion is allowed. I will read Tom's guess first. If Tom's guess is correct, he gets the book. If not, I will read Dick's guess. If Dick's guess is correct, he gets the book. If not, I will read Harry's guess. If Harry is correct, he gets the book but if he is wrong, I keep the book." Find the probability of success associated with each of the prospective borrowers — Tom, Dick, and Harry — under this scheme.

3-30. Flip a penny, a dime, and a quarter in succession. What is the probability that all three come up heads, given

(a) The penny is heads?
(b) At least one is heads?

Can you explain the difference?

3-31. A desk contains two drawers. The right-hand drawer contains three dimes and two nickels. The left-hand drawer contains four nickels and two dimes.

(a) If one coin is taken at random from each drawer, find the probability that

(i) Both coins are dimes.
(ii) Both coins are the same denomination.

(b) A drawer is selected at random and two coins are drawn from it. What is the probability that the coins will be of the same denomination?

3-32. In Problem 3-12, the owner takes his wife and mother-in-law to the warehouse for each to select a coat. The wife is 12, average and the mother-in-law is 10, short. Each chooses a coat.

(a) What is the probability that each has chosen a coat that fits her?
(b) What is the probability that at least one has chosen a coat that will fit her?
(c) What is the probability that, of the two coats chosen, one will fit the wife and the other will fit the mother-in-law?
(d) Show that the probability that the wife picks a coat that will fit her is the same whether the wife chooses first or whether the mother-in-law chooses first.
(e) Suppose the mother-in-law is allowed to continue choosing alone until she has found a coat that fits her. There are then two piles of coats — the coats discarded by the mother-in-law because they did not fit her and the remainder of the original pile. If the mother-in-law got a coat that fit on the tenth try, is the wife likely to have better luck picking from the pile of discards or the pile of remaining originals?

3-33. A die is rolled three times. Find the probability that

(a) The first roll is a 1, the second is a 2, and the third is a 3.
(b) The first roll is not a 1, the second is a 2, and the third is a 3.
(c) The first roll is a 1, the second is not a 2, and the third is not a 3.
(d) The first roll is a 1 *or* {the second roll is not a 2 *and* the third roll is not a 3}.

3-34. Suppose the baseball world series is best of five games (the series ends as soon as one team wins three games). If the teams are evenly matched so that each has probability equal to $\frac{1}{2}$ of winning any game, find the probability that

(a) The series goes a full five games. (It may interest you to know that in the actual seven game world series the probability, assuming the two teams are evenly matched, of a full seven game series is 0.31. Since 1903, 29% of all world series have gone seven games.)

(b) The National League team wins in four games; five games.

(c) The American League team wins at least two games.

3-35. There are two urns, U_1 and U_2. U_1 contains two red and five green balls. U_2 contains four white and seven red balls.

(a) A ball is drawn at random from each urn. What is the probability that

(i) Both are red?

(ii) The two balls differ in color?

(b) One ball is drawn from U_1 and placed in U_2. Then a ball is drawn from U_2. What is the probability that this second ball drawn is

(i) Red?

(ii) Green?

3-36. In Problem 3-29, suppose that instead of keeping the book himself in the case all written guesses are wrong, the lender permits Tom, Dick, and Harry to submit a second written guess. The lender does not reveal what first-round guesses were made but Tom, Dick, and Harry would each know his own first-round guess. In the event of a second round, the lender would again read Tom's guess first. If Tom was wrong again, he would read Dick's second guess, etc. In the event that no one guesses the number on the first two rounds, a third round would ensue. Under this scheme find the probability that Tom will eventually win, that Dick will eventually win, and that Harry will eventually win.

3-37. Three people enter an elevator. What is the probability that at least two have the same birthday (same day of month, not same year of birth)? Assume all years contain 365 days.

3-38. Let A and B partition a sample space S and let $H \subset S$. Further suppose $P(A)$, $P(B)$, $P(H \mid A)$, and $P(H \mid B)$ are all known.

(a) Prove $$P(A \mid H) = \frac{P(A) \cdot P(H \mid A)}{P(A)P(H \mid A) + P(B)P(H \mid B)}.$$

This result is known as Bayes' theorem.

(b) Derive a similar expression for $P(A \mid H)$ when S is partitioned by three events A, B, and C.

3-39. The probability that a certain beginner at golf makes a good shot if he uses the correct club is $\frac{1}{3}$. The probability that he makes a good shot with the wrong club is $\frac{1}{5}$. In his bag are four different clubs, only one of which is correct for the shot he is about to take. Since the beginner knows practically nothing about choice of the proper club, he selects a club at random. He chooses a club and takes a stroke.

(a) With what probability did he get off a good shot?
(b) Given that he got off a good shot, what is the probability that he chose a wrong club?

3-40. Of students who major in statistics, 10% learn econometrics; 5% of the students in business schools learn econometrics; and 15% of economics majors learn econometrics. The junior research staff of a large corporation is made up entirely of graduates of these three fields with 40% having majored in economics and 40% having graduated from business school. A staff member chosen at random is given a research task which involves econometrics. If he does the the problem well, what is the probability that he

(a) Majored in economics?
(b) Is a business school graduate?

4 RANDOM VARIABLES AND PROBABILITY DISTRIBUTIONS

4.1 Introduction

A random variable associated with a *gapped sample space* is referred to as a *discrete random variable*. A random variable which is not discrete is referred to as a *continuous random variable*. We shall discuss the latter in Chapter 6, but the area of application of discrete random variables is so rich that we shall concentrate on the discrete class in developing the important properties of random variables.

Perhaps the most basic notion is that of the *probability distribution*. We shall see, in fact, that all characteristics of a random variable can be derived directly from the probability distribution. In simplest terms, if X is the random variable, any pairing of the possible values of X with their probabilities is the probability distribution of X. Suppose, for example, $X \in \mathcal{S} = \{-1, 1, 2, 5, 10\}$ and $P(X = -1) = 0.2$, $P(X = 1) = 0.1$, $P(X = 2) = 0.3$, $P(X = 5) = 0.1$, and $P(X = 10) = 0.3$. The probability distribution of X can be represented conveniently in at least three ways:

(i) Tabular representation:[1]

x	$P(X = x) = P(x)$
-1	0.2
1	0.1
2	0.3
5	0.1
10	0.3
	1.0

(ii) Set representation:

$$D = \{(x, y) \mid x \in \mathcal{S} \quad \text{and} \quad y = P(x)\}$$
$$= \{(-1, 0.2), (1, 0.1), (2, 0.3), (5, 0.1), (10, 0.3)\}.$$

(iii) Area representation:

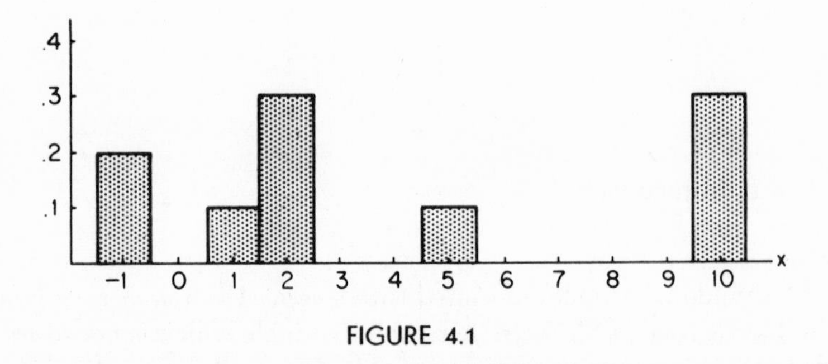

FIGURE 4.1

In Figure 4.1, the area of each shaded rectangle represents a probability. $P(X = 2)$, for example, is represented by the area of the rectangle "sitting on top of" the number 2. The area of the rectangle is base times height. The base of the rectangle is centered at 2 but extends from 1.5 to 2.5 and therefore has a length of 1. The height is 0.3, as seen on the vertical axis, so that $P(X = 2) = (1)(0.3) = 0.3$. An alternative area representation would be Figure 4.2.

[1]Note that the random variable itself is denoted by X, while its possible values (the elements of the sample space) are denoted by x. Thus $x_1 = -1$, $x_2 = 1$, $x_3 = 2$, $x_4 = 5$, $x_5 = 10$; and one of the x's will be the realization of X.

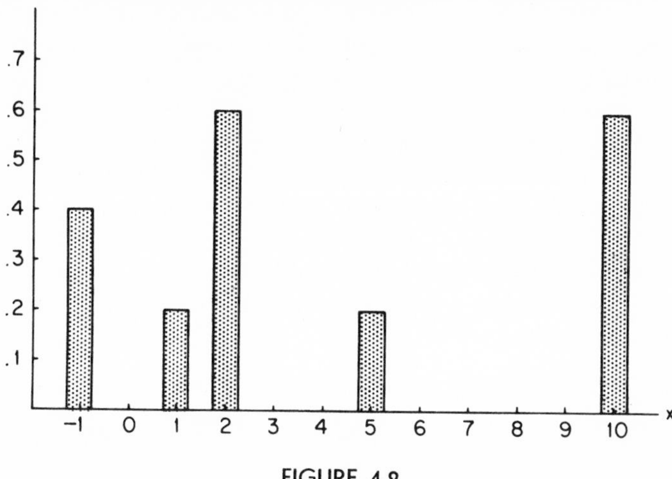

FIGURE 4.2

In this case, $P(X = 2)$ is represented by a base of $\frac{1}{2}$ times a height of 0.6, which is still an area of 0.3. In Figure 4.1, all rectangles have a base of unity so that the heights themselves measure probabilities as well as the areas of the rectangles. In Figure 4.2, all rectangles have a base of $\frac{1}{2}$ so that the heights no longer measure probabilities. The important points are that in a given representation *all* rectangles have equal-sized bases which are centered on the possible values of X and the area of each rectangle is equal to the probability of the particular value on which the rectangle is centered. This means that the sum of the areas of all the rectangles is unity, since the probabilities associated with the points of a sample space must sum to unity. Further, if we form a subset such as $S = \{1, 5\}$, $P(X \in S)$ equals the sum of the areas of the rectangles associated with 1 and 5.

EXAMPLE 4.1.1. A fair coin is tossed twice — or, what is the same thing, two fair coins are tossed simultaneously. Let X equal the number of heads which appear. Find the probability distribution of X.

Solution: The sample space for X is $\mathcal{S} = \{0, 1, 2\}$, which is the set of possibilities for the number of heads in two coin tosses.

We recognize that we can view the situation as a compound experiment with a set of ordered pairs as sample space:

$$\{(\text{H, H}), (\text{H, T}), (\text{T, H}), (\text{T, T})\}.$$

The first element in the pair refers to the result associated with coin No. 1, the second element to coin No. 2. It is important to remember that (H, T) and (T, H) are *different* elementary events even though they both correspond to (form the subset) one head, one tail. If we toss a coin twice,

(H, T) stands for heads on the first toss and tails on the second toss; while (T, H) is tails first, and then heads. If we are tossing a penny and a dime, (H, T) may stand for heads with the penny and tails with the dime; while (T, H) will then represent tails with the penny and heads with the dime. Logically, the situation is exactly the same when two identical coins are tossed simultaneously even though *after* the toss it may be difficult to tell which of the coins landed heads and which tails.

The experiments (or trials) composing the compound experiment are, of course, stochastically independent so that the probabilities of the ordered pairs are easily calculated:

$$P(\text{H, H}) = P[\{\text{H}\} \cap \{\text{H}\}] = P(\text{H})\cdot P(\text{H}) = \tfrac{1}{2}\cdot\tfrac{1}{2} = \tfrac{1}{4},$$

$$P(\text{H, T}) = P(\text{H})\cdot P(\text{T}) = \tfrac{1}{2}\cdot\tfrac{1}{2} = \tfrac{1}{4},$$

$$P(\text{T, H}) = P(\text{T})\cdot P(\text{H}) = \tfrac{1}{2}\cdot\tfrac{1}{2} = \tfrac{1}{4},$$

$$P(\text{T, T}) = P(\text{T})\cdot P(\text{T}) = \tfrac{1}{2}\cdot\tfrac{1}{2} = \tfrac{1}{4};$$

in other words, the ordered pairs are equally likely elementary events. The ordered pairs correspond to the elements of $\mathcal{S}$ as follows:

0 heads: (T, T).
1 head: (H, T) and (T, H).
2 heads: (H, H).

The second correspondence implies

$$\begin{aligned} P(X = 1) &= P\{(\text{H, T}), (\text{T, H})\}^{2} \\ &= P(\text{H, T}) + P(\text{T, H}) \\ &= \tfrac{1}{4} + \tfrac{1}{4} \\ &= \tfrac{1}{2}. \end{aligned}$$

The desired probability distribution is therefore

x	$P(x)$
0	0.25
1	0.50
2	0.25
	1.00

[2]A subset composed of two elementary events of the compound experiment, namely {(H, T), (T, H)}, is equivalent to the event $X = 1$. Therefore, by Theorem 2, Chapter 3, we merely add the probabilities associated with the elementary events which comprise the subset.

4.2 Expectation and Variance

Consider again the random variable X with the following probability distribution:

x	$P(x)$
−1	0.2
1	0.1
2	0.3
5	0.1
10	0.3

By definition it is impossible to predict with certainty what will result when the experiment producing X is conducted. We can ask, however, what the most likely result will be, or in other words, which realization would be the safest on which to bet. The answer is the possible value which has the largest probability. This element of $\mathcal{S}$ is known as the *modal value* or the *mode* of X. In our example two values, 2 and 10, tie for the mode as is seen from the probability distribution. In such a case the distribution (or probability distribution) of X is said to be *bimodal.*

If the experiment is repeated a very large number of times, the most frequent realizations should be the modal values 2 and 10. Exactly what would be expected to occur in a really large number of repetitions? Since the value -1 has a probability of 0.2, we would expect 20% of the realizations to be -1. This does *not* mean that out of 1,000 trials we should expect the first 200 to come out -1. Rather, the -1's will be distributed randomly throughout the 1,000 trials but we should expect 200 of them altogether. Similarly we would expect the number 1 to occur 10% of the time, 2 to occur 30% of the time, 5 to occur 10% of the time, and 10 to occur 30% of the time. Let us agree that a conceptual sequence of trials in which the proportion of times a given realization occurs is equal to its probability will be referred to as a *theoretical sequence.* The sequence in which -1 occurs 20% of the time, 1 occurs 10% of the tine, and so on is therefore a theoretical sequence. If we think in terms of 1,000 trials producing the theoretical sequence, we might wish to summarize the results by calculating the average; that is, by adding up all the results and dividing by 1,000. If we first ordered the results numerically, we would have

$$\underbrace{-1, -1, \ldots, -1,}_{200\text{ times}} \quad \underbrace{1, 1, \ldots, 1,}_{100\text{ times}}$$

$$\underbrace{2, 2, \ldots, 2,}_{300\text{ times}} \quad \underbrace{5, 5, \ldots, 5,}_{100\text{ times}} \quad \underbrace{10, 10, \ldots, 10.}_{300\text{ times}}$$

It is easy to see what the average of the theoretical sequence would be:

$$\frac{(-1)+(-1)+\cdots+(-1)+1+1+\cdots+1+2+2+\cdots+2+5+5+\cdots+5+10+10\cdots+10}{1{,}000}$$

$$= \frac{-1(200) + 1(100) + 2(300) + 5(100) + 10(300)}{1{,}000}$$

$$= -1\left(\frac{200}{1{,}000}\right) + 1\left(\frac{100}{1{,}000}\right) + 2\left(\frac{300}{1{,}000}\right) + 5\left(\frac{100}{1{,}000}\right) + 10\left(\frac{300}{1{,}000}\right)$$

$$= -1(0.2) + 1(0.1) + 2(0.3) + 5(0.1) + 10(0.3)$$

$$= -0.2 + 0.1 + 0.6 + 0.5 + 3.0 = 4.0.$$

The average would thus turn out to be 4.0. An *actual* sequence of 1,000 trials might not produce an average of precisely 4.0, but we would certainly not expect it to be far off. Notice that in calculating the average value of our theoretical or expected sequence of 1,000 trials, we came to the expression

$$-1(0.2) + 1(0.1) + 2(0.3) + 5(0.1) + 10(0.3)$$

which is just

$$-1\,P(X = -1) + 1\,P(X = 1) + 2\,P(X = 2) + 5\,P(X = 5) + 10\,P(X = 10).$$

The average of a theoretical sequence plays an extremely important role in the theory and application of random variables and is referred to as the *expected value of X*.[3]

DEFINITION. The *expected value* of a (discrete) random variable X is denoted by EX and is defined by

$$EX = \sum_x x\,P(x).^4$$

[3]Other common terms are the *expectation of X* and the *mean of X*.

[4]If there are T possible values of X and they are denoted by x_i ($i = 1, 2, \ldots, T$), we can write

$$EX = \sum_{i=1}^{T} x_i\,P(x_i)$$

which is the same as

$$x_1\,P(x_1) + x_2\,P(x_2) + \ldots + x_T\,P(x_T).$$

It is often more convenient, however, not to have to specify the summation index or the number of items being summed. In such a case we write

$$\sum_x x\,P(x)$$

The expected value is thus a weighted sum of the points in the sample space for X, where the weights are precisely the corresponding probabilities of occurrence. The notion of expected value is precisely analogous to the familiar *center of mass* in physics. Consider a uniform bar with weights placed as follows.

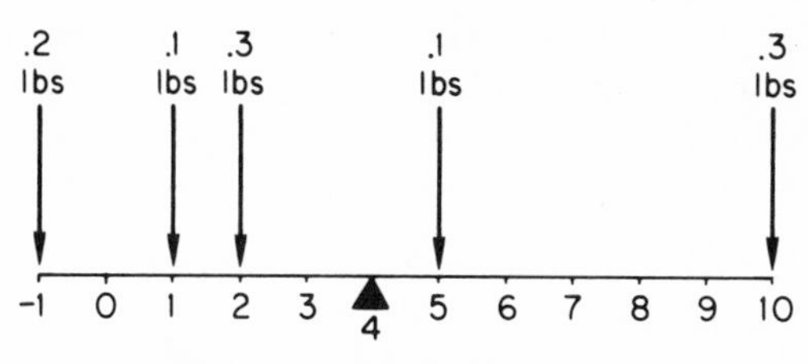

FIGURE 4.3

The center of mass is at 4, which is the point at which a fulcrum must be placed in order for the bar to swing neither left nor right. The expected value thus *balances* the elements of the sample space according to their relative *weights* or probabilities.

Note that while the modal value must be one of the possible values of X, the expected value of X need not be an element of the sample space. Indeed in our example, $EX = 4$, but 4 can never be the realization of X. EX is thus to be interpreted merely as the average of a theoretical sequence of realizations or, as will be noted later, as the average of a very large number of actual realizations.

EXAMPLE 4.2.1. Calculate EX where X equals the number of heads in two tosses of a fair coin.

Solution: In Example 4.1.1 we found the probability distribution of this random variable. Applying the definition

$$EX = \sum_x x\, P(x):$$

x	$P(x)$	$x\,P(x)$
0	0.25	$0(0.25) = 0$
1	0.50	$1(0.50) = 0.50$
2	0.25	$2(0.25) = 0.50$
	1.00	$\sum_x x\,P(x) = 1.00$

---

which means the same as

$$\sum_{i=1}^{T} x_i\, P(x_i)$$

and is read *the sum over* all possible values of x of the products $x\,P(x)$.

Thus, $EX = 1$, which means that in a theoretical sequence of repetitions (or in a very large number of actual repetitions) the average of the number of heads would be 1. Note that for this particular random variable the mode and the expected value are equal.

EXAMPLE 4.2.2. In Example 3.5.1, we found the probability distribution of X = the number of ball bearings of correct size. This random variable resulted from sampling two ball bearings from a machine process which produced 3% defective ball bearings. Calculate EX.

Solution: Using the probability distribution derived in the solution to Example 3.5.1, we calculate

x	$P(x)$	$x\,P(x)$
0	0.0009	$0(0.0009) = 0$
1	0.0582	$1(0.0582) = 0.0582$
2	0.9409	$2(0.9409) = 1.8818$
	1.0000	$\sum_x x\,P(x) = 1.9400$

Thus the expected number of ball bearings of correct size is 1.94. This can be interpreted in several equivalent ways. If the probability of a ball bearing of correct size is 0.97,

(a) A large number of trials (each trial being a sample of 2 ball bearings) will produce 1.94 good ball bearings per trial *on the average*.

(b) In 100 trials (each trial being a sample of 2 ball bearings) we would *expect* a total of 194 [(100)(1.94)] good ball bearings out of 200.

Note that 1.94 good ball bearings out of 2 represents a proportion of $1.94/2 = 0.97$, which is precisely the probability of a good ball bearing.

It is frequently useful to define some function of a random variable X, such as $3X$ or X^2 or $X - 2$. Any such function is itself a random variable since the value of, say, $3X$ cannot be predicted with certainty prior to the performance of a random experiment. Suppose E is the random experiment which produces X. Then the experiment which produces the random variable $3X$ is *carry out experiment E and multiply the result by* 3.

Now what is the expected value of $3X$? If we write $Y = 3X$, then by definition

$$E(3X) = EY = \sum_y y\,P(y),$$

where the possible values of Y are denoted by y. By substituting the definition of Y into the sum, we can write that by definition

$$E(3X) = \sum_{3x} (3x)\, P(3x).$$

Return again to the following:

x	$P(x)$
-1	0.2
1	0.1
2	0.3
5	0.1
10	0.3
	1.0

The possible values of $3X$ are therefore $\{-3, 3, 6, 15, 30\}$. Now $3X = -3$ if and only if $X = -1$; therefore $P(3X = -3) = P(X = -1) = 0.2$. Similarly, $P(3X = 3) = P(X = 1) = 0.1$, and so on. Thus,

x	$3x$	$P(x) = P(3x)$
-1	-3	0.2
1	3	0.1
2	6	0.3
5	15	0.1
10	30	0.3
		1.0

Since $P(x) = P(3x)$, we can write

$$E(3X) = \sum_{3x} (3x)\, P(3x) = \sum_{x} (3x)\, P(x).$$

The middle term is a sum over values of $(3x)$; the term on the right is a sum over values of x. The equality of the two is easily seen in the following tables:

Sum over $3x$

$3x$	$P(3x)$	$(3x)\, P(3x)$
-3	0.2	-0.6
3	0.1	0.3
6	0.3	1.8
15	0.1	1.5
30	0.3	9.0
	1.0	$\sum_{3x} (3x)\, P(3x) = 12$

Sum over x

x	$P(x)$	$(3x)\,P(x)$
-1	0.2	-0.6
1	0.1	0.3
2	0.3	1.8
5	0.1	1.5
10	0.3	9.0
	1.0	$\sum_x (3x)\,P(x) = 12$

Suppose for the same X we define the new random variable $(1 + 2X)$. Then

x	$1 + 2x$	$P(x) = P(1 + 2x)$
-1	-1	0.2
1	3	0.1
2	5	0.3
5	11	0.1
10	21	0.3
		1.0

The third column is correct for the following reason. Since $(1 + 2X) = -1$ if and only if $X = -1$, $P(1 + 2X = -1) = P(X = -1)$, and so on.

Thus again

$$E(1 + 2X) = \sum_{(1+2x)} (1 + 2x)\,P(1 + 2x) = \sum_x (1 + 2x)\,P(x).$$

In tabular form,

x	$(1 + 2x)$	$P(x)$	$(1 + 2x)\,P(x)$
-1	-1	0.2	-0.2
1	3	0.1	0.3
2	5	0.3	1.5
5	11	0.1	1.1
10	21	0.3	6.3
		1.0	$E(1 + 2X) = 9.0$

Finally, consider the new random variable X^2.

x	x^2	$P(x)$
−1	1	0.2
1	1	0.1
2	4	0.3
5	25	0.1
10	100	0.3
		1.0

Here the situation appears to be somewhat different. Indeed, it is true that $X^2 = 4$ if and only if $X = 2$, so that $P(X^2 = 4) = P(X = 2)$. But $X^2 = 1$ when either $X = -1$ or $X = 1$, so that $P(X^2 = 1) = P(X = -1 \text{ or } X = 1) = P(X = -1) + P(X = 1)$. But we shall see that again

$$\sum_{x^2} x^2 P(x^2) = \sum_x x^2 P(x).$$

Sum over x^2

x^2	$P(x^2)$	$x^2 P(x^2)$
1	0.3	0.3
4	0.3	1.2
25	0.1	2.5
100	0.3	30.0
	1.0	$\sum_{x^2} x^2 P(x^2) = 34.0$

Sum over x

x	$P(x)$		$x^2 P(x)$	
−1	0.2	0.3	0.2	0.3
1	0.1		0.1	
2	0.3		1.2	
5	0.1		2.5	
10	0.3		30.0	
	1.0		$\sum_x x^2 P(x) = 34.0$	

In general suppose we define a function $g(X)$. By definition,

$$Eg(X) = \sum_{g(x)} g(x) P[g(x)]$$

and we wish to show

$$\sum_{g(x)} g(x) P[g(x)] = \sum_x g(x) P(x).$$

Suppose the x's are $x_1, x_2, x_3, \ldots, x_6$, and

$$\begin{aligned} g(x_2) &\neq g(x_3), \\ g(x_2) &\neq g(x_4), \\ g(x_2) &\neq g(x_5), \\ g(x_2) &\neq g(x_6), \\ g(x_3) &\neq g(x_4), \\ g(x_3) &\neq g(x_5), \\ g(x_3) &\neq g(x_6), \\ g(x_4) &\neq g(x_5), \\ g(x_4) &\neq g(x_6), \\ g(x_5) &\neq g(x_6), \end{aligned}$$

but

$$g(x_1) = g(x_2).$$

That is to say, all the g-values differ except for $g(x_1)$ and $g(x_2)$. We then have that

$$P[g(x_i)] = P(x_i) \quad (i = 3, 4, 5, 6),$$

precisely as in the $3X$ and $(1 + 2X)$ examples. But $P[g(x_1)] = P(x_1) + P(x_2)$ since x_1 and x_2 produce the same g-value, precisely as -1 and 1 in the X^2 example.

To calculate $Eg(X)$ by its definition, we must first multiply each $g(x)$ value by its probability and then add. We shall be adding over the five different values of $g(x)$: $g(x_1)$, $g(x_3)$, $g(x_4)$, $g(x_5)$ and $g(x_6)$. Consequently,

$$\begin{aligned} Eg(X) = \sum_{g(x)} g(x)\, P[g(x)] &= g(x_1)\, P[g(x_1)] + g(x_3)\, P[g(x_3)] \\ &+ g(x_4)\, P[g(x_4)] + g(x_5)\, P[g(x_5)] + g(x_6)\, P[g(x_6)]. \end{aligned}$$

By substitution, we obtain

$$\begin{aligned} Eg(X) &= g(x_1)[P(x_1) + P(x_2)] + g(x_3)\, P(x_3) + g(x_4)\, P(x_4) \\ &\quad + g(x_5)\, P(x_5) + g(x_6)\, P(x_6) \\ &= g(x_1)\, P(x_1) + g(x_1)\, P(x_2) + g(x_3)\, P(x_3) + g(x_4)\, P(x_4) \\ &\quad + g(x_5)\, P(x_5) + g(x_6)\, P(x_6). \end{aligned}$$

Using $g(x_1) = g(x_2)$,

$$\begin{aligned} Eg(X) &= g(x_1)\, P(x_1) + g(x_2)\, P(x_2) + g(x_3)\, P(x_3) + g(x_4)\, P(x_4) \\ &\quad + g(x_5)\, P(x_5) + g(x_6)\, P(x_6) = \sum_x g(x)\, P(x), \end{aligned}$$

which establishes the following theorem.

THEOREM 1. Let $g(X)$ be a function[5] of the (discrete) random variable X. Then

$$Eg(X) = \sum_{g(x)} g(x)\, P[g(x)] = \sum_{x} g(x)\, P(x).$$

EXAMPLE 4.2.2. Calculate $E(X^2)$ in two ways, where X has the following probability distribution.

x	$P(x)$	x^2
−3	0.10	9
−1	0.20	1
0	0.25	0
1	0.25	1
3	0.10	9
4	0.10	16
	1.00	

Solution: First we use the definition

$$EX^2 = \sum_{x^2} x^2\, P(x^2).$$

x^2	$P(x^2)$
0	0.25
1	0.45
9	0.20
16	0.10
	1.00

The probabilities above are determined as follows:

$X^2 = 0$ if and only if $X = 0$; hence $P(X^2 = 0) = P(X = 0)$.

$X^2 = 1$ if either $X = -1$ or $X = 1$; hence $P(X^2 = 1)$
$= P(X = -1) + P(X = 1)$.

$X^2 = 9$ if either $X = -3$ or $X = 3$; hence $P(X^2 = 9)$
$= P(X = -3) + P(X = 3)$.

$X^2 = 16$ if and only if $X = 4$; hence $P(X^2 = 16) = P(X = 4)$.

[5]For our purposes this statement of the theorem is sufficient. In a more advanced treatment it would be necessary to worry about whether the function were so behaved that the sum defining its expectation existed. At this level it is sufficient to notice merely that we must require $g(x)$ to be a finite number for all x in the sample space.

Then,

$x^2 P(x^2)$
0 (0.25) = 0
1 (0.45) = 0.45
9 (0.20) = 1.80
16 (0.10) = 1.60
$\sum_{x^2} x^2 P(x^2) = 3.85$;

Therefore,

$$EX^2 = 3.85.$$

Now we shall use

$$EX^2 = \sum_x x^2 P(x).$$

x	$P(x)$	$x^2 P(x)$
−3	0.10	9 (0.10) = 0.90
−1	0.20	1 (0.20) = 0.20
0	0.25	0 (0.25) = 0
1	0.25	1 (0.25) = 0.25
3	0.10	9 (0.10) = 0.90
4	0.10	16 (0.10) = 1.60
	1.00	$\sum x^2 P(x) = 3.85$;

Therefore,

$$EX^2 = 3.85.$$

The following two results, which we assemble as a theorem, are extremely useful.

THEOREM 2. Let X be a (discrete) random variable. Then

(a) $E(a + bX) = a + bEX$, where a and b are constants

(b) $E[(X - \mu)^2] = EX^2 - \mu^2$, where $\mu = EX$.

Comment: Let us here interpret (a), leaving (b) for later illustration. First suppose $b = 1$, then the theorem states

$$E(a + X) = a + EX;$$

that is, adding a constant to all values of a random variable adds the same constant to the mean. Think of sampling one individual at random from a large group and inquiring how much money he has with him. Let the random variable X = the amount of money possessed, and suppose the distribution of money held is such that $EX = \$15.30$. Now suppose we give each individual 50 cents *before* the sampling is done. In this second case the amount of money possessed is, say Y, where $Y = X + 0.50$ and the expected value of Y is $EY = EX + 0.50 = \$15.80$.

Now suppose $b = 0$, then the theorem states

$$E(a) = a;$$

that is, the expected value of a constant is precisely the constant. We can think of the constant a as a degenerate random variable assuming the value a with probability one, thus

$$E(a) = aP(a) = a(1) = a.$$

Finally, suppose $a = 0$, then the theorem states

$$E(bX) = bEX;$$

that is, multiplying all values of a random variable by a constant multiplies the expected value by that same constant. Thus, the expected value of $2X$ is twice the expected value of X, and so on.

Proof of (a):

$$\begin{aligned} E(a + bX) &= \sum_x (a + bx)\, P(x) \\ &= \sum_x [a\, P(x) + bx\, P(x)] \\ &= \sum_x a\, P(x) + \sum_x bx\, P(x) \\ &= a \sum_x P(x) + b \sum_x x\, P(x) \\ &= a(1) + b \sum_x xP(x) \\ &= a + b\, EX. \end{aligned}$$

Q.E.D.

Proof of (b):

$$\begin{aligned} E[(X - \mu)^2] &= \sum_x (x - \mu)^2\, P(x) \\ &= \sum_x (x^2 - 2\mu x + \mu^2)\, P(x) \\ &= \sum_x x^2\, P(x) - \sum_x 2\mu x\, P(x) + \sum_x \mu^2\, P(x) \end{aligned}$$

$$= EX^2 - 2\mu \sum_x x\,P(x) + \mu^2 \sum_x P(x)$$
$$= EX^2 - 2\mu\,(EX) + \mu^2\,(1)$$
$$= EX^2 - 2\mu\,(\mu) + \mu^2$$
$$= EX^2 - 2\mu^2 + \mu^2$$
$$= EX^2 - \mu^2. \qquad \text{Q.E.D.}$$

Let us now build up to the point of seeing the usefulness of Theorem 2(b). Suppose X is a random variable with $X \in \{1, 2, 3, 4, 5\}$ and probability distribution $\{(1, 0.45), (2, 0.30), (3, 0.10), (4, 0.10), (5, 0.05)\}$. Then, $EX = 1(0.45) + 2(0.30) + 3(0.10) + 4(0.10) + 5(0.05) = 2.0 = \mu$. Although the expected value is 2, there is only a 0.30 probability that $X = 2$ when the experiment is run. It is more likely that X will turn out to be 1 (its modal value), which is a deviation of -1 from the expected value. On occasion (5% of the time), X will turn out to be 5, which is 3 away from the expected result. In general, therefore, the values of X will often differ from EX. In fact, since $X = EX$ with probability 0.3, X will differ from EX with probability 0.7, that is, in 70% of all trials of the experiment. The random variable $(X - \mu)$ measures the extent to which X differs from its expected value. Suppose we ask for $E(X - \mu)$, that is, the extent to which X differs from its expected value *on the average*. Since μ is a constant, we can apply Theorem 2(a):

$$E(X - \mu) = EX - \mu = \mu - \mu = 0.$$

Thus, although deviations between X and μ will occur in 70% of all trials, the positive and negative deviations tend to cancel so that the average deviation is zero. This is perhaps more easily seen in the following table:

x	$P(x)$	$x\,P(x)$	$(x - \mu)$	$(x - \mu)\,P(x)$
1	0.45	0.45	-1	-0.45
2	0.30	0.60	0	0
3	0.10	0.30	1	0.10
4	0.10	0.40	2	0.20 } 0.45
5	0.05	0.25	3	0.15
	1.00	$\mu = 2.00$		$E(X - \mu) = 0$

Since $E(X - \mu)$ is always zero, it provides no measure of the extent to which X varies around its expected value. If we consider $(X - \mu)^2$, we shall eliminate the canceling of positive and negative deviations. $(X - \mu)^2$

is the square of the discrepancy between X and μ. $E[(X - \mu)^2]$ is the average squared discrepancy. Direct calculation produces $E[(X - \mu)^2] = 1.40$:

$(x - \mu)$	$P(x)$	$(x - \mu)^2$	$(x - \mu)^2 P(x)$
−1	0.45	1	0.45
0	0.30	0	0
1	0.10	1	0.10
2	0.10	4	0.40
3	0.05	9	0.45
	1.00		$E[(X - \mu)^2] = 1.40$

Recall, however, that we proved the theorem $E[(X - \mu)^2] = EX^2 - \mu^2$, so we can calculate as follows:

x	$P(x)$	x^2	$x^2 P(x)$
1	0.45	1	0.45
2	0.30	4	1.20
3	0.10	9	0.90
4	0.10	16	1.60
5	0.05	25	1.25
	1.00		$EX^2 = 5.40$

Then $E[(X - \mu)^2] = EX^2 - \mu^2 = 5.40 - (2)^2 = 5.40 - 4 = 1.40$ as before.

DEFINITION. The expected (or average) squared discrepancy between X and EX is called the *variance of* X, is denoted by σ_X^2, and is defined by

$$\sigma_X^2 = E[(X - \mu)^2],$$

where EX is abbreviated μ.

The theorem which states $\sigma_X^2 = EX^2 - \mu^2$ makes it perfectly obvious that the variance is measured in units of X^2. Thus if X is in units of dollars, σ_X^2 is in units of dollars squared; if X is in pounds, σ_X^2 is in units of pounds squared. A convenient measure of variability in units of the original random variable is the *standard deviation* defined by: the standard deviation of X equals σ_X equals $+\sqrt{\sigma_X^2}$. Note that the standard deviation σ_X is not an average of anything; it is merely the square root of the average squared discrepancy between X and EX.

A measure of variability which *is* in units of X and which *is* an average is the so-called *mean absolute deviation* (M.A.D.) defined by

$$\text{M.A.D.} = E\,|X - \mu|.$$

Here the use of absolute values prevents the canceling of positive and negative deviations. In our example,

x	$P(x)$	$x\,P(x)$	$(x-\mu)$	$\lvert x-\mu\rvert$	$\lvert x-\mu\rvert\,P(x)$
1	0.45	0.45	−1	1	0.45
2	0.30	0.60	0	0	0
3	0.10	0.30	1	1	0.10
4	0.10	0.40	2	2	0.20
5	0.05	0.25	3	3	0.15
	1.00	$EX = 2$			$E\lvert X-\mu\rvert = 0.90$

so that the mean absolute deviation is 0.90. The standard deviation is

$$\sigma_X = +\sqrt{\sigma_X^2} = +\sqrt{1.40} \cong 1.18.$$

Consider the following three probability distributions

$$D_X = \{(1, 0.2), (3, 0.6), (5, 0.2)\},$$

$$D_Y = \{(1, 0.4), (3, 0.2), (5, 0.4)\},$$

and

$$D_Z = \{(0, 0.2), (1, 0.2), (3, 0.2), (5, 0.2), (6, 0.2)\}$$

applying to the random variables X, Y, and Z, respectively. We calculate expected values as follows:

x	$P(x)$	$x\,P(x)$	y	$P(y)$	$y\,P(y)$	z	$P(z)$	$z\,P(z)$
1	0.2	0.2	1	0.4	0.4	0	0.2	0
3	0.6	1.8	3	0.2	0.6	1	0.2	0.2
5	0.2	1.0	5	0.4	2.0	3	0.2	0.6
	1.0	3.0		1.0	3.0	5	0.2	1.0
						6	0.2	1.2
							1.0	3.0
	$EX = 3$			$EY = 3$			$EZ = 3$	

All three random variables have the same expected value, nonetheless a sequence of replications would produce very different patterns of realizations for the three cases. In the case of X, for example, the majority (60%) of realizations would equal EX. For Y, a minority (20%) of realizations would equal EY. It is intuitively clear that Y differs from its expected value far more than X. Specifically,

x	$(x - \mu_X)$	$(x - \mu_X)^2 P(x)$	y	$(y - \mu_Y)$	$(y - \mu_Y)^2 P(y)$
1	−2	4(0.2) = 0.8	1	−2	4(0.4) = 1.6
3	0	0(0.6) = 0	3	0	0(0.2) = 0
5	2	4(0.2) = 0.8	5	2	4(0.4) = 1.6
		1.6			3.2

$\sigma_X^2 = 1.6.$ $\quad \sigma_Y^2 = 3.2.$

$\sigma_X \cong 1.26.$ $\quad \sigma_Y \cong 1.79.$

It is easy to judge the variability of Z relative to Y. Z will assume its expected value as often as Y, that is, 20% of the time. But while Y will differ from EY by two units 80% of the time, Z will differ from EZ by two units only 40% of the time and will differ by as much as three units 40% of the time. Thus Y is on the average closer to EY than is Z to EZ. Specifically,

z	$(z - \mu_Z)$	$(z - \mu_Z)^2 P(z)$
0	−3	9(0.2) = 1.8
1	−2	4(0.2) = 0.8
3	0	0(0.2) = 0
5	2	4(0.2) = 0.8
6	3	9(0.2) = 1.8
		5.2

$\sigma_Z^2 = 5.2.$

$\sigma_Z \cong 2.28.$

The progressively larger variability about the mean is seen clearly if we represent the three probability distributions graphically.

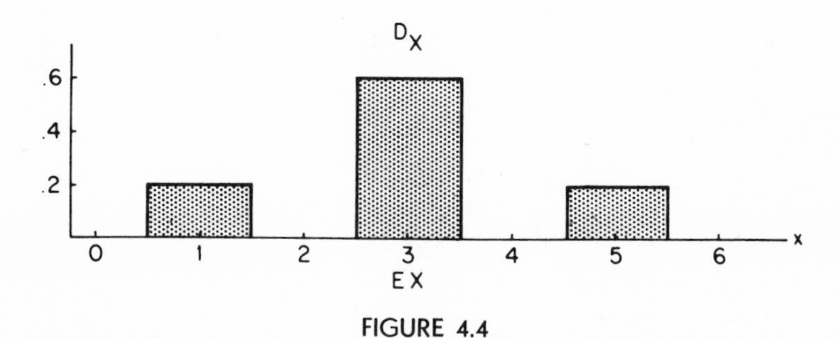

FIGURE 4.4

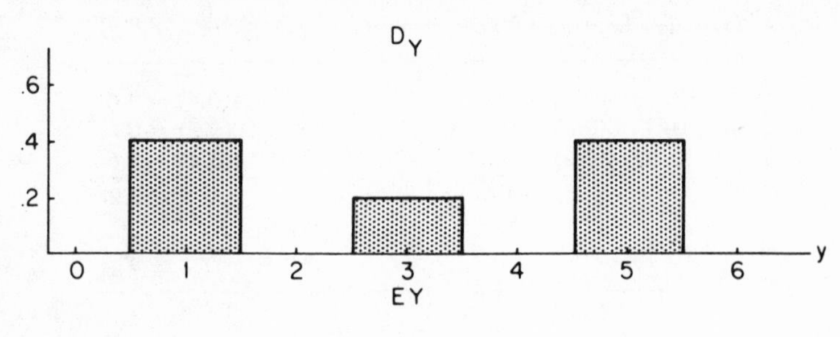

FIGURE 4.5

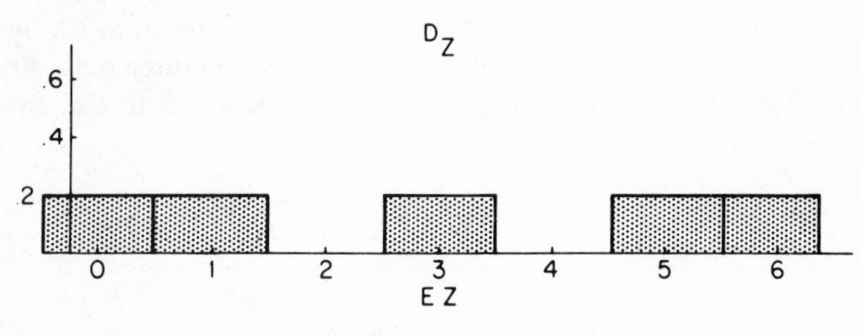

FIGURE 4.6

EXAMPLE 4.2.3. Calculate[6] σ^2, σ, and M.A.D. for the random variable X with probability distribution

$$D = \{(-1, 0.2), (1, 0.1), (2, 0.3), (5, 0.1), (10, 0.3)\}.$$

Solution: We have already found that in this case $EX = 4$.

x	$P(x)$	$(x - \mu)$	$\|x - \mu\|$	$(x - \mu)^2$	$\|x - \mu\| P(x)$	$(x - \mu)^2 P(x)$
−1	0.2	−5	5	25	1.0	5.0
1	0.1	−3	3	9	0.3	0.9
2	0.3	−2	2	4	0.6	1.2
5	0.1	1	1	1	0.1	0.1
10	0.3	6	6	36	1.8	10.8
	1.0				3.8	18.0

Therefore

$$\sigma^2 = 18.0$$
$$\sigma = +\sqrt{18} \cong 4.24,$$
$$\text{M.A.D.} = 3.8$$

[6]When there is only one random variable involved, it is common to omit the subscript from σ_X^2 and σ_X.

EXAMPLE 4.2.4. An urn contains 10 tags of uniform size. One-fifth of the tags are numbered 10, $\frac{1}{2}$ of the tags are numbered 2, and the rest are numbered -10. Two tags are to be drawn from the urn *with replacement* and the number on each tag is to be recorded. Let X = the sum of the two numbers. Calculate and interpret EX and σ^2.

Solution: First, the expression *with replacement* signifies that a tag is drawn and replaced in the urn before the second drawing is made. Further, it is assumed that before each drawing, the tags are thoroughly mixed in the urn.

The experiment described is a compound of

E_1: mix tags, draw a tag, note the number, and return tag to urn,

E_2: mix tags, draw a tag, note the number, and return tag to urn.

E_1 has sample space $\mathcal{S}_1 = \{10, 2, -10\}$ with probability distribution

$$D_1 = \{(10, 0.2), (2, 0.5), (-10, 0.3)\}$$

and the situation is identical for E_2.

$E = E_1 \times E_2$ therefore produces the following sample space of ordered pairs:

$$\mathcal{S} = \left\{\begin{array}{c}(10, 10), (10, 2), (10, -10), (2, 10), (2, 2), \\ (2, -10), (-10, 10), (-10, 2), (-10, -10),\end{array}\right\}$$

where the first number in the pair is the result of E_1 and the second number is the E_2 outcome.

The probability of an ordered pair is easily calculated since the *with replacement* condition assures stochastic independence of the trials E_1 and E_2. Whatever occurs on the first trial has no effect on any probabilities connected with the second trial. Hence

$$P(10, 10) = P(10) \cdot P(10) = (0.2)(0.2) = 0.04 \qquad (20)$$

$$P(10, 2) = (0.2)(0.5) = 0.10 \qquad (12)$$

$$P(10, -10) = (0.2)(0.3) = 0.06 \qquad (0)$$

$$P(2, 10) = (0.5)(0.2) = 0.10 \qquad (12)$$

$$P(2, 2) = (0.5)(0.5) = 0.25 \qquad (4)$$

$$P(2, -10) = (0.5)(0.3) = 0.15 \qquad (-8)$$

$$P(-10, 10) = (0.3)(0.2) = 0.06 \qquad (0)$$

$$P(-10, 2) = (0.3)(0.5) = 0.15 \qquad (-8)$$

$$P(-10, -10) = (0.3)(0.3) = 0.09 \qquad (-20)$$

Note that the probabilities calculated do indeed sum to unity, as they must. The numbers in parentheses to the right of the probabilities give the sum of the tag numbers corresponding to each ordered pair. The sample space for X is therefore

$$X \in \{-20, -8, 0, 4, 12, 20\},$$

and the corresponding probabilities are 0.09, 0.30, 0.12, 0.25, 0.20, and 0.04, respectively. Now calculating mean and variance,

x	$P(x)$	$x\,P(x)$	x^2	$x^2\,P(x)$
−20	0.09	−1.8	400	36.0
−8	0.30	−2.4	64	19.2
0	0.12	0	0	0
4	0.25	1.0	16	4.0
12	0.20	2.4	144	28.8
20	0.04	0.8	400	16.0
	1.00	$EX = 0$		$EX^2 = 104.0$

The expected value of X is thus zero and

$$\sigma^2 = EX^2 - (EX)^2 = 104 - 0 = 104.$$

In a long series of two-tag samplings, the *average* of the two-tag sums will be zero. The *actual* two-tag sums, however, will most often be different from zero. The sums can be expected to be below zero 39% of the time (−8 with probability 0.30 and −20 with probability 0.09), above zero nearly 50% of the time, and 12 or higher nearly 25% of the time. On the average, the squared difference of the two-tag sums from zero will be 104. The standard deviation is $\sigma = +\sqrt{104} \cong 10.2$. Note that if we take an interval of 1 standard deviation on either side of the mean, we find

$$EX - \sigma = 0 - 10.2 = -10.2,$$

$$EX + \sigma = 0 + 10.2 = 10.2,$$

and

$$P[-10.2 \leq X \leq 10.2] = 0.30 + 0.12 + 0.25 = 0.67.$$

Hence the probability is about $\frac{2}{3}$ that a two-tag sum will be within one standard deviation of the expected value zero.

A 2σ interval on either side of the mean is −20.4 to +20.4, and all two-tag sums will therefore be within 2σ of zero; that is, the probability that a two-tag sum will be within 2σ of its expected value is unity.

4.3 Chebyschev's Inequality

In interpreting the standard deviation (and variance) in the tag-sampling problem, it turned out to be instructive to consider the probability that the random variable would be within one or two standard deviations of its expected value. This in fact is a most fruitful way of thinking about the meaning of the standard deviation. This will be formalized in Chebyschev's inequality, but first we shall derive a useful auxiliary result.

Let Y be a random variable defined on the gapped sample space $\mathcal{S}$, where the elements of $\mathcal{S}$ are all nonnegative numbers. It must then be that $Y \geq 0$. Let t be a positive element of $\mathcal{S}$. By definition,

$$EY = \sum_{y} y\, P(y).$$

The term

$$\sum_{y} y\, P(y)$$

can be broken into two parts. If

$$A = \sum_{y<t} y\, P(y) \quad \text{and} \quad B = \sum_{y \geq t} y\, P(y),$$

then

$$A + B = \sum_{y} y\, P(y).$$

That is, A sums all the $y\, P(y)$ products for $y < t$ and B sums them for $y \geq t$. $A + B$ therefore "picks up" *all* the $y\, P(y)$ products.

Therefore,

$$EY = \sum_{y<t} y\, P(y) + \sum_{y \geq t} y\, P(y).$$

Within the B term, all y's are $\geq t$. If we replace all the y's in B by t itself, we find a new term which is smaller (or at least not larger) than B. Thus

$$\sum_{y \geq t} t\, P(y) \leq \sum_{y \geq t} y\, P(y).$$

Then, since

$$EY = \sum_{y<t} y\, P(y) + \sum_{y \geq t} y\, P(y),$$

$$EY \geq \sum_{y<t} y\, P(y) + \sum_{y \geq t} t\, P(y).$$

Factoring out the constant t,

$$EY \geq \sum_{y<t} y\, P(y) + t \sum_{y \geq t} P(y)$$

or

$$EY \geq A + B',$$

where

$$B' = t \sum_{y \geq t} P(y).$$

Since all y's are ≥ 0, A and B' must be ≥ 0. If $EY \geq A + B'$, and A and B' are each ≥ 0, then surely it must be true that

$$EY \geq B' \quad \text{or} \quad EY \geq t \sum_{y \geq t} P(y).$$

Now

$$\sum_{y \geq t} P(y)$$

adds the probabilities for all $y \geq t$, hence

$$\sum_{y \geq t} P(y) = P(Y \geq t).$$

Therefore,

$$EY \geq t\,P(Y \geq t),$$

and since $t > 0$,

$$\boxed{P(Y \geq t) \leq \frac{EY}{t}.}$$

The latter inequality is known as *Markov's inequality*. Suppose, for example, that Y is a nonnegative random variable with $EY = 15$, then

$$P(Y \geq 25) \leq \tfrac{15}{25} = 0.60.$$

The meaning of this is that there can be no nonnegative random variable with mean equal to 15 for which

$$P(Y \geq 25) > 0.60.$$

There are many such random variables for which $P(Y \geq 25)$ is a good deal less than 0.60, but there are *none* for which $P(Y \geq 25) > 0.60$. Consider the nonnegative X, Y, Z random variables which were used to illustrate the concept of variance on pp. 90–92. Each had an expectation of 3. Applying Markov's inequality, the probability of any of these random variables being at least 4 is at most $\frac{3}{4}$. In fact, the probability distributions on p. 90 indicate that the probabilities are 0.2, 0.4, and 0.4 for X, Y, and Z, respectively — all substantially below $\frac{3}{4}$.

Now consider the random variable X with $EX = \mu$. Define a new random variable $Y = (X - \mu)^2$ which is surely nonnegative. Apply Markov's inequality to $(X - \mu)^2$:

$$P[(X - \mu)^2 \geq t^2] \leq \frac{E[(X - \mu)^2]}{t^2},$$

where t^2 is some positive constant. Now $(X - \mu)^2 \geq t^2$ if and only if $|X - \mu| \geq |t|$, so that

$$P[(X - \mu)^2 \geq t^2] = P[|X - \mu| \geq |t|].$$

Therefore,

$$P[|X - \mu| \leq |t|] \leq \frac{E[(X - \mu)^2]}{t^2}.$$

Noticing that $E[(X - \mu)^2] = \sigma_X^2$,

$$\boxed{P[|X - \mu| \geq |t|] \leq \frac{\sigma_X^2}{t^2}.}$$

The latter inequality is known as *Chebyschev's inequality.* For a given $|t|$, Chebyschev's inequality can be interpreted as stating that the larger the variance of X, the more likely is X to deviate from its expected value by at least $|t|$.

Suppose $EX = 65$ and $\sigma_X^2 = 100$. When we run the experiment which yields X, the particular value which occurs might be very different from the expected value. Let us calculate an *upper limit* for the probability that X differs from its mean by at least 25, that is, the probability that X is greater than or equal to $65 + 25 = 90$ or less than or equal to $65 - 25 = 40$. Using Chebyschev's inequality,

$$P[X \leq 40 \text{ or } X \geq 90] = P[|X - 65| \geq 25] \leq \frac{\sigma_X^2}{(25)^2},$$

$$P[|X - 65| \geq 25] \leq \frac{100}{625} = 0.160.$$

Now suppose we ask for the probability that X differs from its expected value by at least two standard deviations. Since $\sigma_X^2 = 100$, $\sigma_X = 10$, and $2\sigma_X = 20$. Therefore

$$P[|X - \mu| \geq 20] \leq \frac{100}{(20)^2} = \frac{1}{4}.$$

Since the probability of differing from the mean by *at least* 2σ is at most $\frac{1}{4}$, the probability of differing from the mean by less than 2σ must be at least $\frac{3}{4}$; hence,

$$P[|X - \mu| < 20] \geq \tfrac{3}{4}.$$

In general, letting k be any constant ≥ 1,

$$P[|X - \mu| \geq k\sigma_X] \leq \frac{\sigma_X^2}{(k\sigma_X)^2} = \frac{1}{k^2}$$

and

$$P[|X - \mu| < k\sigma_X] \geq 1 - \frac{1}{k^2}.$$

Thus, the probability of being within, say, 2σ of the mean is always at least $\frac{3}{4}$; the probability of being within 3σ of the mean is always at least $\frac{8}{9}$, and so on.

Since Chebyschev's inequality must hold true for *all* random variables, it may be quite weak with respect to a particular random variable in which you might be interested. Many important random variables, for example, have a probability far greater than $\frac{8}{9}$ of being within 3σ of their expected values. Nonetheless, Chebyschev's inequality does shed a great deal of light on the meaning and importance of variance and standard deviation.

EXAMPLE 4.3.1. The random variable X has associated with it the sample space $\mathcal{S}$, where

$$X \in \mathcal{S} = \{1, 2, 3, \ldots, 16\}.$$

Further, for $x \in \mathcal{S}$,

$$P(X = x) = \frac{x}{136}.$$

(a) Check that the sum of the probabilities for all points in the sample space is unity.
(b) Calculate EX.
(c) Calculate the exact probability that X differs from its expected value by less than 4.
(d) Calculate the exact probability that X differs from its expected value by less than 5.
(e) Approximate the probabilities in (c) and (d) by use of Chebyschev's inequality.

Hints: (i) $1^2 + 2^2 + 3^2 + \cdots + n^2 = \frac{n}{6}(n + 1)(2n + 1).$

(ii) $1^3 + 2^3 + 3^3 + \cdots + n^3 = \frac{n^2}{4}(n + 1)^2$

Solution: First let us note that the probability distribution of X has been specified somewhat differently in this problem. Rather than specifying the probabilities themselves for each $x \in \mathcal{S}$, we have given a formula or rule by which these probabilities may be calculated. The rule is

$$P(X = x) = \frac{x}{136}.$$

Using this rule, we can find, for example, $P(X = 3) = 3/136$, $P(X = 10) = 10/136$, and so on. However, $P(X = 20) = 0$ since $20 \notin \mathcal{S}$ and the rule holds only for elements of the sample space. A rule which specifies $P(X = x)$ for all $x \in \mathcal{S}$ is referred to as a *probability function*. It is clear that specification of the sample space and probability function is another way of representing the probability distribution.

(a) To check that the sum of the probabilities is unity, we could write a column with elements $\frac{1}{136}$, $\frac{2}{136}$, $\frac{3}{136}$, etc., and add. Alternatively, since the probability function is specified, we can approach the problem as follows.

$$\sum_{i=1}^{16} P(X = x_i) = \sum_{i=1}^{16} \frac{x_i}{136} \stackrel{?}{=} 1.$$

Now

$$\sum_{i=1}^{16} \frac{x_i}{136} = \frac{1}{136} \sum_{i=1}^{16} x_i$$

$$= \frac{1}{136}(1 + 2 + 3 + \cdots + 16).$$

We recognize that the sum in parentheses is the sum of an arithmetic progression. Hence

$$(1 + 2 + 3 + \cdots + n) = \frac{n}{2}(n + 1).$$

In our case

$$(1 + 2 + 3 + \cdots + 16) = \frac{16}{2}(17) = 136;$$

therefore

$$\sum_{i=1}^{16} \frac{x_i}{136} = \frac{1}{136}(136) = 1.$$

(b) By definition,

$$EX = \sum_{x} x\, P(x).$$

In our case,

$$EX = \sum_{i=1}^{16} (x_i) \left(\frac{x_i}{136}\right) = \sum_{i=1}^{16} \frac{x_i^2}{136} = \frac{1}{136} \sum_{i=1}^{16} x_i^2$$

$$= \frac{1}{136}(1^2 + 2^2 + 3^2 + \cdots + 16^2).$$

Using Hint (i),

$$EX = \frac{1}{136}\left[\frac{16}{6}(17)(33)\right] = \frac{1}{136}\left[\frac{(16)(17)(33)}{6}\right]$$

$$= \frac{1}{136}\left[\frac{(2)(8)(17)(33)}{6}\right] = \frac{1}{136}\left[\frac{(2)(136)\,33}{6}\right]$$

$$= \frac{2(33)}{6} = 11.$$

(c) "Deviating from EX by less than 4" means $X > 11 - 4 = 7$ or $X < 11 + 4 = 15$. We therefore need

$$P[7 < X < 15] = \sum_{i=8}^{14} P(X = x_i) = \sum_{i=8}^{14} \frac{x_i}{136} = \frac{1}{136}(8 + 9 + \cdots + 14)$$
$$= \frac{77}{136} \cong 0.566.$$

(d) "Deviating from EX by less than 5" means $X > 11 - 5 = 6$ or $X < 11 + 5 = 16$. Thus

$$P[6 < X < 16] = \sum_{i=7}^{15} P(X = x_i) = \sum_{i=7}^{15} \frac{x_i}{136} = \frac{1}{136}(7 + 8 + \cdots + 15)$$
$$= \frac{99}{136} \cong 0.728.$$

(e) To use Chebyschev's inequality, we first need the variance of X. The easiest approach is to recall the theorem

$$\sigma_X^2 = E[(X - EX)^2] = EX^2 - (EX)^2.$$

Then

$$EX^2 = \sum_x x^2 P(x) = \sum_{i=1}^{16} (x_i)^2 \frac{x_i}{136} = \frac{1}{136} \sum_{i=1}^{16} x_i^3$$
$$= \frac{1}{136}(1^3 + 2^3 + 3^3 + \cdots + 16^3).$$

Using Hint (ii),

$$EX^2 = \frac{1}{136}\left[\frac{(16)^2}{4}(17)^2\right] = \frac{1}{136}\left[\frac{(16)\,(2)\,(8)\,(17)\,(17)}{4}\right]$$
$$= \frac{1}{136}[(4)\,(2)\,(136)\,(17)] = 136.$$

Therefore,

$$\sigma_X^2 = 136 - (11)^2 = 15.$$

Chebyschev's inequality is

$$P[|X - EX| \geq |k|] \leq \frac{\sigma_X^2}{k^2}.$$

Letting $|k| = 4$,

$$P[|X - EX| \geq 4] \leq \frac{15}{(4)^2} = \frac{15}{16};$$

therefore,

$$P[|X - EX| < 4] \geq \frac{1}{16} = 0.0625.$$

This says the probability is at least 0.0625 that X differs from its expected value by less than 4. In (c) we arrived at $77/136 \cong 0.566$, so that the Chebyschev approximation — while correct — is indeed weak.

Letting $|k| = 5$,

$$P[|X - EX| \geq 5] \leq \frac{15}{5^2} = \frac{15}{25} = \frac{3}{5};$$

therefore,

$$P[|X - EX| < 5] \geq \frac{2}{5} = 0.40.$$

Here again the Chebyschev approximation is rather weak. Note, however, that in the first case we were off by a factor of about 9 (that is, 0.566/0.0625), while this time we are off by a factor of about 1.8 (that is, 0.728/0.40).

Generally, the approximation improves the further we go from the expected value of X. For example, the exact probability of deviating by less than 6 is $P[5 < X < 17] = P(X > 5)$, since 16 is the largest possible value. Hence

$$P(X > 5) = \sum_{i=6}^{16} \frac{x_i}{136} = \frac{121}{136} \cong 0.890.$$

The Chebyschev approximation is

$$P[|X - EX| \geq 6] \leq \frac{15}{36} = \frac{5}{12};$$

therefore,

$$P[|X - EX| < 6] \geq \frac{7}{12} \cong 0.584.$$

Now the error factor is down to about 1.5 (that is, 0.890/0.584).

4.4 Sums of Random Variables

We have seen on several occasions that certain experiments can most readily be analyzed in terms of compounds of simple experiments. Often, however, it is not the resulting set of ordered pairs (or triples, etc.) which is of prime interest to the experimenter. Thus, for example, sampling two ball bearings produced a set of ordered pairs as elementary events, but the experimenter was interested only in the *number* of good ball bearings. Public opinion polls produce a sequence of responses, some favorable, some unfavorable, but interest centers on the *proportion* of favorable responses rather than the ordered sequence of responses. Many such situations can be viewed as a case of adding random variables.

Suppose a random experiment (perhaps compound) produces two random variables $X \in \mathcal{S}_1$ and $Y \in \mathcal{S}_2$. When the experiment is run, interest centers not on X or Y, but on their sum $Z = X + Y$.

We shall lead up to an analysis of the sum $X + Y$ by first asking for the probability that a running of the experiment produces $X = x$ and $Y = y$. If we think in terms of a compound experiment, the event $\{X = x$ and $Y = y\}$ is of course an intersection of Cartesian products $(x \times \mathcal{S}_2) \cap (\mathcal{S}_1 \times y)$[7] which has probability

$$P\{(x \times \mathcal{S}_2) \cap (\mathcal{S}_1 \times y)\}.$$

We shall now show that if x is held fixed at x_1,

$$\sum_y P\{(x_1 \times \mathcal{S}_2) \cap (\mathcal{S}_1 \times y)\} = P(X = x_1).$$

For y_1 we have

$$\begin{aligned}(x_1 \times \mathcal{S}_2) \cap (\mathcal{S}_1 \times y_1) &= \{(x_1, y_1), (x_1, y_2), (x_1, y_3), \ldots\} \cap \\ &\quad \{(x_1, y_1), (x_2, y_1), (x_3, y_1), \ldots\} \\ &= \{(x_1, y_1)\}.\end{aligned}$$

For y_2 we have

$$\begin{aligned}(x_1 \times \mathcal{S}_2) \cap (\mathcal{S}_1 \times y_2) &= \{(x_1, y_1), (x_1, y_2), (x_1, y_3), \ldots\} \cap \\ &\quad \{(x_1, y_2), (x_2, y_2), (x_3, y_2), \ldots\} \\ &= \{(x_1, y_2)\}.\end{aligned}$$

For y_3 we would similarly arrive at

$$(x_1 \times \mathcal{S}_2) \cap (\mathcal{S}_1 \times y_3) = \{(x_1, y_3)\}, \text{ and so on.}$$

Then adding the probabilities,

$$\begin{aligned}\sum_y P\{(x_1 \times \mathcal{S}_2) \cap (\mathcal{S}_1 \times y)\} &= P\{(x_1, y_1)\} + P\{(x_1, y_2)\} + P\{(x_1, y_3)\} \\ &\quad + P\{(x_1, y_4)\} + \cdots \\ &= P\{(x_1, y_1), (x_1, y_2), (x_1, y_3), (x_1, y_4), \ldots\} \\ &= P\{(x_1 \times \mathcal{S}_2)\}.\end{aligned}$$

We thus have the set of ordered pairs in which x_1 is paired with all possible y values. This is the subset of the compound experiment which corresponds to the event $X = x_1$. Hence

$$\sum_y P\{(x_1 \times \mathcal{S}_2) \cap (\mathcal{S}_2 \times y)\} = P\{(x_1 \times \mathcal{S}_2)\} = P(X = x_1). \text{ Q.E.D.}$$

[7]It is more convenient to write $(\mathcal{S}_1 \times y)$ than $(y \times \mathcal{S}_1)$ but both produce the same points in the Cartesian product space.

From now on we shall abbreviate $P\{(x \times \mathcal{S}_2) \cap (\mathcal{S}_1 \times y)\}$ to simply $P(x \cap y)$. We can restate the result just derived as

$$\sum_y P(x_1 \cap y) = P(X = x_1).$$

The derivation of the latter is perfectly general and establishes the following two rules:

(i) For x_i fixed,

$$\sum_y P(x_i \cap y) = P(X = x_i).$$

(ii) For y_j fixed,

$$\sum_x P(x \cap y_j) = P(Y = y_j).$$

Suppose now that we wish to calculate the expected value of the sum $(X + Y)$. By definition, we should first take each possible value of $(X + Y)$ and multiply it by its probability and then add all the resulting products. Instead, let us consider the following sum A, where we assume there are only four possible values for the X variable (x_1, x_2, x_3, x_4) and an unspecified number of values for the Y variable $(y_1, y_2, y_3, \ldots)$.

$$\begin{aligned} A = {} & [(x_1 + y_1)\, P(x_1 \cap y_1) + (x_1 + y_2)\, P(x_1 \cap y_2) \\ & + (x_1 + y_3)\, P(x_1 \cap y_3) + \cdots] \\ & + [(x_2 + y_1)\, P(x_2 \cap y_1) + (x_2 + y_2)\, P(x_2 \cap y_2) \\ & + (x_2 + y_3)\, P(x_2 \cap y_3) + \cdots] \\ & + [(x_3 + y_1)\, P(x_3 \cap y_1) + (x_3 + y_2)\, P(x_3 \cap y_2) \\ & + (x_3 + y_3)\, P(x_3 \cap y_3) + \cdots] \\ & + [(x_4 + y_1)\, P(x_4 \cap y_1) + (x_4 + y_2)\, P(x_4 \cap y_2) \\ & + (x_4 + y_3)\, P(x_4 \cap y_3) + \cdots]. \end{aligned}$$

In Section 4.4 of the appendix, we shall show first that $A = E(X + Y)$. Then it will be demonstrated that a judicious rearranging of the terms in the expression for A yields the result

$$\begin{aligned} A = {} & EX + [y_1 \sum_x P(x \cap y_1) + y_2 \sum_x P(x \cap y_2) + y_3 \sum_x P(x \cap y_3) \\ & + y_4 \sum_x P(x \cap y_4) + \cdots]. \end{aligned}$$

Now applying Rule (ii) to the

$$\sum_x P(x \cap y_j),$$

$$A = EX + [y_1P(y_1) + y_2P(y_2) + y_3P(y_3) + y_4P(y_4) + \cdots] = EX + EY.$$

Thus $E(X + Y) = A = EX + EY$, which establishes the important

THEOREM 3. If Z is a random variable defined as the sum of the random variables X and Y, $Z = X + Y$, then $EZ = E(X + Y) = EX + EY$.

This theorem can be extended to the sum of any finite number of random variables. Provided that EZ exists, which it always will in this book and in most practical applications, EZ can be calculated as the sum of the expected values of the random variables whose sum defines Z.

EXAMPLE 4.4.1. Return to the two-tag problem in Example 4.2.3 and calculate EX using the results of Theorem 3.

Solution: Let $X_1 \in \mathcal{S}_1 = \{10, 2, -10\}$ be the random variable *number on first tag drawn;* and $X_2 \in \mathcal{S}_2 = \{10, 2, -10\}$ be the random variable *number on second tag drawn.* The probability distribution for X_1 was $D_1 = \{(10, 0.2), (2, 0.5), (-10, 0.3)\}$. The probability distribution for X_2 was identical to D_1. When two random variables have the same probability distribution, they are said to be *identically distributed.* Since X_1 and X_2 are identically distributed, it is clear that

$$EX_1 = EX_2.$$

Now, $EX_1 = 10(0.2) + 2(0.5) + (-10)(0.3) = 0.$

Since X is the sum of the numbers on both tags,

$$X = X_1 + X_2.$$

Therefore,

$$EX = EX_1 + EX_2 = 0 + 0 = 0,$$

precisely as calculated directly in Example 4.2.4.

We already know the meaning of stochastic independence of events. Let $X \in \mathcal{S}_1$, $Y \in \mathcal{S}_2$, and consider the compound experiment which produces the set of ordered pairs $\{(x, y) \mid x \in \mathcal{S}_1, y \in \mathcal{S}_2\}$. If it is true that S and T are independent for all S which are subsets of $\mathcal{S}_1$ and all T which are subsets of $\mathcal{S}_2$, then X and Y are said to be *stochastically independent random variables.* In other words, if any and all events from $\mathcal{S}_1$ are independent of any and all events from $\mathcal{S}_2$, then X and Y are independent. This implies the following useful definition of stochastic independence of X and Y.

DEFINITION. X and Y, with sample spaces $\mathcal{S}_1$ and $\mathcal{S}_2$ respectively, are said to be stochastically independent random variables if and only if $P(X = x \text{ and } Y = y) = P\{(x \times \mathcal{S}_2) \cap (\mathcal{S}_1 \times y)\} = P(X = x)P(Y = y)$ for all $x \in \mathcal{S}_1$ and all $y \in \mathcal{S}_2$. In our abbreviated notation,

$$P(X = x \quad \text{and} \quad Y = y) = P(x \cap y) = P(x)P(y).$$

In deriving the theorem that the expected value of a sum is the sum of the expected values, it was never necessary to specify whether or not $P(x \cap y) = P(x)P(y)$. The theorem is therefore perfectly general and applies regardless of the dependence or independence of X and Y.

Suppose now that X and Y *are* independent and we consider the random variable defined as their product XY. By analogy with the calculation of $E(X + Y)$, the expectation of the product can be represented as[8]

$$\begin{aligned} EXY = &\sum_y (x_1y)\, P(x_1 \cap y) + \sum_y (x_2y)\, P(x_2 \cap y) + \sum_y (x_3y)\, P(x_3 \cap y) \\ &+ \sum_y (x_4y)\, P(x_4 \cap y), \end{aligned}$$

where again we have, for ease of exposition, considered X to have only four possible values. At this point we shall invoke independence of X and Y so that

$$\begin{aligned} EXY &= \sum_y (x_1y)\, P(x_1)\, P(y) + \sum_y (x_2y)\, P(x_2)\, P(y) \\ &\quad + \sum_y (x_3y)\, P(x_3)\, P(y) + \sum_y (x_4y)\, P(x_4)\, P(y) \\ &= \sum_y x_1\, P(x_1)\, y\, P(y) + \sum_y x_2\, P(x_2)\, y\, P(y) \\ &\quad + \sum_y x_3\, P(x_3)\, y\, P(y) + \sum_y x_4\, P(x_4)\, y\, P(y) \\ &= x_1\, P(x_1) \sum_y y\, P(y) + x_2\, P(x_2) \sum_y y\, P(y) \\ &\quad + x_3\, P(x_3) \sum_y y\, P(y) + x_4\, P(x_4) \sum_y y\, P(y) \\ &= x_1\, P(x_1)EY + x_2\, P(x_2)EY + x_3\, P(x_3)EY + x_4\, P(x_4)EY \\ &= [x_1\, P(x_1) + x_2\, P(x_2) + x_3\, P(x_3) + x_4\, P(x_4)](EY) \\ &= (EX)\, (EY). \end{aligned}$$

Thus, *if* X and Y are independent,

$$E(XY) = (EX)(EY).$$

This is *not* an if and only if proposition. If $E(XY) = (EX)(EY)$, then X and Y may or may not be independent; but if they *are* independent, then it must be that the expectation of their product is the product of their expectations. Consider, for example, the random variables X and Y where X has the probability distribution

$$D_X = \{(-1, 0.\ 4), (0, 0.2), (1, 0.4)\}$$

and Y is defined by $Y = X^2$. Now $Y = 0$ if and only if $X = 0$ so that $P(Y = 0) = P(X = 0) = 0.2$, and $Y = 1$ if $X = -1$ or $X = 1$ so that

[8]The reader should verify this as a correct representation of EXY in precisely the way it was done for $E(X + Y)$; see Appendix, Section 4.4.

$P(Y = 1) = 0.4 + 0.4 = 0.8$. We can calculate $EX = -1(0.4) + 0(0.2) + 1(0.4) = 0$ and $EY = 0(0.2) + 1(0.8) = 0.8$.

Now consider the product XY. $XY = -1$ if and only if $X = -1$ and $Y = 1$, so that, applying the general multiplication rule, $P(XY = -1) = P[(X = -1) \cap (Y = 1)] = P[(X = -1)]\, P[(Y = 1) \mid (X = -1)]$. Now the conditional probability $P[(Y = 1) \mid (X = -1)]$ is equal to unity, since if $X = -1$, the condition $Y = X^2$ means that Y *must* be equal to one. Therefore,

$$P(XY = -1) = P[(X = -1)]\, P[(Y = 1) \mid (X = -1)]$$
$$= (0.4)(1) = 0.4.$$

But $0.4 \neq P(X = -1) \cdot P(Y = 1) = (0.4)(0.8) = 0.32$. Therefore it is clear — if it was not already — that X and Y are *dependent* random variables.

$XY = 1$ if and only if $X = 1$ and $Y = 1$, which occurs with probability $P(X = 1)\, P(Y = 1 \mid X = 1) = 0.4(1) = 0.4$.

$XY = 0$ if and only if $X = 0$ and $Y = 0$, which occurs with probability $P(X = 0)\, P(Y = 0 \mid X = 0) = 0.2(1) = 0.2$.

We therefore find directly that $EXY = -1(0.4) + 1(0.4) + 0(0.2) = 0$, which indeed is $(EX)(EY) = (0)(0.8) = 0$. Thus we have two clearly dependent random variables for which $E(XY) = (EX)(EY)$.[9]

We are now ready to consider the variance of a sum of random variables.

Let $Z = X + Y$. By definition,

$$\text{Variance of } Z = \sigma_Z^2 = E[(Z - EZ)^2].$$

By using $Z = X + Y$ and $E(X + Y) = EX + EY$, we find

$$\sigma_Z^2 = E[(X + Y - EX - EY)^2] = E[\{(X - EX) + (Y - EY)\}^2].$$

Performing the indicated squaring,

$$\sigma_Z^2 = E[(X - EX)^2 + (Y - EY)^2 + 2(X - EX)(Y - EY)].$$

Now $(X - EX)^2$, $(Y - EY)^2$, and $2(X - EX)(Y - EY)$ are random variables, so that the expectation of their sum is the sum of their expectations; hence

$$\sigma_Z^2 = E(X - EX)^2 + E(Y - EY)^2 + E2(X - EX)(Y - EY).$$

[9]Advanced treatments refer to dependent variables for which $EXY = (EX)(EY)$ as *orthogonal random variables.*

But

$$E(X - EX)^2 = \sigma_X^2, \quad E(Y - EY)^2 = \sigma_Y^2,$$

and

$$E2(X - EX)(Y - EY) = 2E(X - EX)(Y - EY);$$

therefore,

$$\sigma_Z^2 = \sigma_X^2 + \sigma_Y^2 + 2E(X - EX)(Y - EY).$$

Working on the last term on the right,

$$\begin{aligned} E(X - EX)(Y - EY) &= E[XY - Y(EX) - X(EY) + (EX)(EY)] \\ &= EXY - E[Y(EX)] - E[X(EY)] \\ &\quad + E[(EX)(EY)]. \end{aligned}$$

Now EX and EY are constants, not random variables, so that by Theorem 2,

$$\begin{aligned} E(X - EX)(Y - EY) &= EXY - (EY)(EX) - (EX)(EY) + (EX)(EY) \\ &= EXY - (EX)(EY). \end{aligned}$$

If X and Y are independent, then $EXY = (EX)(EY)$, so that

$$E(X - EX)(Y - EY) = (EX)(EY) - (EX)(EY) = 0.$$

We have thus proved the following theorem.

THEOREM 4. If X and Y are independent random variables, the variance of their sum is the sum of their variances; that is,

$$\text{Variance } (X + Y) = \sigma_X^2 + \sigma_Y^2.$$

The term $E(X - EX)(Y - EY)$, which we showed to be zero if X and Y are independent, is of great importance in probability theory and is known as the *covariance of* X *and* Y, abbreviated cov (X, Y). Suppose that whenever X is far above its mean, the probability that Y will also be far above its mean is large. Further, whenever X is far below its mean, the probability that Y will be far below its mean is large. In that case, when $(X - EX)$ is large and positive, $(Y - EY)$ will also tend to be large and positive; when $(X - EX)$ is far below zero, $(Y - EY)$ will also tend to be far below zero. The random variable $(X - EX)(Y - EY)$ will therefore tend to be large and positive whenever X is not close to EX. When X is close to EX, Y will tend to be close to EY so that the product $(X - EX)(Y - EY)$ will tend to be relatively small. $E(X - EX)(Y - EY)$ will therefore be an average of large positive values and small values; hence

$$\text{cov } (X, Y) = E(X - EX)(Y - EY) > 0.$$

Thus a positive covariance indicates that X and Y tend to "move together" directly; that is, when X is large, Y tends to be large and when X is small, Y tends to be small.

On the other hand if $(X > EX)$ implies a high probability that Y will be $< EY$, and if $(X < EX)$ implies a high probability that Y will be $> EY$, the products $(X - EX)(Y - EY)$ will tend to be negative whenever X is not close to EX and small whenever X is close to EX. In this case,

$$\text{cov}(X, Y) = E(X - EX)(Y - EY) < 0.$$

A negative covariance indicates that X and Y tend to "move together" inversely; that is, when X is large, Y tends to be small and when X is small, Y tends to be large.

If X and Y are independent, their covariance is zero, indicating that they do not tend to "move together" at all; that is, a large X implies nothing about Y at all.

In general then, if $Z = X + Y$,

$$\text{Variance}(X + Y) = \sigma_X^2 + \sigma_Y^2 + 2\,\text{cov}(X, Y),$$

which specializes to

$$\text{Variance}(X + Y) = \sigma_X^2 + \sigma_Y^2$$

if X and Y are independent.[10]

EXAMPLE 4.4.2. Suppose $EX = 50$, $\sigma_X^2 = 25$ $EY = 80$, $\sigma_Y^2 = 35$, and $\text{cov}(X, Y) = -20$. Let $Z = X + Y$.

(a) Are X and Y independent?
(b) What is the probability that $Z \leq 120$ or $Z \geq 140$?
(c) How would the answer to (b) change if all conditions were as given except $\text{cov}(X, Y) = 0$? How do you motivate this change in the answer to (b)?

Solution:

(a) Since $\text{cov}(X, Y) \neq 0$, X and Y must be dependent. The negative covariance in fact implies that Y has a higher probability of being below 80 ($= EY$) when X is above 50 ($= EX$) than when X is below 50. Hence probabilities connected with Y *are* affected by what value of X occurs.

[10]The reader can show easily that $\text{cov}(X,Y) = 0$ if X and Y are independent or orthogonal so that (1) X and Y independent implies that variance $(X + Y) = \sigma_X^2 + \sigma_Y^2$; and (2) variance $(X + Y) = \sigma_X^2 + \sigma_Y^2$ implies that X and Y are either independent or orthogonal.

(b) Exact probability calculations are impossible without knowing the relevant probability distributions. However, we can calculate an upper limit for the desired probability via Chebyschev's inequality.

$$Z = X + Y;$$

therefore,

$$EZ = EX + EY = 50 + 80 = 130.$$

If $Z \leq 120$ or $Z \geq 140$, then

$$|Z - EZ| \geq 10.$$

To apply Chebyschev's inequality, we need the variance of Z:

$$\begin{aligned}\sigma_Z^2 &= \sigma_X^2 + \sigma_Y^2 + 2 \operatorname{cov}(X, Y)\\ &= 25 + 35 + 2(-20)\\ &= 25 + 35 - 40 = 20.\end{aligned}$$

Therefore,

$$P[|Z - EZ| \geq 10] \leq \frac{\sigma_Z^2}{(10)^2} = \frac{20}{100} = 0.2.$$

Thus the desired probability must be no more than 0.2.

(c) If $\operatorname{cov}(X, Y) = 0$,

$$\begin{aligned}\sigma_Z^2 &= \sigma_X^2 + \sigma_Y^2\\ &= 25 + 35 = 60.\end{aligned}$$

Therefore,

$$P[|Z - EZ| \geq 10] \leq \frac{60}{100} = 0.60.$$

Now the desired probability need no longer be ≤ 0.2 and in fact may be as high as 0.6.

Imposing a zero covariance has increased the variance of the random variable Z and thus made a given deviation from the mean more likely. When X and Y have a negative covariance, a large X tends to be accompanied by a small Y more often[11] than when X and Y have zero covariance. Thus when X is large, $X + Y$ tends to be relatively smaller when the covariance is negative than when it is zero. Similarly a large Y will be accompanied by a small X more often when the covariance is negative than

[11]Interpret *more often* as *with higher probability*.

when it is zero. Relative to a zero covariance, then, a negative covariance creates a bias against extremely large (or extremely small) $X + Y$ sums. This has the effect of reducing the extent of variability of Z relative to what it would be with zero covariance.[12]

PROBLEMS

4-1. Suppose a student is taking a three-question, true-false exam. Suppose also that he has not studied, so that he must guess at each question and, therefore, has a probability of $\frac{1}{2}$ of answering any particular question correctly. Let the random variable X = the number of questions he answers correctly.

(a) Find the probability distribution of X.
(b) Find $E(X)$ and give it an interpretation.

4-2. Repeat Problem 1 for a four-question exam.

4-3. Using the following information,

x = values of a random variable X	-2	-1	0	1	2
$P[X = x]$	0.2	0.1	0.2	0.3	0.2

(a) Compute $E(X)$.
(b) Find the probability distribution of the random variable $(3X - 1)$.
(c) Verify that $E(3X - 1) = 3E(X) - 1$.
(d) Find the probability distribution and expected value of the random variable $(X^2 - 1)$.

4-4. A marksman is to fire two shots at a target. He scores 100 for a bull's-eye, 65 for a near miss, 40 for hitting anywhere else on the target, and 0 for not hitting the target at all. In previous experience on this particular range, $\frac{1}{10}$ of all his shots were bull's-eyes, $\frac{2}{5}$ were near misses, and $\frac{1}{5}$ of the remainder missed the target completely. Let X = the sum of his two scores.

[12] A positive covariance would go further and create a bias in favor of extremely large (or extremely small) $X + Y$ sums. σ_Z^2 is smallest for X and Y having a negative covariance, largest for X and Y having a positive covariance, and in between for X and Y having a zero covariance.

(a) Is X a random variable? If so, what random experiment ($\mathcal{E}$) generates X?
(b) Find $E(X)$ and $P(X = EX)$.
(c) Would your answer to (b) be different if the score for a near miss were 60 instead of 65? How?

4-5. A retailer has purchased 2 widgets (a perishable commodity) for his inventory this week. Weekly demand for widgets is a random variable (X) with the following probability distribution:

$X = x$	0	1	2	3	4
$P[X = x]$	0.1	0.1	0.3	0.4	0.1

The retailer charges his customers a price of \$2 per widget and buys them from the producer for \$1.50 apiece.

(a) What is the retailer's expected profit (or loss) from the sale of widgets this week?
(b) What is the value of his optimum profit for this week and what is its probability?
(c) If the retailer wanted to stock the same quantity of widgets every week, what quantity would you recommend? Why?

4-6. You can play a game which has the following set of possible outcomes: {you lose \$50 with probability 0.10, you lose \$2 with probability 0.50, you win \$15 with probability 0.35, you win \$50 with probability 0.05}. It costs you an entry fee of \$.75 to play the game. Let the random variable X = the next gain (or loss) from one play of the game.

(a) What is the probability distribution of X?
(b) What is the expected net gain in playing this game?
(c) It is clear from (a) and (b) that you cannot possibly win the expected net gain on any single play. Explain, then, the meaning of the *expected net gain* and discuss its usefulness as a criterion for deciding whether to play the game.

4-7. Let us use I to denote the game described in Problem 4-6. Suppose there is another game — game II — which has the following set of possible outcomes: {you lose \$10 with probability 0.10, you lose \$1 with probability 0.10, you win the chance to play game I with no entry fee with probability 0.80}. Game II has no entry fee.

(a) What is the expected net gain from playing game II?

(b) If you could play a game only once and wanted to maximize the probability of a positive net gain, which game would you choose?

4-8. In a certain city there are four employment agencies — A, B, C, and D. A handles only engineering jobs and places 50% of all applicants. B specializes in engineering jobs but handles others as well and places $\frac{1}{3}$ of all engineers who apply. C handles few engineering jobs and can place only 10% of applicant engineers. D handles only temporary, low-paying jobs and can place any applicant who applies. An unemployed engineer seeking a job will naturally go to A first. If A cannot place him, he will go to B next; then, if necessary, he will go to C. If A, B, and C fail to place him, he will go to D.

(a) Let the random variable Y = the number of agencies visited at the time a job is secured; that is, $Y = 2$ if the applicant is placed in a job by agency B. Find the probability distribution of Y.
(b) How many agencies should the applicant expect to have to try in order to get a job?
(c) Suppose agencies A and B charge each applicant a \$5 fee while agency C charges a \$3 fee and D charges \$1. What is the expected cost of obtaining a job? (The agency fee is for the privilege of applying and having the application processed. It must, therefore, be paid whether the agency is able to place the applicant or not.)

4-9. X is a random variable distributed as follows:

$X = x$	-4	-3	-1	4	7	12
$P[X = x]$	0.1	0.2	0.2	0.1	0.3	0.1

(a) Calculate $E(X)$ and var (X) and give an interpretation of the latter.
(b) Calculate $E(Y)$ and var (Y) for the random variable $Y = 2X - 2$. What is the relationship between var (Y) and var (X)?

4-10. Prove var $(aX + b) = a^2$ var (X), where a and b are constants and X is a random variable.

4-11. Calculate the variance, standard deviation, and M.A.D. of the net gain in Problem 4-6. Give an interpretation of each result.

4-12. Suppose X is a random variable with expected value μ. Prove $E[(X - \mu)^2] < E[(X - b)^2]$, where b is a constant and $b \neq \mu$.

Hint: any constant b may be expressed as $b = \mu + a$, where a is also a constant.

Express the statement $E[(X - \mu)^2] < E[(X - b)^2]$ verbally.

4-13. Let X be a random variable with expected value μ and variance σ^2. Consider the random variable $Y = (X - \mu)/\sigma$. What is $E(Y)$; var (Y)?

(*Note:* Y is called the *standardized* form of X. The notion of a *standardized* random variable plays an important role in the theory of statistics, as will become evident in later chapters.)

4-14. A salesman receives a commission of \$35 per sale. In the past 100 weeks his efforts have produced the following results:

X = Number of sales per week	0	1	2	3	4	5	6	7	8	>8
Number of weeks this has occurred	3	12	15	20	12	18	10	7	3	0

Assign reasonable probabilities to each possible realization of X, then

(a) Compute the income the salesman can expect to earn in a week and its variance.
(b) With what probability will the salesman earn at least \$150 next week?
(c) Find an upper limit for P[next week's income $\geq$ \$150] by use of Markov's inequality. Comment on the utility of this figure.
(d) Calculate the exact probability that next week's income will deviate from expected income by at least \$50.
(e) Find an upper limit for the probability of a deviation from expected income of at least \$50 by means of Chebyschev's inequality. Comment on the utility of this figure.

4-15. To illustrate the weakness of Chebyschev's inequality in some cases, consider the experiment of throwing a die one time. Let X be the random variable *score on the die*. Calculate $E(X)$ and σ_X^2. What is the maximum value of $|X - E(X)|$? What does Chebyschev's inequality have to say about the probability of a deviation at least this large?

4-16. Let X_1 denote the random variable outcome of the first performance of a random experiment. Let X_2 denote the random variable outcome of the second performance of the same random experiment. Why must $E(X_1) = E(X_2)$ and $\sigma_{X_1}^2 = \sigma_{X_2}^2$?

4-17. Consider the random experiment of rolling a die two times. Let X_1 = the score on the first roll and X_2 = the score on the second roll. Define $Y = X_1 + X_2$. Calculate $E(Y)$, var (Y).

4-18. Urn A contains three tags numbered 2, 6, and 13 respectively. Urn B contains three tags numbered 5, 9, and 13 respectively. Let $\mathcal{E}_A$ denote the random experiment of drawing one tag from urn A and let $\mathcal{E}_B$ denote the random experiment of drawing one tag from urn B. Suppose we define $Y = X_B - X_A$ where X_B and X_A are the random variables generated by the random experiments $\mathcal{E}_B$ and $\mathcal{E}_A$ respectively.

(a) What random experiment generates Y?
(b) What is the probability distribution of Y?
(c) Calculate $E(Y)$ and σ_Y^2.
(d) Calculate $P[Y \geq (EY + \sigma_Y)]$ and $P[Y \leq (EY - \sigma_Y)]$.

4-19. Suppose the six numbered tags of Problem 4-18 were all in the same urn. Consider the random experiment of drawing two tags from the urn — one at a time, without replacement. Let the random variable Z denote the difference between the number on the first tag drawn and the number on the second tag drawn. Find the probability distribution of Z and calculate EZ, σ_Z^2.

4-20. Private gross national product (Y) is defined as the sum of personal consumption expenditures (C) and gross private domestic investment (I); that is, $Y = C + I$. An economist wants to forecast private gross national product by summing forecasts of C and I. Both C and I are random variables. Suppose it is known that var C = 2,600, var I = 1,000, and cov (C, I) = 1,400. Assume that C, I, and hence Y are measured in millions of dollars so that variances and covariances are in units of millions of dollars squared.

(a) Explain the meaning of the covariance term. Can you give an economic reason for the existence and sign of cov (C, I) in this problem?
(b) Find an upper limit for the probability that this economist's forecast of Y will be less than \$100 million from expected Y.

4-21. Let X_1, X_2, X_3 be random variables with variances $\sigma_{X_1}^2$, $\sigma_{X_2}^2$, $\sigma_{X_3}^2$ respectively. Define the random variable $S = X_1 + X_2 + X_3$. Prove

var $(S) = \sigma^2_{X_1} + \sigma^2_{X_2} + \sigma^2_{X_3} + 2 \text{ cov } (X_1, X_2) + 2 \text{ cov } (X_1, X_3) + 2 \text{ cov } (X_2, X_3)$.
(Can you see how this result, along with Theorem 4, can be generalized to the sum of any finite number of random variables?)

4-22. Consider the random experiment of rolling a fair die twice. Let X_1 denote the larger of the two outcomes and let X_2 denote the other. Define $Y = X_1 - X_2$.

(a) Find the probability distributions of X_1, X_2, and Y.
(b) Using the results of (a), verify that $E[Y] = E[X_1] - E[X_2]$ and var $[Y] = \text{var } X_1 + \text{var } X_2 - 2 \text{ cov } (X_1, X_2)$.
(c) Give an interpretation of cov $[X_1, X_2]$.

4-23. X and Y are stochastically independent random variables. Prove that U and V are also stochastically independent where $U = a + bX$ and $V = c + dY$ and a, b, c, d are constants.

4-24. X is a random variable with probability distribution

x	-1	0	1
$P[X = x]$	$\frac{1}{3}$	$\frac{1}{3}$	$\frac{1}{3}$

Show that the random variables X and Y are orthogonal random variables but are not stochastically independent, where Y is defined by $Y = X^2$.

4-25. Prove cov $[(X - a), (Y - b)] = \text{cov } [X, Y]$ for any pair of constants a, b.

4-26. Instead of stocking two widgets per week, suppose the retailer in Problem 4-5 follows a random purchase pattern from week to week. Assume this random purchase pattern is restricted to the purchase of one, two, or three widgets with equal probabilities. Find the expected value of net weekly profit under this scheme. Would you recommend this method of purchasing to the retailer?

5 THE BINOMIAL RANDOM VARIABLE (Analysis of a Dichotomy)

5.1 Introduction

Experimenters and decision-makers are frequently faced with dichotomous situations. For example, a survey undertaken before the marketing of a new product elicits either a favorable or unfavorable response from each individual sampled; inspection of the output of a production run results in either defective or nondefective items; and so on.

In this chapter we shall study the probabilistic implications of such dichotomous situations and present several applications. The earliest careful studies of the probability aspects of a dichotomy were undertaken by James Bernoulli in the 17th century, and we begin with what is referred to as the Bernoulli variable.

5.2 The Bernoulli Variable

Consider a random experiment with only two possible outcomes referred to as success, S, and failure, F. Let p denote the probability of success, and $q = 1 - p$ the probability of failure. Our interest centers on the random variable

$$X = \text{the number of successes.}$$

Clearly, $X \in \mathcal{S} = \{0, 1\}$ and the probability distribution of X is

$$D = \{(0, q), (1, p)\}.$$

It is quite easy to specify a probability function for X; namely

$$P(X = x) = p^x q^{1-x}, \qquad x \in \{0, 1\}.$$

Thus,[1]

$$P(X = 0) = p^0 q^{1-0} = (1)(q) = q$$

and

$$P(X = 1) = p^1 q^{1-1} = p(q^0) = p.$$

The random experiment which produces either success with probability p or failure with probability $q = 1 - p$ is referred to as a *Bernoulli trial;* the random variable which measures the number of successes in a Bernoulli trial is said to be a *Bernoulli variable* or to have the *Bernoulli distribution.*

Let us calculate the expected value and variance of the Bernoulli variable X.

$$\begin{aligned} EX &= \sum_x x\, P(x) \\ &= (0)(q) + 1(p) = p. \\ \sigma_X^2 &= \sum_x (x - EX)^2 P(x) \\ &= (0 - p)^2 q + (1 - p)^2 p \\ &= p^2 q + (1 - p)^2 p \\ &= p[pq + (1 - p)^2] \\ &= p[pq + q^2] \\ &= pq[p + q] \\ &= pq. \end{aligned}$$

The last line above follows from the fact that $p + q = p + (1 - p) = 1$.

5.3 The Case of Two Independent Bernoulli Trials

The Bernoulli variable itself is extremely limited in application since it is almost never sufficient for any purposes to carry out only one Bernoulli trial. In any important application one would generally wish to analyze the results of several Bernoulli trials. Let us begin with two

[1]Recall that $t^0 = 1$ for $-\infty < t < \infty$.

Bernoulli trials run under identical conditions so that they are stochastically independent with the same probability of success p on each trial. If X_1 is the Bernoulli variable for the first trial and X_2 is that for the second trial, then X_1 and X_2 are *independent and identically distributed* random variables. Thus

$$EX_1 = EX_2 = p.$$

$$\sigma_{X_1}^2 = \sigma_{X_2}^2 = pq.$$

Further, the number of successes in the *two* trials is a random variable X defined by

$$X = X_1 + X_2.$$

The expected number of successes in two trials is

$$EX = EX_1 + EX_2 = 2p.$$

By virtue of the independence of X_1 and X_2, the variance of X is

$$\sigma_X^2 = \sigma_{X_1}^2 + \sigma_{X_2}^2 = 2pq.$$

EXAMPLE 5.3.1. In a given population of 100 people, 15 favor a proposition to be voted upon and the rest are against it. The sentiment of the population is, however, unknown to the proponents of the proposition. If 2 individuals are sampled at random, with replacement, what is the expected number who will favor the proposition and what is the standard deviation of the number favoring the proposition?

Solution: First note that the *with replacement* condition is necessary to cast the problem in such a way as to produce independent Bernoulli trials. In the first trial the probability of success is

$$p = \tfrac{15}{100} = 0.15.$$

If the second sampling were then made from the remaining 99 individuals, the probability of success would be either $\frac{15}{99}$ or $\frac{14}{99}$, *depending* on whether the first individual had been *for* or *against.* In any case the probability of success would then not be 0.15 and the trials would be stochastically dependent. In the case of random sampling *with* replacement, the trials are independent and the probability of success is $p = 0.15$ on each trial.

Consequently, letting $X =$ the number favoring the proposition (that is, the number of successes),

$$EX = 2p = 0.30.$$

$$\sigma_X^2 = 2pq = 2(0.15)(0.85) = 0.255.$$

Thus, the expected number of seccesses is 0.3 and the standard deviation is $+\sqrt{0.255} \cong 0.505$.

Three-tenths of a success can never be observed of course. Each observation on X must be either 0, 1, or 2, but the average of the results of many replications (each replication being a sample of two individuals) or the average of a theoretical sequence of replications would be 0.3.

Further, Chebyschev's inequality implies that the probability is at least $\frac{3}{4}$ that the number of favorable responses on a given trial will be between -0.71 $(EX - 2\sigma)$ and $+1.31$ $(EX + 2\sigma)$. Since the interval -0.71 to $+1.31$ contains the subset $\{0, 1\}$ of possible values of X, it must be that the probability is at least $\frac{3}{4}$ that fewer than two successes will occur when the two-person sampling is made.

At the end of Example 5.3.1 we used Chebyschev's inequality to make a statement about the probability that X, the sum of two Bernoulli variables, would be less than 2. It is convenient to be able to make exact probability statements about X, that is, to be able to calculate the probability distribution of X. Viewed as a compound experiment, the two Bernoulli trials produce the following sample space of ordered pairs:

$$\{(S, F), (S, S), (F, S), (F, F)\},$$

where, as usual, the first element of the pair is the result of the first trial and so on. Since the trials are independent, the probabilities of the ordered pairs are easily calculated:

$$P(S, F) = P(S)\,P(F) = pq. \quad (1)$$

$$P(S, S) = P(S)\,P(S) = p^2. \quad (2)$$

$$P(F, S) = P(F)\,P(S) = qp. \quad (1)$$

$$P(F, F) = P(F)\,P(F) = q^2. \quad (0)$$

The numbers in parentheses to the right of the probabilities above give the number of successes in each ordered pair. We therefore derive the following probability distribution for X:

x	$P(x)$
0	q^2
1	$2pq$
2	p^2

To prove that the sum of the probabilities is unity,

$$q^2 + 2pq + p^2 = q^2 + p(2q + p)$$
$$= q^2 + p(q + q + p)$$

$$= q^2 + p(q + 1)$$
$$= q^2 + qp + p$$
$$= q(q + p) + p$$
$$= q + p$$
$$= 1.$$

Using the probability distribution above we can, for example, calculate EX directly:

$$\begin{aligned} EX &= (0)(q^2) + (1)(2pq) + (2)(p^2) \\ &= 2pq + 2p^2 \\ &= 2p(q + p) \\ &= 2p. \end{aligned}$$

That the variance of X is $2pq$ could be similarly calculated directly by its definition.[2]

The reader might have noticed that the probabilities of 0, 1, and 2 successes are simply the successive terms in the binomial expansion of $(q + p)^2$ for

$$(q + p)^2 = q^2 + 2pq + p^2.$$

Indeed, this is no accident as we shall discover when we extend our discussion to more than two Bernoulli trials.

5.4 The Binomial Random Variable

The area of application of Bernoulli trials is extremely rich once we learn to analyze any finite number of trials. We begin with the following

DEFINITION. The random variable, $X =$ the number of successes in n stochastically independent Bernoulli trials with equal probability p of success on each, is said to be a *binomial random variable.* The number of trials n may be any finite, positive number.

A shorthand way of denoting that X is a binomial random variable resulting from n independent Bernoulli trials each with probability of success p is to write

$$X \text{ is } B(n, p),$$

[2]It is suggested that the reader do this himself.

which is read X *is binomial* n, p. Thus, 10 trials with probability of success 0.25 on each would produce the particular random variable denoted by

$$X \text{ is } B(10, 0.25)$$

with $X \in \{0, 1, 2, \ldots, 10\}$.

Let $X_1, X_2, X_3, \ldots, X_n$ be the Bernoulli random variables for the n trials mentioned in the definition of the binomial variable. It is clear that all these variables are stochastically independent[3] and identically distributed.[4] The binomial variable X = the number of successes on all n trials is

$$X = \sum_{i=1}^{n} X_i.$$

For the expectation of X we have

$$EX = E(\sum_{i=1}^{n} X_i).$$

Since the expectation of a sum is the sum of the expectations, and $EX_i = p$,

$$\begin{aligned} EX &= \sum_{i=1}^{n} EX_i \\ &= \sum_{i=1}^{n} p \\ &= np. \end{aligned}$$

[3]The definition of stochastic independence of three random variables X, Y, and Z is the following extension of the definition given for two variables in Chapter 4: Let $X \in \mathcal{S}_1$, $Y \in \mathcal{S}_2$, and $Z \in \mathcal{S}_3$. X, Y, and Z are said to be mutually stochastically independent if and only if

$$P(X = x \text{ and } Y = y \text{ and } Z = z) = P(X = x)\, P(Y = y)\, P(Z = z)$$

for all $x \in \mathcal{S}_1$, $y \in \mathcal{S}_2$, and $z \in \mathcal{S}_3$.

We note that mutual independence of X, Y, and Z implies that X and Y are stochastically independent, and similarly for X and Z and also Y and Z. However, pairwise independence does not imply mutual independence of all three. (See problem 5-3, p. 143.) The reader can easily extend the definition of mutual independence to any finite number of random variables.

[4]We can envision independent Bernoulli trials which do not produce identically distributed random variables. For example, consider flipping a fair coin and then a loaded coin and counting the number of heads each time. These are independent Bernoulli trials, but the resulting Bernoulli variables are not identically distributed since the probability of heads differs for the two coins. In this case the number of heads in the two trials would *not* be a binomial random variable. *Both* the independence *and* the constant probability of success from trial to trial are necessary to define the binomial variable.

For the variance of X we have

$$\sigma_X^2 = \text{variance } (\sum_{i=1}^{n} X_i).$$

Although we shall not prove it, Theorem 4, Chapter 4 extends to any finite number of mutually independent random variables so that the variance of the sum of the X_i is the sum of their variances, and since $\sigma_{X_i}^2 = pq$,

$$\begin{aligned}\sigma_X^2 &= \sum_{i=1}^{n} \sigma_{X_i}^2 \\ &= \sum_{i=1}^{n} pq \\ &= npq.\end{aligned}$$

If $n = 2$, these results specialize to

$$EX = 2p$$

and

$$\sigma_X^2 = 2pq$$

as calculated in Section 5.3. We also remark that the Bernoulli variable itself is a *degenerate binomial*, namely $B(1, p)$.

EXAMPLE 5.4.1. A two-question exam is taken by 30 students, none of whom has studied the necessary material. Question 1 is multiple choice with four choices given; the second question is multiple choice with five possibilities listed. Let X = the number of students with at least one question correct.

(a) What is the expected number of students with at least one question correct?

(b) Calculate an upper limit for the probability that at least half the class gets at least one question correct.

Solution: First we must recognize that each student taking the exam is performing a Bernoulli trial since he either does or does not get at least one question correct. The 30 trials can be considered independent provided all students work alone. Since none of the students has studied, we shall regard each as having to guess on each question so that each student should have the same probability of getting at least one right answer. X is therefore $B(30, p)$ and what is left is to determine p, a student's probability of getting at least one right answer.

Each Bernoulli trial is itself a compound experiment, namely guessing on the first question and then guessing on the second. Assuming the questions themselves are unrelated so that the first guess does not influence the second guess, the trials (guesses) composing the Bernoulli trial are stochastically independent. The event *at least one question correct* is the complement of the event *neither question correct,* which is the ordered pair: (wrong guess on No. 1, wrong guess on No. 2). With four choices on No. 1 and five on No 2, the probability of the latter ordered pair is

$$\tfrac{3}{4}\cdot\tfrac{4}{5} = \tfrac{3}{5}.$$

Thus, Prob (at least one question correct) $= p = 1 - \frac{3}{5} = \frac{2}{5}$.

Therefore

$$X \text{ is } B(30, \tfrac{2}{5})$$

(a) $EX = np = 30(\frac{2}{5}) = 12$.

Twelve students can be expected to get at least one question correct (by independent guessing).

(b) The probability that at least half the class gets at least one correct answer is

$$P(X \geq 15).$$

Since X is nonnegative and $EX = 12$, Markov's inequality yields

$$P(X \geq 15) \leq \tfrac{12}{15} = 0.8.$$

Logically, our next task would be to attempt to derive the binomial probability distribution for any finite, positive n. Thus far we have determined the probability distribution only for $n = 1$ (the Bernoulli case) and $n = 2$. Looking back, for $n = 1$, the probabilities of $X = 0$ and $X = 1$ are the successive terms in

$$(q + p)^1 = q + p.$$

For $n = 2$, the probabilities of $X = 0$, $X = 1$, and $X = 2$ are the successive terms in

$$(q + p)^2 = q^2 + 2pq + p^2.$$

If the reader should guess that for any $n \geq 1$ the probabilities of 0, 1, 2, . . ., n respectively are the successive terms in $(q + p)^n$, he would be correct. Deriving this result is made very much easier if we first digress long enough to learn something about permutations.

5.5 Digression on Counting

Suppose we have three distinct objects a, b, and c. How many different arrangements of these objects are possible? The following enumeration clearly shows the answer to be six:

abc
acb
bac
bca
cab
cba

The different arrangements are referred to as permutations. What we have done is to find that there are six permutations of three objects. This fact is written ${}_3P = 6$. For future reference we note that this can be written

$${}_3P = 3 \cdot 2 \cdot 1.$$

How many permutations are there of four different objects; that is, what is ${}_4P$? We shall use the device of "counting-trees" to show that the answer is ${}_4P = 24$. Denote the four objects by a, b, c, and d. If we start with a in the first position, we have three choices for the second position. Once the letter in the second position is chosen, we have two choices for the third

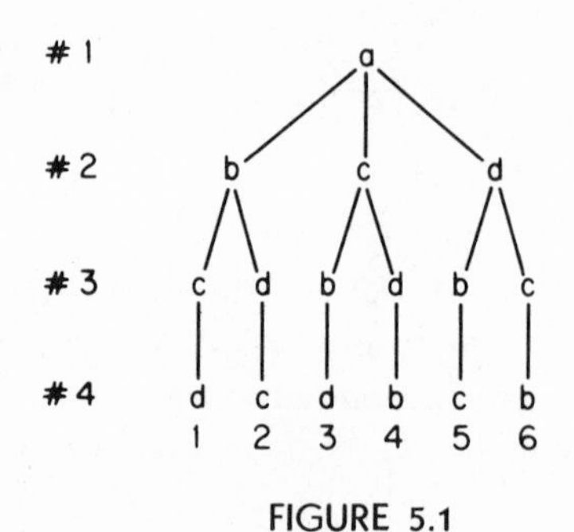

FIGURE 5.1

position, and so on. Starting with a, then, we arrive at the "tree" in Figure 5.1. This tree produces six permutations, reading the "branches" from left to right:

$a\,b\,c\,d$
$a\,b\,d\,c$
$a\,c\,b\,d$
$a\,c\,d\,b$
$a\,d\,b\,c$
$a\,d\,c\,b$

There are three more such trees: one tree starting with b in the first position, one with c in the first position, and finally a tree beginning with d. Each of the four trees will produce six permutations so that we have $4 \cdot 6 = 24$ in all. Note that this can be written

$$_4P = 24 = 4 \cdot 3 \cdot 2 \cdot 1.$$

With only two objects there are two permutations:

$$ab$$
$$ba,$$

while one object produces only one arrangement. Thus

$$_1P = 1,$$

$$_2P = 2 \cdot 1,$$

$$_3P = 3 \cdot 2 \cdot 1,$$

$$_4P = 4 \cdot 3 \cdot 2 \cdot 1.$$

The reader can now easily convince himself that

$$_5P = 5 \cdot 4 \cdot 3 \cdot 2 \cdot 1,$$

$$_6P = 6 \cdot 5 \cdot 4 \cdot 3 \cdot 2 \cdot 1,$$

and so on. Fortunately, mathematicians have an abbreviation for a product such as $5 \cdot 4 \cdot 3 \cdot 2 \cdot 1$, namely $5!$, which is read *five factorial.* The expression $6!$ stands for the product $6 \cdot 5 \cdot 4 \cdot 3 \cdot 2 \cdot 1$, etc.[5] The permutation results then become

$$_1P = 1!,$$

$$_2P = 2!,$$

$$_3P = 3!,$$

$$_4P = 4!.$$

In general, if n is a positive integer,

$$_nP = n! = n(n - 1)(n - 2)(n - 3) \cdots (2)(1).$$

Suppose now that we have n objects but we wish to permute them in groups of $(n - 1)$; that is, we want the permutations of n objects but only $(n - 1)$ at a time. In the case of $n = 3$, we would have

[5]Note that $1! = 1$. By convention $0! = 1$ also. Saying that $0!$ equals one may not make a great deal of sense, but simple arithmetic fails unless we make $0!$ equal to one and that is probably justification enough!

ab
ba
ac
ca
bc
cb

or, six permutations of three objects in groups of two. The abbreviation for *the permutations of three objects in groups of two* is ${}_3P_2$ and we have found that

$${}_3P_2 = 6 = 3!.$$

Usually if we are permuting n objects in groups of $(n-1)$, we shall have the same number of counting-trees as for ${}_nP$, namely n, but the last position on each tree will be unfilled. A look at Figure 5.1 will show that eliminating the last position still leaves the same number of branches per tree. The last position is said to be a one-branch position.[6] Thus,

$${}_nP_{(n-1)} = {}_nP = n!.$$

Suppose we want to permute n objects in groups of $(n-2)$. We still have the n counting-trees of ${}_nP$ but now we eliminate the last *two* positions. Eliminating the last position does not alter the number of branches because the last position is a one-branch position. Eliminating the next to the last position, however, leaves only half as many branches since the next to the last position is a two-branch position.[7] Thus,

$${}_nP_{(n-2)} = \left(\frac{1}{2}\right){}_nP_{(n-1)} = \left(\frac{1}{2}\right)n! = \frac{n!}{2!}.$$

To find the permutations of n items in groups of $(n-3)$, we begin with the n trees of ${}_nP_{(n-2)}$ and eliminate the last position which is now a three-branch position[8] and therefore leaves only one-third as many branches. Thus,

$${}_nP_{(n-3)} = \frac{1}{3}\,{}_nP_{(n-2)} = \left(\frac{1}{3}\right)\frac{n!}{2!} = \frac{n!}{3!}.$$

The general formula for the permutations of n objects in groups of $(n-r)$ is easily seen to be[9]

$${}_nP_{(n-r)} = \frac{n!}{r!}, \qquad [r = 0, 1, \ldots, (n-1)].$$

[6]Notice the *single-branch* lines leading to the last position in Figure 5.1.

[7]Notice the *double-branch* lines leading to the next to the last position in Figure 5.1.

[8]Notice the *triple-branch* lines leading to the second from the last position in Figure 5.1.

[9]Here we see the necessity for the convention $0! = 1$. Suppose we want to permute in groups of $(n-r)$ and $r = 0$. This means permuting the whole group of n and the answer is $n!$. Substituting in the formula,

$${}_nP_{(n-0)} = \frac{n!}{0!} = \frac{n!}{1} = n!.$$

Suppose now that we want to permute n objects when r are of one kind and the rest are of another kind, that is, r red balls and $(n - r)$ black balls with all the red balls identical and all the black balls identical. The number of permutations is abbreviated ${}_nP_{r,(n-r)}$, which is read *the permutations of n objects when r are of one kind and $(n - r)$ are of another kind.* Suppose we start with a particular ordering of, say, $n = 6$ balls with two red and four black:

$$R\ B\ B\ B\ R\ B$$

Keeping the reds in positions No. 1 and No. 5, let us pretend that the four blacks are somehow distinguishable. There would then be 4! arrangements (by permuting the four distinguishable blacks) which would keep the red-black arrangement unchanged. If now the two reds were also distinguishable, then for each permutation of the distinguishable blacks there would be 2! permutations of the reds. Thus if the reds and the blacks were both distinguishable, there would be (2!)(4!) arrangements which would keep the reds in positions No. 1 and No. 5 and the blacks in positions No. 2, No. 3, No. 4, and No. 6. Whatever the initial arrangement of reds and blacks, there would be (2!)(4!) as many if they were all distinguishable. But if they are all distinguishable, then we are just talking about the permutations of six different objects. Hence there are (2!)(4!) as many permutations when the six objects are different as when there are two reds and four blacks, or

$${}_6P = (2!)(4!)\,{}_6P_{2,4};$$

Therefore

$${}_6P_{2,4} = \frac{{}_6P}{2!4!} = \frac{6!}{2!4!}.$$

The reasoning above applies to any n when r are one kind and the other $(n - r)$ are of a second kind. Thus[10]

$${}_nP_{r,(n-r)} = \frac{{}_nP}{r!(n-r)!} = \frac{n!}{r!(n-r)!}.$$

5.6 The Binomial Probability Function

We are now in a position to derive the binomial probability function. Suppose we have a binomial random variable X derived as the sum of five independent and identically distributed Bernoulli variables with success

[10]Another common abbreviation for ${}_nP_{r,\,(n-r)}$ is $\binom{n}{r}$. Thus

$${}_nP_{r,(n-r)} = \binom{n}{r} = \frac{n!}{r!(n-r)!}.$$

probability $p = 0.2$. How do we arrive at the probability that $X = 3$? To answer this, we first ask how it can happen that $X = 3$. Clearly, $X = 3$ requires that three of the five Bernoulli experiments produce success and the other two result in failure. Thus, a sequence such as $(S\ S\ S\ F\ F)$, which indicates success on the first three trials and failure on the last two trials, is an element of the subset of ordered quintuples which satisfies $X = 3$. Stochastic independence of the trials leads to

$$P(S\ S\ S\ F\ F) = (0.2)(0.2)(0.2)(0.8)(0.8) = (0.2)^3(0.8)^2.$$

Other ordered sequences also result in $X = 3$, for example, $(S\ F\ F\ S\ S)$, $(F\ S\ S\ F\ S)$, and so on. Calculating the probability of the latter,

$$\begin{aligned} P(F\ S\ S\ F\ S) &= (0.8)(0.2)(0.2)(0.8)(0.2) \\ &= (0.2)(0.2)(0.2)(0.8)(0.8) \\ &= (0.2)^3(0.8)^2, \end{aligned}$$

which is precisely the same as $P(S\ S\ S\ F\ F)$. It is clear in fact that any permutation of three S's and two F's will, by virtue of independence, have precisely the same probability of occurrence. The probability of three successes, therefore, is merely the number of different ways in which three successes can occur multiplied by their common probability of occurrence, $(0.2)^3(0.8)^2$. Since the number of permutations of five items of which three are S's and two are F's is simply

$${}_5P_{3,2} = \binom{5}{3} = \frac{5!}{3!2!} = 10,$$

we arrive at the following result. If X is $B(5, 0.2)$,

$$\begin{aligned} P(X = 3) &= \binom{5}{3}(0.2)^3(0.8)^2 \\ &= \frac{5!}{3!2!}(0.2)^3(0.8)^2 \\ &= 10(0.008)(0.64) \\ &= 0.0512. \end{aligned}$$

In general, if X is $B(n, p)$,

$$P(X = x) = \binom{n}{x}p^x q^{n-x} = \frac{n!}{x!(n-x)!}p^x q^{n-x}.$$

This is so because any sequence satisfying $X = x$ will contain x S's and $(n - x)$ F's and will therefore have probability $p^x q^{n-x}$. Further, the number of such sequences will be the permutations of n items when x are S's and the rest, $(n - x)$, are F's, that is, ${}_nP_{x,(n-x)}$. Hence $P(X = x)$ is the number of sequences which are acceptable multiplied by the common probability of each. If X is $B(n, p)$, the binomial probability function is

$$P(X = x) = \binom{n}{x} p^x q^{n-x}; \quad q = 1 - p \quad (x = 0, 1, \ldots, n).$$

Suppose we ask for the probability of zero successes ($X = 0$). The answer is immediately obvious. Zero successes means n failures and the only sequence which suffices is that with n F's, hence probability q^n. Using the probability function,

$$\begin{aligned} P(X = 0) &= \binom{n}{0} p^0 q^{n-0} = \frac{n!}{0!(n-0)!} p^0 q^{n-0} \\ &= \frac{n!}{(1)n!}(1)q^n \\ &= q^n. \end{aligned}$$

Summing all the binomial probabilities for $0, 1, \ldots, n$ successes, we must find

$$\sum_{x=0}^{n} \binom{n}{x} p^x q^{n-x} = 1.$$

Those who recall from high school algebra that the left-hand side of the equation above is merely the binomial expansion of $(q + p)^n$ will be convinced at once that the sum is indeed unity since $q + p = 1$ and $1^n = 1$. A general proof of this proposition is rather involved. We have already proved it for the cases $n = 1$ and $n = 2$, and the reader can easily derive the result in similar fashion for $n = 3$ or 4.[11]

When we introduced the binomial as the sum of n independent and identically distributed Bernoulli variables, we found that the expected number of successes was np. It is also possible to derive this result by direct calculation using the binomial probability function. We show in Section 5.6 of the Appendix that it is indeed true that

$$EX = \sum_x xP(x) = \sum_{x=0}^{n} x \binom{n}{x} p^x q^{n-x} = np.$$

EXAMPLE 5.6.1. Two percent of the items coming from a factory assembly line are defective. A customer has purchased five items.

(a) What is the probability that he gets all perfect merchandise?

[11]The result is proved for the special case $p = q = \frac{1}{2}$ in Section 5.6 of the Appendix.

(b) If more than one item is defective, the customer intends to return the merchandise and cancel his order. If exactly one item is defective, the customer returns it for a replacement. In this event the manufacturer merely sends an item chosen randomly without first inspecting it. If the replacement is also defective, the customer cancels his order. What is the probability that the order is canceled?

Solution: First we recognize this as a binomial situation (assuming the 2% defective items are turned out randomly by the production process) where $X =$ the number of defectives and X is $B(5, 0.02)$.

$$\text{(a)}\ P(X = 0) = \frac{5!}{0!5!}(0.02)^0(0.98)^5$$
$$= (0.98)^5 = 0.9039.$$

(b) Cancellation can occur in two mutually exclusive ways: either two or more defectives in the original order or one defective in the original and a defective replacement. Calculating first the probability of two or more defectives in the original order,

$$P(X \geq 2) = 1 - P(X \leq 1)$$
$$= 1 - [P(X = 0) + P(X = 1)].$$

$P(X = 0)$ is known from (a) to be 0.9039.

$$P(X = 1) = \frac{5!}{1!4!}(0.02)^1(0.98)^4$$
$$= 5(0.02)(0.98)^4 = 5(0.02)(0.92237)$$
$$\cong 0.0922.$$

Therefore

$$P(X \geq 2) = 1 - (0.9039 + 0.0922) = 0.0039.$$

We are now interested in the ordered pair,

[(1 defective in original order), (defective replacement)].

Using the general multiplication rule, the probability of this ordered pair is

$$P(\text{1 defective in original order})$$
$$\cdot P(\text{defective replacement} \mid \text{1 defective in original order}).$$

Since the replacement is not inspected, this becomes

$$(0.0922)(0.02) \cong 0.0018,$$

which is the probability of cancellation due to a defective replacement.

The overall probability of cancellation is therefore obtained by adding the probabilities of the two mutually exclusive events which result in cancellation.

$$P(\text{order canceled}) = 0.0039 + 0.0018 = 0.0057.$$

EXAMPLE 5.6.2. A woman claims to be able to distinguish between brewed and instant coffee with 80% accuracy and presents her claim to an agency interested in combating the use of instant coffee. The agency is interested in hiring this woman to perform at public demonstrations, provided her claim is well-founded. The agency proposes to test the woman as follows: The woman is to be given a cup of brewed and a cup of instant coffee to taste and she is then to distinguish between them. After a few moments of resting her taste buds, the test is to be repeated with two new cups. In all, the two-cup test is to be run seven times and the agency agrees to hire the woman if she is correct at least six out of seven times.

(a) Does this test provide the agency sufficient protection against the possibility that the woman has made a fraudulent claim?

(b) Does this test give the woman a sufficient chance to be hired if she really can distinguish brewed from instant coffee?

Solution:

(a) If the woman has made a fraudulent claim, then she will have to guess on each trial and should have a probability of $\frac{1}{2}$ of correctly identifying the brewed coffee in each pair. Letting X = number of correct identifications, X is $B(7, \frac{1}{2})$. The agency is in store for future embarrassment if the claim is fraudulent and the woman is hired; that is, if $X \geq 6$ when the woman merely guesses each time. Since then X is $B(7, \frac{1}{2})$,

$$\begin{aligned}
P(X \geq 6) &= \sum_{x=6}^{7} \binom{n}{x} \left(\frac{1}{2}\right)^{x} \left(\frac{1}{2}\right)^{n-x} \\
&= \frac{7!}{6!1!} \left(\frac{1}{2}\right)^{7} + \left(\frac{1}{2}\right)^{7} \\
&= 8\left(\frac{1}{2}\right)^{7} = (2^3)\,\frac{1}{(2)^7} = \frac{1}{(2)^4} = \frac{1}{16} \\
&= 0.0625.
\end{aligned}$$

"Sufficiency" of the agency's protection depends on many factors about which we have no information; suffice it to say here that there is a rather small likelihood (probability 0.0625) that a fraudulent claim would pass the agency's test.

(b) If the claim is not fraudulent, then X is $B(7, 0.8)$ and again the hiring occurs if $X \geq 6$.

$$\begin{aligned} P(X \geq 6) &= \sum_{x=6}^{7} \binom{n}{x} (0.8)^x (0.2)^{n-x} \\ &= \frac{7!}{6!1!} (0.8)^6 (0.2)^1 + (0.8)^7 \\ &= 7(0.8)^6(0.2) + (0.8)^7 \\ &= (0.8)^6(1.4 + 0.8) \\ &= (0.8)^6(2.2) \\ &= 0.5767. \end{aligned}$$

If the woman has not made a fraudulent claim, she may well regard the test as unfair to her since it gives her little more chance of being hired than would a test consisting simply of the flipping of a coin. Indeed, if finding a person with such ability is important enough to the agency, then the agency itself might not like the test. While the proposed test protects the agency rather well against fraudulence, it leaves the agency with a probability of 0.4233 (1 − 0.5767) of passing up a well-founded claim.

(The reader should be able to show that requiring only five correct identifications as the minimum criterion leaves the agency with only about a 15% chance of passing up a well-founded claim, but raises to nearly 23% the chance of not detecting a fraudulent claim. If this situation is not desirable, the agency should expand the test to more than seven trials.)

5.7 Quality Control

The practical importance of the binomial distribution is partially illustrated by its usefulness in the area of industrial quality control. We shall present two illustrations, one in *process control* and one in the area of *acceptance sampling*.

Process Control

Suppose production machinery is considered to be operating *in control* if the proportion of defective items produced is $\leq r$. If the proportion of defectives being produced is $> r$, the machinery is said to have gone *out of control*. At the end of each daily production run, n items are sampled at random and the number of defectives X is determined. X is binomially distributed with probability of success $\leq r$ if the process is in control, and probability of success $> r$ if the process is out of control. (X being binomially distributed assumes a very large production run relative to n so that the probability of success remains essentially constant from trial to trial. See the discussion of Example 5.7.2 below.)

Let the probability of success be denoted by p, then X is $B(n, p)$ with $EX = np$ and $\sigma_X^2 = npq$. According to Chebyschev's inequality,

$$P[|X - EX| \geq 3\sigma_X] \leq \tfrac{1}{9}.$$

If the process is barely in control, then $p = r$, $EX = nr$, $\sigma_X^2 = nr(1 - r)$, and the probability is at most $\frac{1}{9}$ that on a given day the number of defectives will differ from nr by at least $3\sqrt{nr(1 - r)}$. The number $nr + 3\sqrt{nr(1 - r)}$ then takes on critical importance as the so-called 3σ *upper control limit* (UCL).

If $p < r$, then $EX = np < nr$ and $\sigma_X^2 = npq < nr(1 - r)$. The latter inequality is correct provided $r < \frac{1}{2}$, and since r is the maximum acceptable fraction defective, it will be a good deal below $\frac{1}{2}$. If then $p < r$, $np + 3\sqrt{npq}$ is smaller than the UCL. Note that the UCL depends only on r, not p. While the UCL is 3σ from the mean of X if $p = r$, the UCL is more than 3σ from the mean of X if $p < r$. Consequently, if $p < r$, it is highly unlikely that the observed number of defectives will exceed the UCL.

If the process is out of control, $p > r$. Then $EX = np > nr$, and $\sigma_X^2 = npq > nr(1 - r)$ (if r is below $\frac{1}{2}$). Consequently, if $p > r$, UCL $< np + 3\sqrt{npq}$. The more out of control the process, the greater the discrepancy between UCL and $np + 3\sqrt{npq}$ and the larger the probability that the number of defectives will exceed the UCL.

The process control scheme then works as follows. First, the UCL is calculated. As long as the daily X values (realizations) remain below the UCL, the process is considered in control. Once an observed number of defectives exceeds the UCL, the process is considered to have gone out of

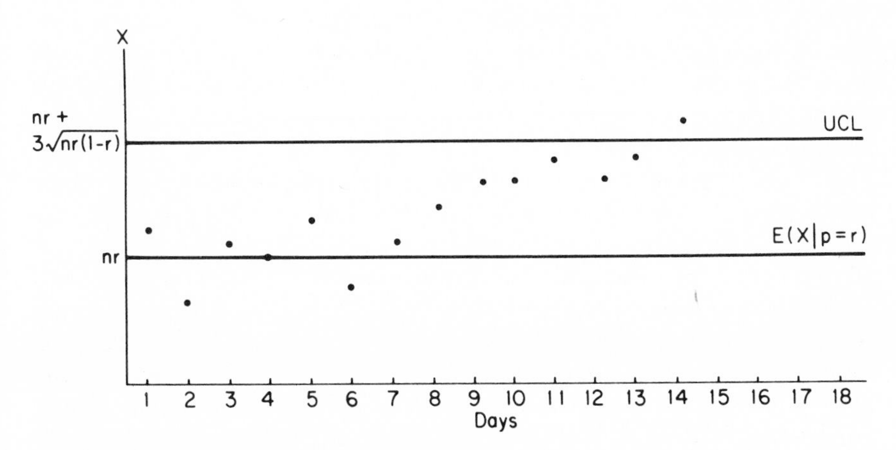

FIGURE 5.2

control. Since machinery often moves out of control a little at a time rather than all at once, it is useful to keep a "running inventory" of the daily number of defectives. This is done by using a process control chart such as the one illustrated in Figure 5.2. Each dot on the chart is the observed number of defectives on a given day. Note the pattern for the first 7 days: a randomly distributed pattern around and close to nr, indicating that the process is in control. The pattern becomes suspicious between days 9 and 13 with the daily number of defectives *all* close to the UCL and trending upwards. By the 14th day suspicion that the machinery is going out of adjustment is confirmed by the number of defectives being greater than the UCL.

Consider the following numerical example. A particular process is in control if $p \leq r = 0.04$. Each day 50 items are inspected. If $p = r$, $EX = 50(0.04) = 2$, $\sigma_X^2 = 50(0.04)(0.96) = 1.92$, $3\sigma_X \cong 4.16$; hence $\text{UCL} = 2 + 4.16 = 6.16$. Suppose the following pattern of daily X's has been observed:

Day No.	Observed X
1	1
2	3
3	0
4	2
5	0
6	4
7	3
8	4
9	6
10	7*

The daily observations indicate that the process remained in control for 9 days. By the 10th day the observed number of defectives, 7, became too large to continue to believe $p \leq 0.04$ and adjustment of the machinery was indicated.

It must be pointed out that although the use of a 3σ upper control limit can be partially justified by Chebyschev's inequality and is a common rule of thumb in process control work, it is often far from optimal. As an example, take the case of $n = 10$ and $r = 0.05$. The 3σ UCL would be $nr + 3\sqrt{nr(1 - r)} = 0.50 + 3\sqrt{0.475} \cong 2.57$. Now the process is indeed out of control if more than 5% defectives are being produced, but suppose the situation is not considered financially serious unless the process gets out of control to the point of 8% defectives. That is, the producers would like to be able to detect 6 or 7% defectives but detection is not really crucial unless the proportion defective rises to 8%. If $p = 0.08$, the probability of detecting that the process is out of control is $P(X > 2.57 \mid p = 0.08)$, which is

$$\begin{aligned} P(X > 2.57 \mid p = 0.08) &= P(X \geq 3 \mid p = 0.08) \\ &= 1 - P(X \leq 2 \mid p = 0.08) \\ &= 1 - \sum_{x=0}^{2} \binom{10}{x} (0.08)^x (0.92)^{10-x} \\ &\cong 1 - 0.96 \\ &\cong 0.04. \end{aligned}$$

Thus using a 3σ UCL leaves the management with little chance to detect a process which is producing 8% defectives. If an out-of-control process is detected, the producer can be reasonably certain that the process is a good deal worse than 8% defective. If the UCL is cut back to 2σ, UCL $= 0.50 + 2\sqrt{0.475} = 1.88$. Then the probability of detecting an 8% process is

$$P(X \geq 2 \mid p = 0.08) \cong 0.19.$$

If the process is producing only 5% defectives, it will exceed the 2σ UCL with probability

$$\begin{aligned} P(X \geq 2 \mid p = 0.05) &= 1 - P(X \leq 1 \mid p = 0.05) \\ &= 1 - \sum_{x=0}^{1} \binom{10}{x} (0.05)^x (0.95)^{10-x} \\ &\cong 1 - 0.914 \\ &\cong 0.086. \end{aligned}$$

Thus the probability is at worst only 0.086 that a process in control will register out of control, but a process seriously out of control will be detected with a probability of only 0.19. The producer therefore has reasonable protection against wrongly concluding that a good process is out of control, but poor protection in the sense of detecting a process as bad as 8% defective.

Calculations such as those made above should always precede the construction of a process control plan in order to judge how effective the plan will be. In the case we just examined, neither the 3σ nor 2σ UCL plan is very worthwhile. In this case the firm would have to resort to sampling more than 10 items per day if it wished sufficient protection against both

(i) Falsely concluding that a good process was out of control.
(ii) Failing to detect a process that was seriously out of control.

EXAMPLE 5.7.1. A production process turns out a milled part which is supposed to have certain specified dimensions. If the part is nondefective, it is used in a precision instrument; if the dimensions of the part are not within the specified tolerances (defective), the part can be used in an inexpensive instrument which the company also produces. Since the inexpensive item comprises 25% of the company's final production, it is desirable to have 25% "defective" milled parts. The process producing the milled part is therefore considered to be out of control if it produces either less than or more than 25% defective. Each day the firm samples 80 milled parts and uses a 2σ process control plan.

(a) On a given day, 10 parts are defective. Is the process in control?

(b) Evaluate the plan from the point of view of detecting a process producing 38% defectives.

Solution: In this example it is not only too many defectives that are to be avoided, but also too few defectives. Thus, we need not only a UCL, but also a *lower control limit* (LCL). If the process is in control, $p = 0.25$ and the number of defectives X is distributed $B(80, 0.25)$. Consequently $EX = 80(0.25) = 20$ and $\sigma^2 = 80(0.25)(0.75) = 15$. The 2σ UCL is then

$$\text{UCL} = 20 + 2\sqrt{15} \cong 27.7.$$

The 2σ LCL is

$$\text{LCL} = 20 - 2\sqrt{15} \cong 12.3.$$

(a) The process is in control if the observed number of defectives is at least 13 but no more than 27. If 10 defectives are observed, this indicates that the process has gone out of control on the low side; that is, too few parts are being produced for the inexpensive instrument and too many for the precision instrument.

(b) If $p = 0.38$, X is $B(80, 0.38)$. Such a process which is producing too few parts for the precision instrument will be detected if the number of defectives on a given day is above 27.7, the UCL; that is, if $X \geq 28$.

$$P(X \geq 28 \mid p = 0.38) = \sum_{x=28}^{80} \binom{80}{x} (0.38)^x (0.62)^{80-x}$$
$$\cong 0.75.$$

The 2σ plan which consists of sampling 80 milled parts is therefore reasonably satisfactory in the sense of having a probability of 0.75 of detecting a process producing 38% defectives.

Acceptance Sampling

If the purchaser of a product had complete faith in the manufacturer's process control system and agreed with the manufacturer's choice of r and UCL, the purchaser would have little need to inspect the products he purchased. Realistically, however, this is not the case and purchasers frequently resort to product testing before deciding whether to accept a shipment. Suppose a purchaser receives a lot of 100 large metal washers, the inner diameter of which is supposed to be 2 inches. The purchaser's use of these washers permits a tolerance of ± 0.05 inches in the diameter. A washer with diameter outside the range of 1.95–2.05 inches is considered defective and the purchaser is willing to tolerate no more than 5 defectives per lot of 100 washers. There are many sampling schemes which are available to the purchaser to aid him in deciding whether or not to accept a lot. The most obvious scheme is to inspect the entire lot, but let us assume that this is rejected immediately as being too expensive. We shall use the device of operating characteristic (OC) curves to choose between the following two fairly typical types of plan.

Plan 1: Sample 10 items with replacement and reject the lot if more than 1 item is defective.

Plan 2: Sample 7 items with replacement and accept the lot if none are defective. If 2 or more are defective, reject the lot. If 1 is defective, sample 5 (with replacement) of the remaining 93;[12] accept the lot if none of these are defective and reject the lot otherwise.

We begin with Plan 1, which is the simple binomial situation. The probability of accepting a lot depends on p, the proportion of defectives in the lot. If $p = 0$, the lot is accepted with probability one. Suppose $p = 0.03$, then X (= the number of defectives out of 10) is distributed $B(10, 0.03)$. The lot is accepted if $X = 0$ or $X = 1$. Thus

$$P(\text{accept lot} \mid p = 0.03) = (0.97)^{10} + \frac{10!}{1!9!}(0.03)^1(0.97)^9$$

$$\cong 0.966.$$

Suppose p $= 0.05$, then X is $B(10, 0.5)$. The lot is accepted again if $X = 0$ or $X = 1$, hence with probability

$$P(\text{accept lot} \mid p = 0.05) = (0.95)^{10} + \frac{10!}{1!9!}(0.05)^1(0.95)^9$$

$$\cong 0.914.$$

If $p = 0.08$, we have

$$P(\text{accept lot} \mid p = 0.08) = (0.92)^{10} + \frac{10!}{1!9!}(0.08)^1(0.92)^9$$

$$\cong 0.812.$$

[12]If the first 7 items are sampled *with replacement*, there may be more than 93 items remaining after the first stage of inspection. Since the probability that the first stage of sampling results in 7 different items is 0.83, we introduce relatively little error in the calculations by making the simplifying assumption that there are 93 items remaining for the second stage of the inspection. See problem 5-19, p. 146.

If $p = 0.12$, we have

$$P(\text{accept lot} \mid p = 0.12) = (0.88)^{10} + \frac{10!}{1!9!}(0.12)^1(0.88)^9$$

$$\cong 0.657.$$

If $p = 0.16$, we have

$$P(\text{accept lot} \mid p = 0.16) = (0.84)^{10} + \frac{10!}{1!9!}(0.16)^1(0.84)^9$$

$$\cong 0.508.$$

The results above are plotted in Figure 5.3, known as an OC curve, with intermediate points sketched in. The OC curve continues beyond what is shown and trails off toward a probability of zero for a lot with all defectives. The OC curve clearly indicates that Plan 1 is highly unsatisfactory. Good lots, those with $p < 0.05$, have a high probability of being accepted, which of course is desirable. But even if a lot is as bad as 15% defective, there is still a probability in excess of 0.5 of accepting it. Use of Plan 1 would rarely result in rejection of a good lot but will invariably accept many bad lots

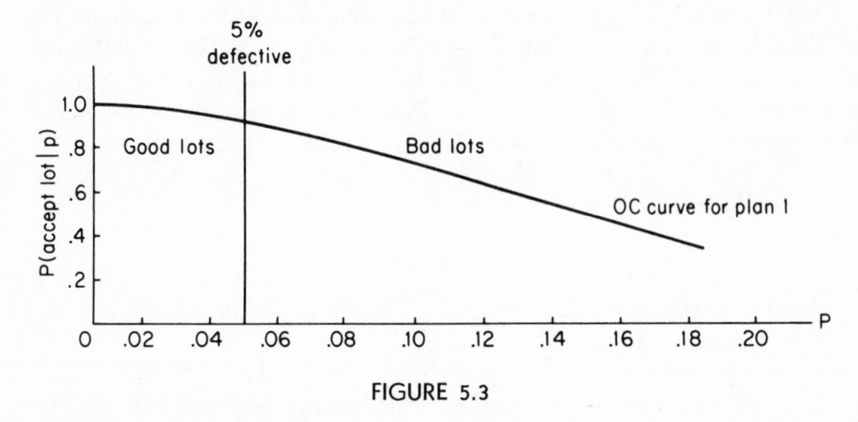

FIGURE 5.3

Plan 2 is a bit more difficult to analyze since it involves combining binomials. Under the second plan a lot is accepted if either

(i) Zero out of seven are nondefective,

or

(ii) One out of seven is defective and none of the next five is defective.

These two conditions are clearly mutually exclusive so we simply add their separate probabilities to determine the probability of accepting a lot. Let g represent the number of nondefectives in a lot.

Starting with (i), the number of defectives X is distributed

$$B\left(7, p = \frac{100 - g}{100}\right);$$

hence

$$P(X = 0) = \left(\frac{g}{100}\right)^7. \tag{A}$$

For (b), we want

$P[(1 \text{ defective in first } 7), (0 \text{ defective in next } 5)]$

$$= P(1 \text{ defective in first } 7)\, P(0 \text{ defective in next } 5 \mid 1 \text{ defective in first } 7).$$

Now one defective in the first seven trials leaves 93 items of which $(g - 6)$ are nondefective. Hence,

$$P(0 \text{ defective in next } 5 \mid 1 \text{ defective in first } 7) = \left(\frac{g-6}{93}\right)^5;$$

therefore

$P[(1 \text{ defective in first } 7), (0 \text{ defective in next } 5)]$

$$= \left[\frac{7!}{1!6!}\left(\frac{100-g}{100}\right)^1\left(\frac{g}{100}\right)^6\right]\left[\left(\frac{g-6}{93}\right)^5\right]. \tag{B}$$

Adding formulas (A) and (B), we arrive at

$$P(\text{accept lot} \mid g \text{ nondefectives}) = (A) + (B)$$

$$= \left(\frac{g}{100}\right)^6\left[\frac{g}{100} + 7\,\frac{(100-g)}{100}\left(\frac{g-6}{93}\right)^5\right].$$

If the entire lot is nondefective ($g = 100$), the probability of accepting the lot is clearly unity. If $g = 97$ (that is, the proportion defective is $p = 0.03$),

$$P(\text{accept lot} \mid 97 \text{ nondefectives}) = (0.97)^6\,[0.97 + 7\,(0.03)(\tfrac{91}{93})^5]$$

$$\cong 0.965.$$

If $g = 95$ (that is, $p = 0.05$),

$$P(\text{accept lot} \mid 95 \text{ nondefectives}) = (0.95)^6\,[0.95 + 7\,(0.05)(\tfrac{89}{93})^5]$$

$$\cong 0.905.$$

If $g = 92$ (that is, $p = 0.08$),

$$P(\text{accept lot} \mid 92 \text{ nondefectives}) = (0.92)^6\,[0.92 + 7\,(0.08)(\tfrac{86}{93})^5]$$

$$\cong 0.787.$$

If $g = 88$ (that is, $p = 0.12$,

$$P(\text{accept lot} \mid 88 \text{ nondefectives}) = (0.88)^6 \left[0.88 + 7\,(0.12)\left(\tfrac{82}{93}\right)^5\right] \cong 0.616.$$

If $g = 84$ (that is, $p = 0.16$),

$$P(\text{accept lot} \mid 84 \text{ nondefectives}) = (0.84)^6 \left[0.84 + 7\,(0.16)\left(\tfrac{78}{93}\right)^5\right] \cong 0.458.$$

Putting the results for Plan 2 together in the form of an OC curve (Figure 5.4) and then superimposing the Plan 1 OC curve on the same figure, we can compare the two plans directly. While Plan 2 clearly leaves a great deal to be desired in any absolute sense, it is superior to Plan 1. Both plans have about the same probabilities of accepting good lots ($p < 0.05$) and

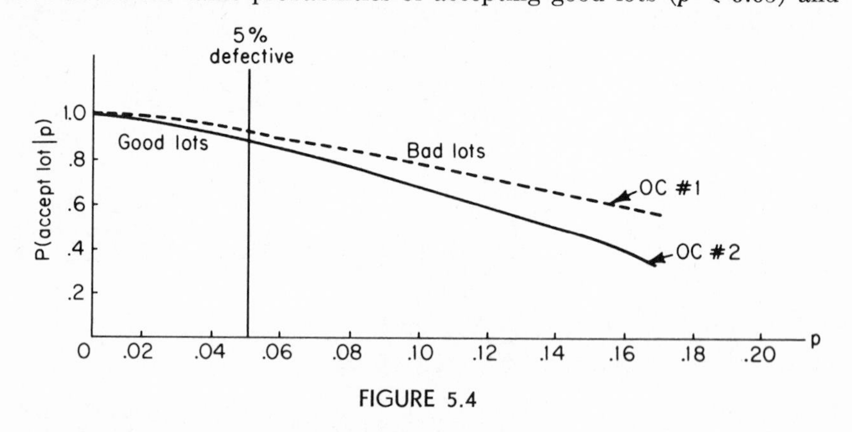

FIGURE 5.4

Plan 2 has lower probabilities for accepting bad lots.

Note that an OC curve is incapable of revealing the true composition of a submitted lot. The OC curve reveals the operating characteristics of the *sampling plan* in the sense of making the following kind of statement: The sampling plan is such that *if* a lot contains 12% defective items, then the probability is 0.616 that the lot will be accepted despite its having 12% defectives. An ideal OC curve would remain close to unity for $p < 0.05$ and then fall rapidly for p increasing beyond 0.05.

The whole point in investigating a plan such as Plan 2 (known as a *multiple sampling plan*) is that it is often at least as good as one of the *single sampling plans* typified by Plan 1, but less expensive. Thus, decisions with Plan 1 always require sampling 10 items; with the superior Plan 2, decisions can frequently be reached with only 7 items being sampled. Indeed, there are times when Plan 2 will require 12 items, but such a multiple sampling plan will frequently permit decisions with fewer items having to be sampled *on the average* over a large number of lots.

EXAMPLE 5.7.2. The U.S. Department of Defense purchases a particular mortar shell in lots of 100,000. The shipment arrives in 2,000 crates, each containing 50 mortar shells. One crate is chosen at random and all 50 shells are fired. To accept the entire lot of 100,000, it is required that there be no defective shells in the examined crate. What are the operating characteristics of this plan?

Solution: Since the crate is randomly chosen, the plan amounts to sampling 50 out of 100,000 shells without replacement. Since the sampling is without replacement, the probabilities change from trial to trial. Suppose, however, that the lot of 100,000 contains only 500 defective shells ($\frac{1}{2}$ of 1%). When the first shell is sampled, the probability of a defective is $\frac{500}{100{,}000} = 0.005$. By the time the 50th shell is reached, the probability of a defective may be as much as $\frac{500}{99{,}951} = 0.00502$ if no defectives were obtained on the first 49 trials, or as little as $\frac{451}{99{,}951} = 0.00451$ if all the first 49 shells were defective. The latter of course would be exceedingly unlikely if there were only 500 out of 100,000 defectives to begin with. The point of this is that the 50 shells being sampled are so few relative to the 100,000 that we can safely neglect the fact that the corresponding Bernoulli trials have different probabilities of a defective shell. We shall therefore treat X, the number of defectives in the crate of 50 shells, as a binomial variable; that is, X is $B(50, p)$ where p is the proportion of defectives in the lot of 100,000.

The entire lot is accepted if $X = 0$. If $p = 0$,

$$P(X = 0 \mid p = 0) = 1.$$

If $p = 0.005$,

$$P(X = 0 \mid p = 0.005) = (0.995)^{50} \cong 0.78.$$

If $p = 0.008$,

$$P(X = 0 \mid p = 0.008) = (0.992)^{50} \cong 0.67.$$

If $p = 0.01$,

$$P(X = 0 \mid p = 0.01) = (0.99)^{50} \cong 0.61.$$

If $p = 0.015$,

$$P(X = 0 \mid p = 0.015) = (0.985)^{50} \cong 0.47.$$

If $p = 0.02$,

$$P(X = 0 \mid p = 0.02) = (0.98)^{50} \cong 0.36.$$

If $p = 0.025$,

$$P(X = 0 \mid p = 0.025) = (0.975)^{50} \cong 0.28.$$

If $p = 0.03$,

$$P(X = 0 \mid p = 0.03) = (0.97)^{50} \cong 0.22.$$

If $p = 0.05$,

$$P(X = 0 \mid p = 0.05) = (0.95)^{50} \cong 0.08.$$

If $p = 0.06$,

$$P(X = 0 \mid p = 0.06) = (0.94)^{50} \cong 0.05.$$

The results above have been assembled as the OC curve in Figure 5.5. Evaluation of the plan in absolute terms is impossible since we have no information as to what proportion of defective shells is considered tolerable. If, for example, the department is willing to accept no more than 1% defectives, then the plan is clearly unacceptable since with 1% defectives

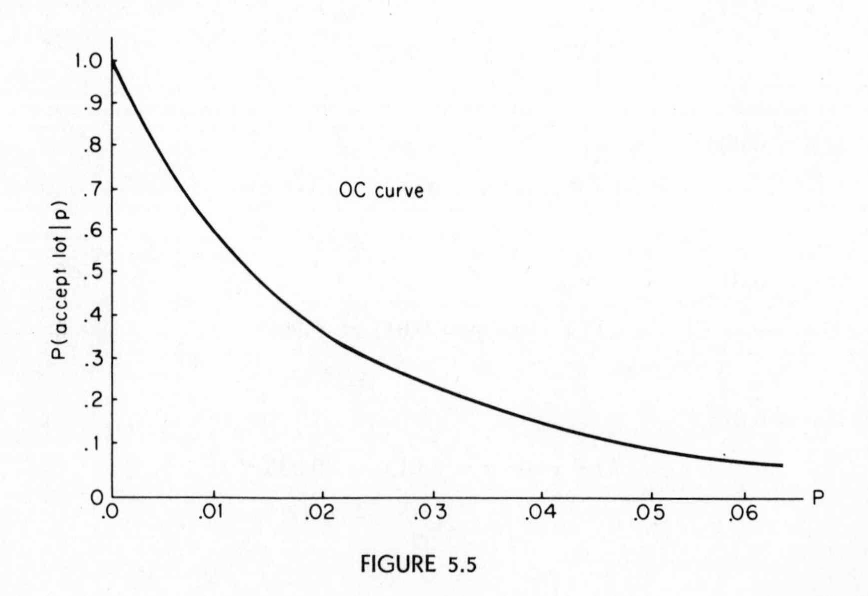

FIGURE 5.5

in the lot, the probability is 0.61 that the lot will be accepted. If the cutoff point is 6% defectives, the plan would probably be perfectly adequate since the OC curve indicates a probability of only about 0.05 of accepting a lot with as many as 6% defective shells.

Even though 6% defectives may be unthinkable in some applications, it is nonetheless a remarkable fact that it is necessary to sample only 50 items out of 100,000 to obtain a probability as small as 0.05 of accepting a lot with 6% defectives. In other words, sampling only 50 out of 100,000 items results in a probability as large as 0.95 of rejecting a lot which is 6% defective.

Note to Chapter 5

Calculations of the probabilities associated with various realizations of a binomially distributed random variable can be extremely time-consuming. Fortunately the probabilities of the most commonly incurred of these realizations have been calculated and published in tabular forms called *Binomial Tables*. A binomial table is reproduced in this book as Appendix Table A. This table will enable the student to avoid unnecessary calculations in working any of the problems of Chapter 5 which involve the numerical magnitudes of probabilities of realizations of a binomially distributed random variable.

PROBLEMS

5-1. Suppose you draw a card from a deck five times, replacing each card drawn and shuffling the deck before the next drawing. Define a random variable X as the number of spades obtained in the five draws.

(a) Is X a binomial variable? Why?
(b) Calculate the expected value of X and also its variance.

5-2. A baseball player is currently hitting 0.325. What is the expected number of hits he will get in his next 80 times at bat? Calculate an upper limit for the probability that he will get a hit on at least $\frac{1}{2}$ of these next 80 times at bat.

5-3. An urn contains a red ball, a white ball, a blue ball, and a red, white, and blue ball. One ball is drawn at random and observed. Let R, W, and B denote the event that the color seen is red, white, or blue respectively.

(a) Are the events R, W, B pairwise independent? Why?
(b) Are the events R, W, B mutually independent events? Why?

5-4. A woman is giving a dinner party for six guests. In how many ways may the guests be seated around a dinner table?

5-5. In how many ways may a student answer an eight-question, true-false exam if

(a) He marks no two consecutive answers the same?
(b) He answers four true, four false?

5-6. In how many distinguishable ways can three white and four black balls be arranged in a row?

5-7. Suppose the three white and four black balls in Problem 5-6 are individually numbered.

(a) Now how many distinguishable arrangements are there?
(b) Show that the probability that a random arrangement will consist of four black balls in succession, followed by three white balls is the same regardless of whether the balls are numbered. What is this probability?

5-8. Suppose the six dinner guests in Problem 5-4 were composed of three husband-wife combinations. Find the probability that a certain guest and his wife will be seated next to one another if the seating is arranged at random and the guests are seated

(a) Around a circular table.
(b) Along one side of a rectangular table.

5-9. Suppose a computer is controlled by a keyboard consisting of five distinguishable keys. Depression of any number (from zero to five) of keys relates an instruction to the computer. If nonidentical combinations of key depressions yield nonidentical instructions, find the total number of instructions which can be conveyed.

5-10. A fair coin is tossed 10 times. Find the probability that heads appear at least half the time.

5-11. A fair die is thrown six times. Find the probability that a 6 appears

(a) Exactly twice.
(b) At least twice.
(c) At least twice given that at least one 6 is known to have appeared.

5-12. You are going to Boston from San Francisco with brief stops at Chicago and Washington, D.C. Since you are bored with jet travel, you want to try something new. Suppose you have a choice of going by plane, train, or bus and that you decide to throw a die in order to choose among these alternatives; that is, if you get a 1 or 2, take a plane; if 3 or 4, train; if 5 or 6, bus.

Accordingly you throw a die at San Francisco and decide which transportation to use. At Chicago and at Washington, D.C., you repeat the procedure. Assume the die is unbiased.

(a) How many different ways are there of reaching Boston?
(b) What is the probability you will go all the way by train?
(c) Let X denote the number of times that you ride a train on the way to Boston. Show that X can be considered as a binomial variable and find $P[X = 2]$.
(d) Consider the possibility of choosing the plane at least twice somewhere along the way to Boston. Call this event Y. Show that Y may be considered one of the possibilities in a Bernoulli random experiment. What is the probability corresponding to Y?

5-13. Merchant A's store is located adjacent to merchant B's. Both merchants sell the same goods. Three customers enter A's store and two enter B's store. If the probability of a customer making a purchase is $\frac{1}{2}$, with what probability will A have a larger number of sales than B?

5-14. Show that the answer to Problem 5-13 is the same for any number $(n + 1)$ customers entering A's store and n customers entering B's store.

Hint: First consider the possible outcomes of the experiment involving A's first n customers and B's n customers. The sample space for this experiment is partitioned by the three events A makes more sales, B makes more sales, and they make the same number of sales. The first two events are equiprobable and the final solution does not require evaluation of these probabilities.

5-15. Five percent of the items produced by a certain process are defective.

(a) In a sample of 20 items, what is the probability that at least 4 of them will be defective?
(b) Use logarithms to find the smallest sized sample that would contain at least 1 defective with probability ≥ 0.99.

5-16. A certain machine is shut down for repairs whenever a sample of five items of its output yields three *successive* defectives. What is the probability that the machine will be shut down after an inspection if

(a) It is producing 50% defectives?
(b) It is producing 25% defectives?
(c) It is producing 10% defectives?

5-17. A pianist is contemplating joining either a band which already has three members or a band which already has five members. The pianist would consider a position with either as his full-time job. Both bands have offered him the same salary per performance. He is, therefore, anxious to choose the band which will perform more often. It so happens that the two bands have opportunities to perform equally often but all the current members of both bands have other jobs. Each of the current members has a probability p of not being able to attend any given performance due to job conflicts. A four-man band (the three-man band plus the pianist who would be able to attend all performances) can give a performance if at least three of its members are present and a six-man band (the five-man band plus the pianist) can give a performance if at least four of its members are present.

(a) If $p = 0.80$, which band should the pianist join?
(b) For what values of p is the smaller band to be preferred?

5-18. A river which empties into Lake Erie is suspected of containing a chemical which prevents extraction of drinking water from the lake. This chemical is used by four factories which dump wastes into this river. The factories try to prevent the chemical from getting into the wastes dumped into the river but this is difficult to do. It has been established that the probability of the chemical entering the wastes is 0.20 for each factory. Public health officials have devised a test to measure the amount of this chemical which is contained in water. Unfortunately the equipment involved in this test is very bulky and expensive to move. The public health officials have decided to assemble the equipment at the mouth of the river. Here they will test whether the chemical is indeed in the river. If it is, they will direct the first factory upstream to stop dumping all wastes into the river while a second test is made. If the second test reveals a reduction in the chemical content of the water, officials will know that the first factory is guilty of chemical pollution. However, there may still be chemicals in the water which indicates that at least one of the remaining factories is polluting the river and lake. In this case the officials will direct the second factory upstream to halt waste dumping and run a third test. The testing will continue until the polluting factories are individually identified. How many tests should the officials expect to make?

5-19. Repeated sampling *with* replacement from a population whose members have one of two characteristics (for example, success or failure) constitutes a series of Bernoulli trials and yields a random variable which is binomially distributed. If the same population is sampled one at a time *without* replacement, the random variable generated (X = the number of successes) is distributed *hypergeometrically*. Consider the experiment of drawing r items, without replacement, from a population of size $M + N$—where M = the number of items which produce a success and N = the number of items which produce a failure. The hypergeometric probability function is:

$$P(X = x) = \frac{\binom{M}{x}\binom{N}{r-x}}{\binom{M+N}{r}}.$$

(a) Verify that $\sum_{x=1}^{r} P(X = x) = 1$ for $M = 3$, $N = 2$, and $r = 2$.

(b) Compare the probabilities of drawing two spades in two draws from a standard deck with and without replacement.

(c) Repeat (b) when the two cards are drawn from two pooled decks.

(d) Under what conditions might one be justified in approximating a hypergeometrically distributed random variable by a binomially distributed random variable? What circumstances would make the approximation better? Worse?

5-20. Let X denote a hypergeometrically distributed random variable (see Problem 5-19). Prove $EX = r \cdot \left(\frac{M}{M+N}\right)$.

5-21. The machinery involved in a certain production process is readjusted if a sample of 25 units of its output yields 4 or more defectives.

(a) With what probability will the machinery be readjusted after one sampling if it is actually producing 1% defectives? When it is producing 5% defectives, 10%, 20%, 30%?

(b) The probability that the machinery will be readjusted when the actual rate of defective production is p is given for various values of p in the table below. Using this table and your answers to (a), graph the conditional probability of acceptance (= probability the machinery will not be readjusted | p) against the process percent defective. Explain the meaning of this OC curve.

p	0.09	0.08	0.07	0.06	0.04	0.03	0.02
P[readjustment | p]	0.183	0.135	0.094	0.060	0.017	0.006	0.002

5-22. A company produces two variants of the same product — one is more expensive than the other. The inexpensive version is constructed from parts considered defective for the expensive version. The company has found that its profits are highest when the inexpensive version comprises 15% of total physical output. The production process is considered to be in control when 15% defective parts are being produced. Each day the company samples 100 parts and uses a 2σ control plan.

(a) On one day, 20 parts were defective. Is the process in control? Explain.

(b) On another day, 5 parts were found to be defective. Is the process in control? Explain.

5-23. A dairy which produces its own milk cartons considers its carton production process to be in control if 5% or fewer of the cartons it produces are defective. Each day the dairy samples 20 cartons and uses a 2σ control plan.

(a) Evaluate the plan's efficiency in detecting a process producing 10% defectives.

(b) What level of control plan (that is, how many σ) would detect a process producing 15% defectives with probability at least 0.8?

5-24. A certain process is considered to be in control if 10% or less of its output is defective. There are two alternative plans for determining whether the process is out of control. Under Plan I, the process is judged to be out of control if more than 3 in a sample of 20 are defective. Under Plan II, the process is judged to be out of control if 1 or more in a sample of 6 is defective. Compare the efficiency of the two plans with respect to

(a) Falsely concluding that a good process is out of control.

(b) Detecting a process which is producing 15% defectives.

6 THE CONVERGING BINOMIAL

6.1 Introduction

The reader might well have come away from Chapter 5 with the following impression: The binomial may be important and useful, but computing binomial probabilities can quickly become very tedious. Such an impression is entirely correct and even though binomial probability tables exist, it is frequently difficult to find a table which contains probabilities for precisely the n and p values desired, particularly if n is reasonably large. Fortunately when n is fairly large and p is neither very small nor very large,[1] it is a relatively simple matter to approximate the binomial probabilities rather closely. The availability of a fairly simple approximation to the binomial is one of the many important results flowing from the beneficent *central limit theorems* of mathematical statistics. Central limit theorems themselves are beyond the scope of this book; nonetheless we may reap their harvest with great profit.

6.2 The Converging Binomial

Suppose X_n is distributed $B(n, 0.4)$; that is, X_1 is $B(1, 0.4)$, X_2 is $B(2, 0.4)$, X_3 is $B(3, 0.4)$, etc. Let us display the probability distributions

[1]Roughly, $0.2 \leq p \leq 0.8$.

for these random variables geometrically. In each case we use the binomial probability function

$$P(X_n = x) = \binom{n}{x}(0.4)^x(0.6)^{n-x}$$

to obtain probabilities and then plot the results in a diagram. The results are plotted for $n = 2, 4, 10, 15$, and 20 in Figure 6.1a–6.1e respectively. The expected values are shown as μ_2, μ_4, μ_{10}, μ_{15}, and μ_{20}. It is clear from Figure 6.1 that as n increases several things begin to happen to the probability distribution of X_n.

(i) The distribution spreads horizontally. This is obviously necessary since the possible values increase directly with n.
(ii) The mean and modal values both increase.
(iii) The probability of the modal value diminishes. This makes intuitive sense since the total probability of unity has to be divided among more and more possible realizations as n increases.
(iv) The "tails" of the distribution, that is, realizations near zero and near n, become less and less important in terms of their probabilities of occurrence.
(v) In conjunction with (iv), the distribution begins to look more nearly symmetric about its expected value.

One's overall impression is that, aside from the continuous horizontal spreading, the distribution seems to be undergoing some sort of process of standardization as n increases. This standardization is made even more apparent if we perform a slight transformation. X_n is distributed $B(n, p)$ so that

$$\text{Variance } (X_n) = npq$$

and the variance clearly increases as n increases. This is related to the spreading phenomenon noted above. Suppose we attempt to modify X_n just to the extent of keeping the variance constant. Specifically, consider the new random variable Y_n defined by

$$Y_n = \frac{1}{\sqrt{npq}} X_n.$$

It has already been shown (Problem 4-10, p. 112) that the variance of a constant times a random variable is equal to the square of the constant multiplied by the variance of the random variable; consequently

$$\text{Variance } (Y_n) = \left(\frac{1}{\sqrt{npq}}\right)^2 \text{variance } (X_n)$$

$$= \frac{1}{npq}(npq) = 1.$$

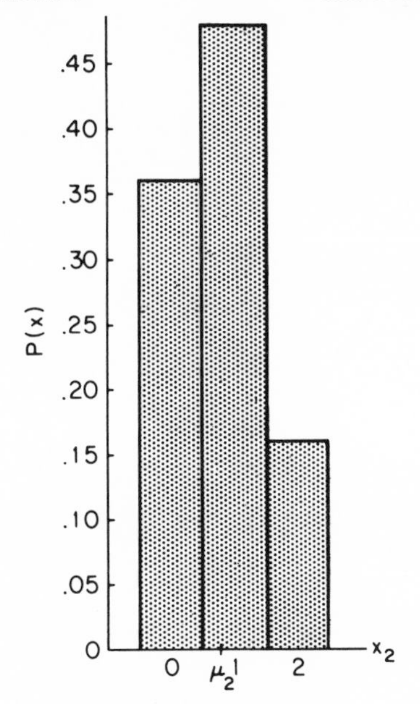

FIGURE 6.1a

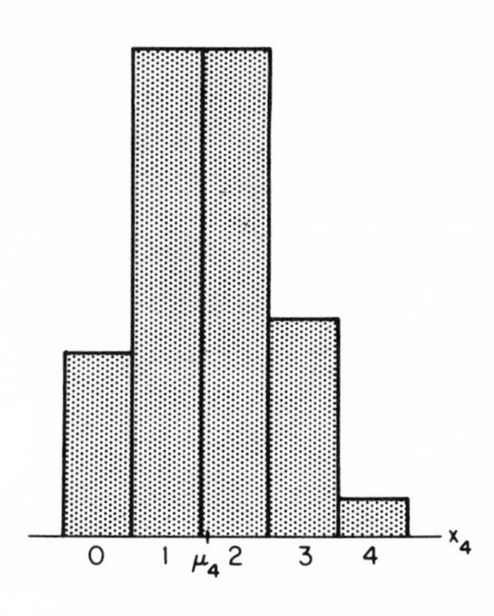

FIGURE 6.1b

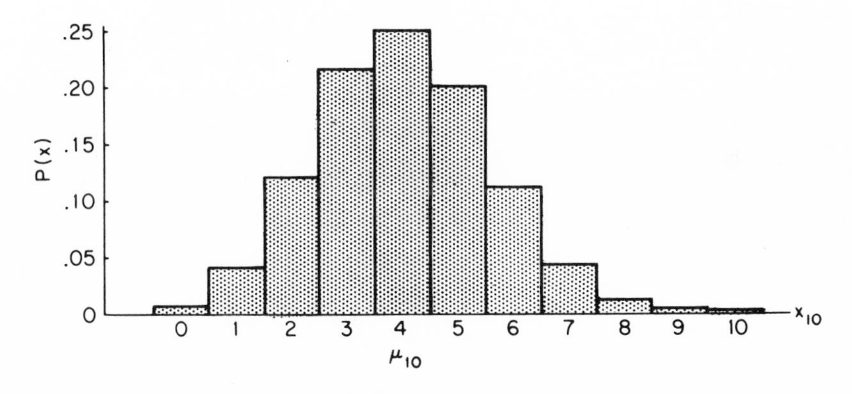

FIGURE 6.1c

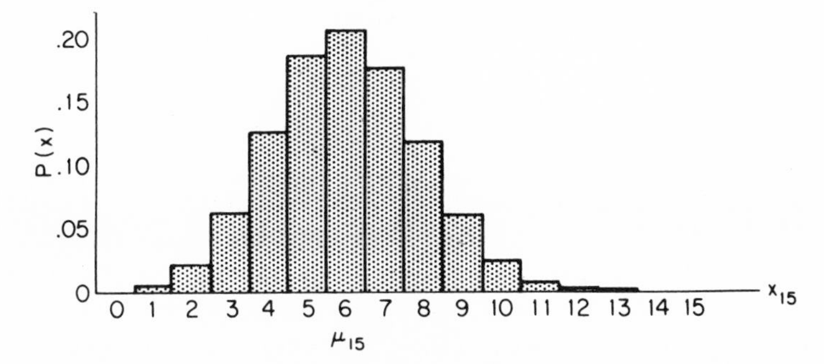

FIGURE 6.1d

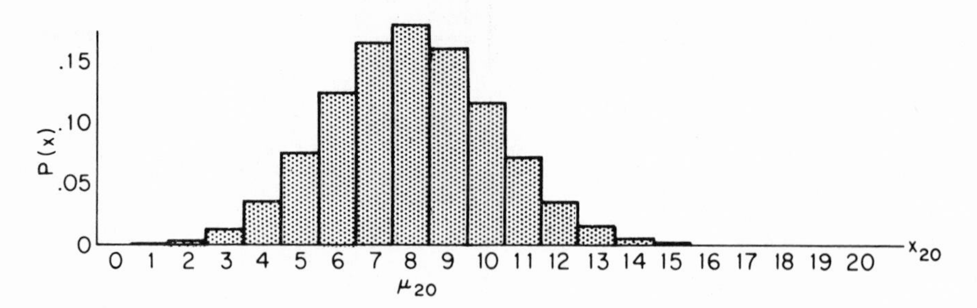

FIGURE 6.1e

Further,

$$\begin{aligned} E(Y_n) &= E\left(\frac{1}{\sqrt{npq}} X_n\right) \\ &= \frac{1}{\sqrt{npq}} EX_n \\ &= \frac{1}{\sqrt{npq}} np \\ &= \sqrt{\frac{np}{q}}. \end{aligned}$$

Also, since

$$Y_n = \frac{1}{\sqrt{npq}} X_n \quad \text{and} \quad X_n \in \mathcal{S} = \{0, 1, 2, \ldots, n\},$$

it follows that

$$Y_n \in \mathfrak{J} = \left\{\frac{0}{\sqrt{npq}}, \frac{1}{\sqrt{npq}}, \frac{2}{\sqrt{npq}}, \ldots, \frac{n}{\sqrt{npq}}\right\}.$$

Finally,

$$\begin{aligned} P\left(Y_n = \frac{x}{\sqrt{npq}}\right) &= P\left(\frac{1}{\sqrt{npq}} X_n = \frac{x}{\sqrt{npq}}\right) \\ &= P\left(X_n = \sqrt{npq}\, \frac{x}{\sqrt{npq}}\right) \\ &= P(X_n = x). \end{aligned}$$

Hence, once the probability distribution of X_n is known, so is the probability distribution of Y_n and vice versa. In an important sense, then, all that the introduction of Y_n does is to give us a new random variable which is just like the binomial X_n except that the variance has been stabilized at unity for all n. If we then observe the Y_n distributions as n increases, we can see what happens to the binomial with a stabilized variance. Before looking at the result geometrically, we present the case $n = 2$ in tabular form (again $p = 0.4$, so that $npq = 0.48$):

x_2	$P(x_2)$	$y_2 = \frac{1}{\sqrt{0.48}} x_2$	$P(y_2)$	$y_2 P(y_2)$	$y_2^2 P(y_2)$
0	0.360	$\frac{0}{\sqrt{0.48}} = 0$	0.360	0	0
1	0.480	$\frac{1}{\sqrt{0.48}} = 1.44338$	0.480	0.6928	1.0000
2	0.160	$\frac{2}{\sqrt{0.48}} = 2.88675$	0.160	0.4619	1.3333
	1.000		1.000	1.1547	2.3333

From the table above we find that indeed

$$EY_2 = \sum_{y_2} y_2 P(y_2) = 1.1547 = \sqrt{\frac{2(0.4)}{0.6}}$$

and

$$\begin{aligned} \text{Variance } (Y_2) &= E(Y_2^2) - (EY_2)^2 \\ &= 2.3333 - 1.3333 \\ &= 1.0000. \end{aligned}$$

We also notice that while the possible values of X_2 are separated by a distance of 1 unit, the possible values of Y_2 are separated by approximately 1.4434, which is $1/\sqrt{0.48}$. Each rectangle in the Y_2 distribution will therefore have a base of $1/\sqrt{0.48}$ so that its height must therefore be $\sqrt{0.48}$ times the corresponding probability in order to have the area of the rectangle itself equal to the probability. In general, consecutive values of Y_n are separated by a distance of $1/\sqrt{npq}$ so that the rectangles have bases equal to $1/\sqrt{npq}$ and heights equal to $\sqrt{npq}$ times the corresponding probabilities. The Y_n distributions for $p = 0.4$ and $n = 2, 4, 10, 15$, and 20 are plotted in Figure 6.2a–6.2e. When the corresponding portions of Figures 6.1 and 6.2 are compared, it becomes apparent that the stabilization of the variance has been accomplished solely by "squeezing" the X_n distributions for $n \geq 10$ and "stretching" them for $n \leq 4$.[2] That is to say, the distribution of Y_{10} is the distribution of the corresponding X_{10} "squeezed" together from either end. The squeezing must be accomplished in such a way that the total area of the figure remains equal to unity. Consequently, the squeezing is accom-

[2]In general, if n is such that $npq < 1$, the distribution must be "stretched" to increase the variance to unity; if n is such that $npq > 1$, the distribution must be "squeezed" to reduce the variance to unity.

panied by a simultaneous vertical growth of the distribution. The more n increases, the more the need to squeeze in order to hold the variance at unity and the taller the distribution must grow to maintain a total area of unity.

It should be apparent from Figures 6.1 and 6.2 that as n increases the binomial (or variance-stabilized binomial) distribution approaches more and more a standardized form which can be described as symmetrical and bell-shaped. Of course, no matter how large n becomes, the binomial is never exactly symmetrical unless $p = 0.5$, but the progressively declining importance of the tails of the distribution as n increases makes the lack of symmetry decidedly unimportant.[3] InFigure 6.2e, for example, the possible values of Y_{20} extend from $0/\sqrt{4.8}$ to $20/\sqrt{4.8}$. However,

$$P\left[\frac{2}{\sqrt{4.8}} \leq Y_{20} \leq \frac{14}{\sqrt{4.8}}\right] = 0.998.$$

Thus the tails ($0/\sqrt{4.8}$, $1/\sqrt{4.8}$ and $15/\sqrt{4.8}$, $16/\sqrt{4.8}$, . . . , $20/\sqrt{4.8}$) contain very nearly no probability, and very nearly all the probability is concentrated in the bell-shaped and approximately symmetric figure extending from $2/\sqrt{4.8}$ to $14/\sqrt{4.8}$.

In view of the remarks above, it might be conjectured that if n is large enough there should exist a symmetrical, bell-shaped figure which is enough like the corresponding binomial distribution to be usable as an approximation to the latter. That such a conjecture proves to be correct is the practical meaning of the following remarkable theorem.

THE BINOMIAL CENTRAL LIMIT THEOREM. If the random variable X_n is distributed $B(n, p)$, the distribution of the random variable Z_n, defined by

$$Z_n = \frac{X_n - np}{\sqrt{npq}},$$

approaches the distribution of the *normal* random variable with mean zero and variance unity as n increases.

Although we cannot possibly hope to prove the binomial central limit theorem, we must understand it in order to use it. Let us first deal with the normal random variable mentioned in the theorem. If X is a normal random variable, then $X \in \mathcal{S} = \{x \mid -\infty < x < +\infty\}$ and the probability graph of X is given by the rather formidable function

$$f(x) = \frac{1}{\sqrt{2\pi\sigma^2}} e^{-1/2\,(x-\mu)^2/\sigma^2}$$

[3]The smaller p is, the larger n must be before the lower tail really becomes of negligible importance. Similarly, the larger p is, the larger n must be before the upper tail really becomes of negligible importance.

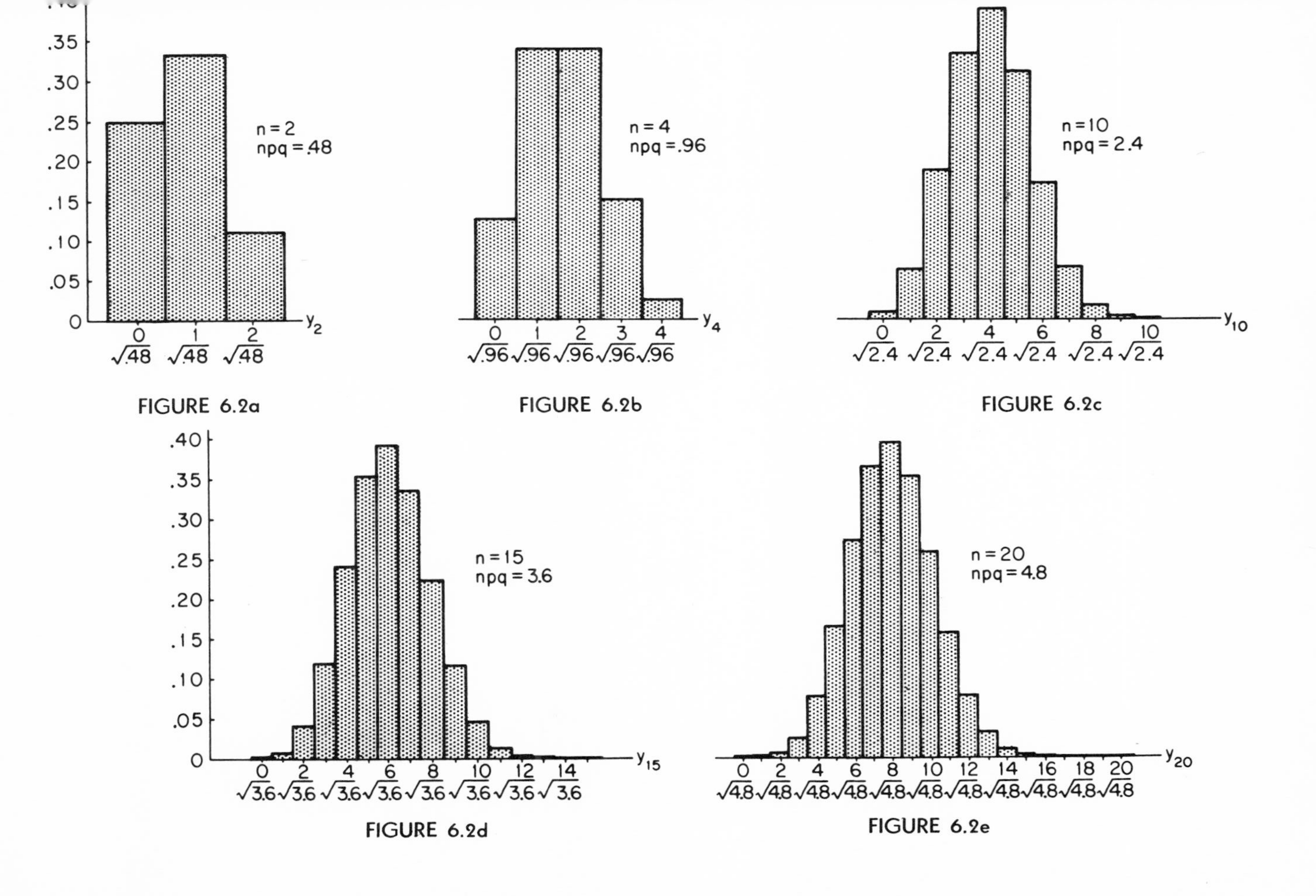

FIGURE 6.2a

FIGURE 6.2b

FIGURE 6.2c

FIGURE 6.2d

FIGURE 6.2e

where[4] $\pi = 3.14159\ldots$, $e = 2.71828\ldots$, $\mu = EX$, and $\sigma^2 =$ variance (X). For our purposes it is sufficient to know that the normal probability graph looks like the one depicted in Figure 6.3.

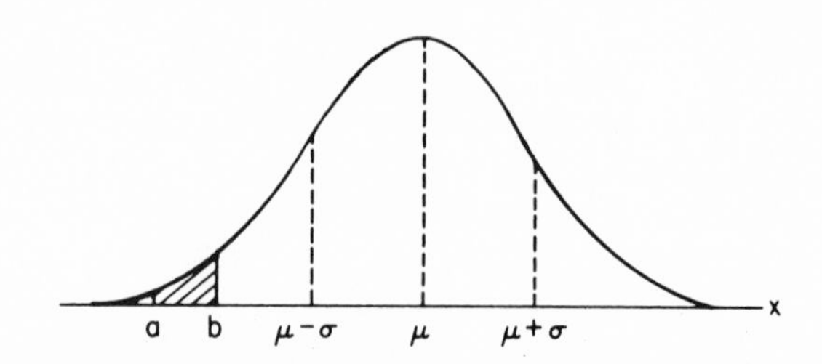

FIGURE 6.3. The Normal Probability Graph.

The curve is smooth, bell-shaped, and symmetrical about its mean. From $(-\infty)$ to $(\mu - \sigma)$ the curve rises with increasing rapidity. From $(\mu - \sigma)$ to μ the curve rises with diminishing rapidity, reaching its maximum at μ which is therefore both the mean and mode of the distribution. By symmetry, the curve falls with increasing rapidity between μ and $(\mu + \sigma)$ and thereafter falls with decreasing rapidity. Since this is a probability graph, the total area under the curve is unity; that is, $P(-\infty < X < +\infty) = 1$, while

$$P(a \leq X \leq b)$$

is given by the shaded area in Figure 6.3.

There are an infinite number of normal distributions, one for each possible μ, σ^2 combination. A shorthand way of stating that *X is a normal random variable with mean μ and variance σ^2* is to write

$$X \text{ is } \eta(\mu, \sigma^2),$$

which is read precisely as the italicized statement above. Thus X is $\eta(10, 50)$ means that *X is a normal random variable with mean equal to* 10 *and variance equal to* 50. The binomial central limit theorem mentions the particular random variable which is $\eta(0, 1)$, that is, the normal random variable with mean zero and variance unity. This is the so-called *standard normal* variable. According to the theorem, then, the distribution of some variable Z_n approaches the distribution of the standard normal variable as n increases. To understand the theorem, we must now do two things:

(i) See what this Z_n variable is.

[4] π is the number which appears in the familiar formula for the area of a circle: Area $= \pi$ times radius squared. e is another important mathematical constant and, among other things, is the base of natural logarithms.

(ii) Learn precisely what it means for one distribution to *approach* another.

Learning about Z_n is perfectly straightforward, for Z_n is defined in terms of the binomial X_n. Thus,

$$Z_n = \frac{X_n - np}{\sqrt{npq}}.$$

We have already studied

$$Y_n = \frac{X_n}{\sqrt{npq}}$$

and found that it is merely a variance-stabilized binomial, that is, *a binomial with variance stabilized at unity*. The Y_n distribution has the same shape as that of the corresponding binomial except for the "stretching" or "squeezing" necessary to keep the variance at unity.[5] Further, we have seen that any Y_n probability can be derived from the corresponding X_n probability and vice versa. Now

$$\begin{aligned} Z_n &= \frac{X_n - np}{\sqrt{npq}} \\ &= \frac{X_n}{\sqrt{npq}} - \frac{np}{\sqrt{npq}} \\ &= \frac{X_n}{\sqrt{npq}} - \sqrt{\frac{np}{q}} \\ &= Y_n - E(Y_n). \end{aligned}$$

Thus, Z_n is merely Y_n minus its expected value. Hence

$$\begin{aligned} EZ_n &= E[Y_n - E(Y_n)] \\ &= EY_n - EY_n \\ &= 0 \end{aligned}$$

and[6]

$$\begin{aligned} \text{Variance } Z_n &= \text{variance } [Y_n - E(Y_n)] \\ &= \text{variance } Y_n \\ &= 1. \end{aligned}$$

[5]The "stretching" ("squeezing") is accompanied by a simultaneous reduction (increase) in the height of the distribution.

[6]We are using the result of Problem 4-10, p. 112 which is that

$$\text{Variance } (aX + b) = a^2 \text{ variance } X$$

where X is a random variable and a and b are constants.

The transformations producing the Z_n variable can now be described as follows: First we either stretch or squeeze the X_n distribution so that its variance is unity; this results in Y_n, which has variance unity and mean $\sqrt{np/q}$. Next we "move" the Y_n distribution to the "left" until its expected value becomes zero; this involves neither squeezing nor stretching so that the result is Z_n which still has variance unity, but a mean of zero.[7] The process of producing the mean- and variance-stabilized binomial is illustrated for the case $n = 10$, $p = 0.4$ in Figure 6.4.

Now that we understand what the random variable Z_n is, we can take up the question of precisely what it means for the distribution of Z_n to approach the distribution of the standard normal variable as n increases. In general, the approach or *convergence* of two distributions has the following interpretation. Let $Z_1, Z_2, Z_3, \ldots, Z_n, Z_{n+1}, Z_{n+2}, \ldots$ be a sequence of random variables, let S be some other random variable, and let a and b be any constants with $a < b$. We want to compare

$$P(a \leq Z_n \leq b) \quad \text{with} \quad P(a \leq S \leq b).$$

[7]Another fruitful way of looking at the transformations producing Z_n follows: First take X_n with mean np and move it to the left a distance of np. This results in a new random variable $W_n = X_n - np$, where

$$EW_n = E(X_n - np) = 0$$

and

$$\begin{aligned}\text{Variance } W_n &= \text{variance } (X_n - np)\\ &= \text{variance } X_n = npq.\end{aligned}$$

Then "stretch" or "squeeze" the W_n distribution so that its variance is unity. This results in

$$Z_n = \frac{W_n}{\sqrt{npq}}$$

where

$$EZ_n = \frac{1}{\sqrt{npq}} E(W_n) = 0$$

and

$$\begin{aligned}\text{Variance } Z_n &= \text{variance}\left(\frac{1}{\sqrt{npq}} W_n\right)\\ &= \left(\frac{1}{\sqrt{npq}}\right)^2 \text{variance } W_n\\ &= \frac{1}{npq}(npq) = 1.\end{aligned}$$

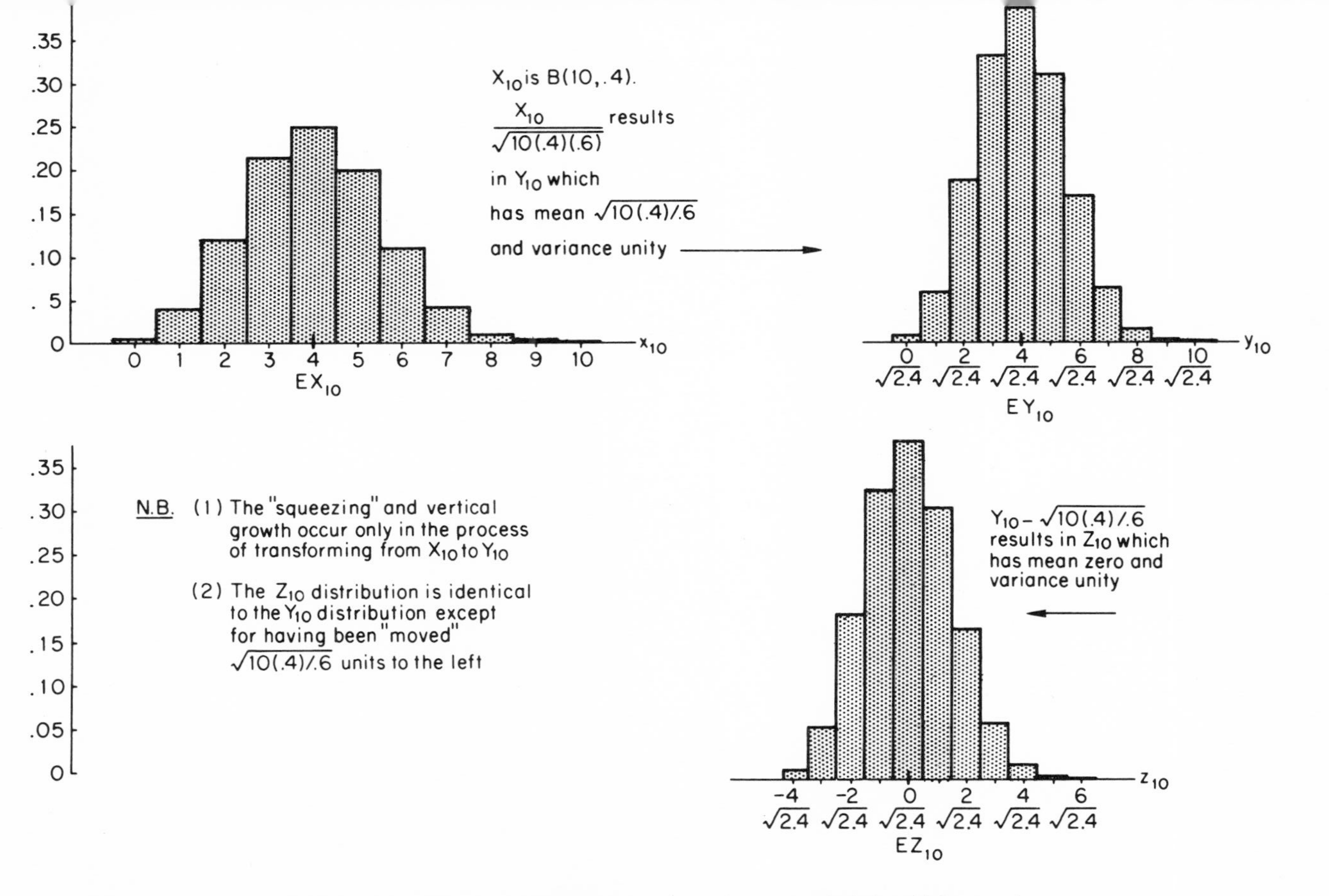

FIGURE 6.4. Transformation to the "Mean-and-Variance Stabilized" Binomial.

We can therefore look at the following sequence of differences:

$$P(a \leq Z_1 \leq b) - P(a \leq S \leq b)$$
$$P(a \leq Z_2 \leq b) - P(a \leq S \leq b)$$
$$P(a \leq Z_3 \leq b) - P(a \leq S \leq b)$$
$$P(a \leq Z_4 \leq b) - P(a \leq S \leq b)$$

.

.

.

$$P(a \leq Z_{100} \leq b) - P(a \leq S \leq b)$$
$$P(a \leq Z_{101} \leq b) - P(a \leq S \leq b)$$

etc.

If the differences continue to get smaller and smaller as the subscript on Z increases (that is, as n increases), then the probability that Z_n lies between a and b is getting closer and closer to the probability that S lies between a and b. We denote this by saying *as n approaches infinity, the error in approximating $P(a \leq Z_n \leq b)$ by $P(a \leq S \leq b)$ approaches zero.* A shorthand way of writing this is

$$\lim_{n \to \infty} [P(a \leq Z_n \leq b) - P(a \leq S \leq b)] = 0,$$

which may be read precisely as the previous statement in italics. If the approximation error approaches zero as n approaches infinity for all possible choices of a and b such that $a < b$, then the distribution of Z_n is said to *converge to* or *approach* the distribution of S as n increases. Common alternative statements which convey precisely the same notion of convergence of distributions[8] are

(i) The distribution of S is the *asymptotic distribution* of Z_n.
(ii) Z_n is *asymptotically distributed* as S.

This brief discussion of the meaning of convergence of distributions should make it clear that if Z_n is asymptotically distributed as S, then S can be used to approximate probabilities involving Z_n. The approximation might

[8]Note that the S distribution is fixed, while each Z_n has a different probability distribution. Convergence means, roughly, that as n increases the Z_n distribution gets to be more and more like the distribution of S.

well be quite poor in the case of Z_2 or Z_5, but it should be much better for Z_{20} and still better for Z_{50}, and so on as n increases.

We can now rephrase the binomial central limit theorem to: if X_n is $B(n, p)$,

$$Z_n = \frac{X_n - np}{\sqrt{npq}} \text{ is asymptotically } \eta(0, 1).$$

We should therefore be able to use the standard normal distribution to approximate binomial probabilities. The theorem states that Z_n, which has mean zero and variance unity, is asymptotically distributed as the standard normal variable, which also has mean zero and variance unity. Suppose X_n is $B(20, 0.3)$, then

$$P(X_n = 5) = \binom{20}{5}(0.3)^5(0.7)^{15} = 0.179.$$

To avoid the tedious arithmetic necessary to arrive at 0.179, we wish to approximate the probability that $X_n = 5$ by using the standard normal distribution. Two things must be noticed. First, convergence implies the ability to approximate the probability that a random variable will lie in some interval; second, it is Z_n, not X_n, which is asymptotically $\eta(0, 1)$. Suppose the "interval problem" has been solved, then the "X_n versus Z_n" part of the problem is easily handled. For if we wish to approximate the probability that X_n is between a and b, all we do is use the definition

$$Z_n = \frac{X_n - np}{\sqrt{npq}}$$

to find the corresponding Z_n interval thus: If $X_n = a$,

$$Z_n = \frac{a - np}{\sqrt{npq}} = a',$$

if $X_n = b$,

$$Z_n = \frac{b - np}{\sqrt{npq}} = b'.$$

Hence $P(a \leq X_n \leq b) = P(a' \leq Z_n \leq b')$, and then we approximate $P(a' \leq Z_n \leq b')$ by $P(a' \leq S \leq b')$, where S is the standard normal variable.

Now recall that the approximation actually occurs in the form of using an area from the normal probability graph to approximate some area of the binomial probability graph. The binomial probability graph can be constructed in essentially two ways. Figure 6.5 displays these two ways in which the probabilities of 4, 5, and 6 can be represented for the case X_n is $B(20, 0.3)$.

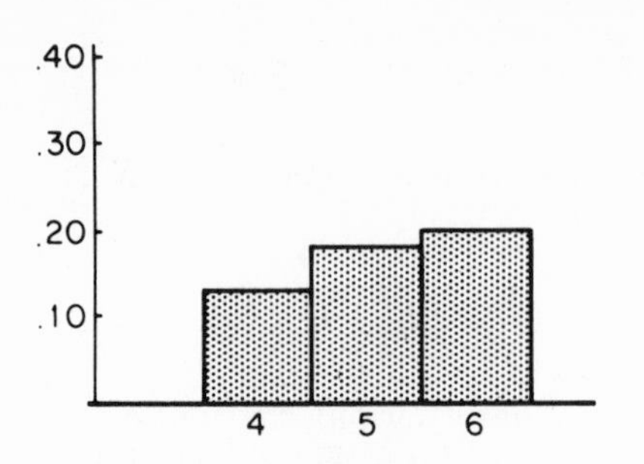

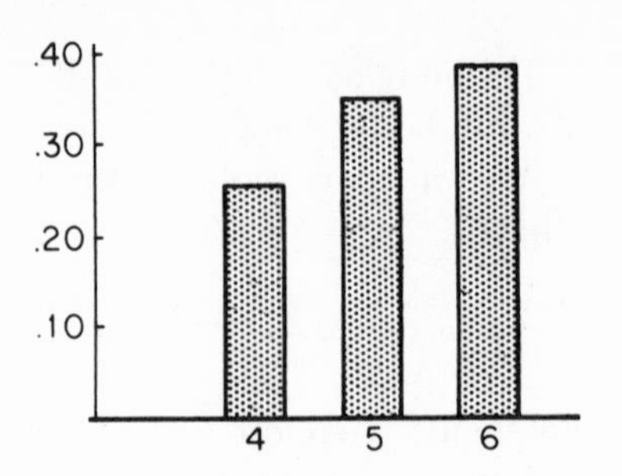

FIGURE 6.5. Probabilities of 4, 5, and 6 for B (20, 0.3)

(a) (b)

Figure 6.5b represents the case in which the base of a probability rectangle is given some arbitrary length (in this case $\frac{1}{2}$) and the height is adjusted so that the area of the rectangle is equal to a probability. Figure 6.5a represents the case of contiguous rectangles. In Figure 6.5b, the probability of 5 is represented by the area over the interval from 4.75 to 5.25; in Figure 6.5a, that same probability is represented by the area over the interval from 4.5 to 5.5. The prime difference is that the Figure 6.5b representation contains empty spaces whereas the Figure 6.5a representation does not. Thus, there is no probability (that is, area) over the interval from 4.25 to 4.75 in Figure 6.5b, while the same interval in Figure 6.5a is not empty. Recall that the normal probability graph is also free of empty spaces. Suppose we say that to approximate $P(X_n = 4)$ we use the interval 3.75 to 4.25 and to approximate $P(X_n = 5)$ we use the interval 4.75 to 5.25. The corresponding Z_n intervals are[9]

$$(-1.10 \leq Z_n \leq -0.85) \quad \text{for} \quad (3.75 \leq X_n \leq 4.25)$$

and

$$(-0.61 \leq Z_n \leq -0.36) \quad \text{for} \quad (4.75 \leq X_n \leq 5.25).$$

Then using S which is $\eta(0, 1)$, the standard normal approximation to $P(X_n = 4)$ would be $P(-1.10 \leq S \leq -0.85)$, and the approximation to $P(X_n = 5)$ would be $P(-0.61 \leq S \leq -0.37)$. These areas are shown on the standard normal graph in Figure 6.6.

[9]Since X_n is B (20, 0.3), $np = 6$, $npq = 4.2$.

Then,

$$\frac{3.75 - 6}{\sqrt{4.2}} \cong -1.10 \quad \text{and} \quad \frac{4.25 - 6}{\sqrt{4.2}} \cong -0.85,$$

and

$$\frac{4.75 - 6}{\sqrt{4.2}} \cong -0.61 \quad \text{and} \quad \frac{5.25 - 6}{\sqrt{4.2}} \cong -0.36.$$

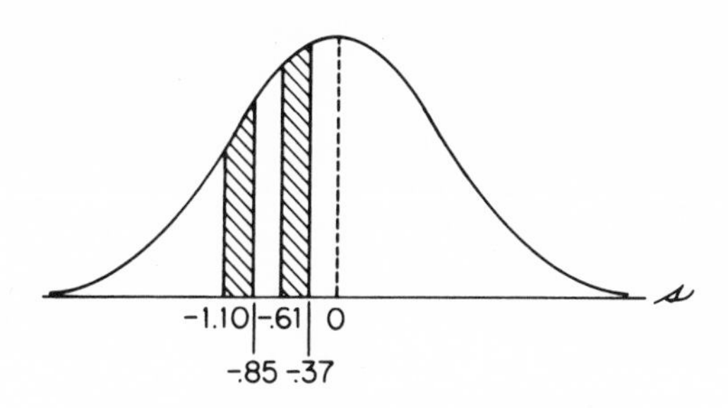

FIGURE 6.6

But what of $P(-0.85 \leq S \leq -0.61)$? This probability would obviously never be used in approximating the binomial. It is clear, then, that if we use a representation such as Figure 6.5b to determine intervals corresponding to the binomial realizations and then use these intervals to approximate (via the corresponding Z_n intervals) the binomial probabilities, the probability approximations summed over all possible realizations of X_n will not total unity. This results from the fact that while the area under the *entire* standard normal graph is unity, the proposed approximation method will leave out such areas as that between -0.85 and -0.61 in Figure 6.6. It is therefore evident that in approximating binomial probabilities it must be the *contiguous rectangle graph*, such as Figure 6.5a, which is used to determine an interval corresponding to a binomial realization. Only in this way will *all* the area of the standard normal graph be assigned to the binomial.[10] To approximate $P(X_n = 5)$, we must then use the interval from 4.5 to 5.5. The corresponding Z_n interval is

$$\frac{4.5 - np}{\sqrt{npq}} \quad \text{to} \quad \frac{5.5 - np}{\sqrt{npq}}.$$

Since X_n is $B(20, 0.3)$, we find

$$\frac{4.5 - np}{\sqrt{npq}} = \frac{4.5 - 6}{\sqrt{4.2}} \cong -0.73$$

and

$$\frac{5.5 - np}{\sqrt{npq}} = \frac{5.5 - 6}{\sqrt{4.2}} \cong -0.24.$$

[10]This process of using the *contiguous rectangle graph* to assign an interval to each of the binomial realizations is referred to as a *continuity correction* process. Some such process is always necessary when a continuous random variable is used to approximate a discrete random variable. The standard normal variable S is continuous since

$$S \in \{s \mid -\infty < s < +\infty\}.$$

We then say

$$P(X_n = 5) = P(4.5 \leq X_n \leq 5.5) = P(-0.73 \leq Z_n \leq -0.24),$$

and the desired probability is approximated by

$$P(-0.73 \leq S \leq -0.24).$$

It will be the task of the next section to show that the latter probability can easily be found to be

$$P(-0.73 \leq S \leq -0.24) = 0.173,$$

which is then our normal approximation to the true binomial probability $P(X_n = 5) = 0.179$.

6.3 The Normal Probability Table

Suppose X is $\eta(20, 16)$; that is, X is normally distributed with mean 20 and variance 16. The probability graph of X would be represented as in Figure 6.7, which is the geometric representation of the equation

$$f(x) = \frac{1}{\sqrt{2\pi(16)}} e^{-1/2\ (x-20)^2/16}.$$

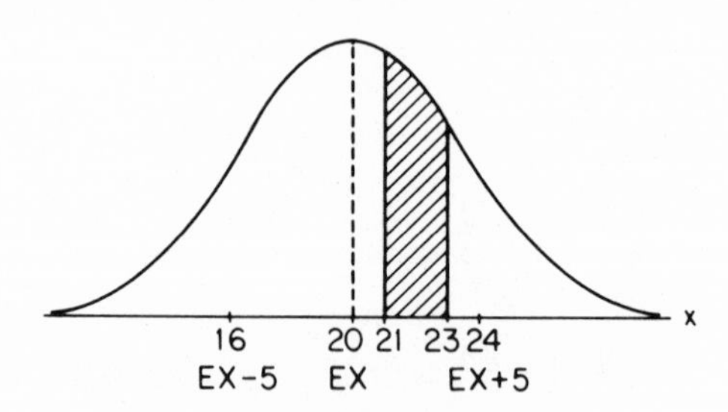

FIGURE 6.7. The Probability Graph for the η (20,16) Variable

The shaded area in Figure 6.7 depicts $P(21 \leq X \leq 23)$ and the question now is how to evaluate the shaded area. Since the equation of the graph is known, evaluation of an area such as that shown in Figure 6.7 is, conceptually, a straightforward problem in mathematics. It would be quite convenient, however, to avoid the complicated mathematics by resorting to a table which lists the results of such computations performed by someone else. In a sense, this is too much to hope for since there would then have to be an infinite number of such tables — one for each possible choice of the mean and variance. The latter problem is overcome by considering the random variable

$$S = \frac{X - EX}{\sigma_X}.$$

We find that since X is $\eta(20, 16)$,

$$\begin{aligned} ES &= E\left(\frac{X - 20}{4}\right) \\ &= E\tfrac{1}{4}(X - 20) \\ &= \tfrac{1}{4}[EX - 20] \\ &= \tfrac{1}{4}(20 - 20) = 0, \end{aligned}$$

and

$$\begin{aligned} \text{Variance } (S) &= \text{variance } [\tfrac{1}{4}(X - 20)] \\ &= (\tfrac{1}{4})^2 \text{ variance } (X - 20) \\ &= (\tfrac{1}{16}) \text{ variance } X \\ &= (\tfrac{1}{16})(16) = 1. \end{aligned}$$

Further, if $X \geq 21$,

$$S \geq \frac{21 - 20}{4} = \tfrac{1}{4},$$

and if $X \leq 23$,

$$S \leq \frac{23 - 20}{4} = \tfrac{3}{4},$$

so that

$$P(21 \leq X \leq 23) = P(\tfrac{1}{4} \leq S \leq \tfrac{3}{4}).$$

Now the random variable S is clearly the standard normal variable — S is $\eta(0, 1)$ — and we see that all that is really needed is a probability table for the standard normal variable in order to determine any normal probability. If such a table should indicate that

$$P(\tfrac{1}{4} \leq S \leq \tfrac{3}{4}) = 0.175,$$

we would conclude that if X is $\eta(20, 16)$,

$$P(21 \leq X \leq 23) = 0.175.$$

Suppose Y is $\eta(50, 100)$ and we wish to find $P(52.5 \leq Y \leq 57.5)$. Using $S = (Y - EY)/\sigma_Y$, we find if $Y \geq 52.5$,

$$S \geq \frac{52.5 - 50}{10} = \tfrac{1}{4},$$

and if $Y \leq 57.5$,

$$S \leq \frac{57.5 - 50}{10} = \tfrac{3}{4}.$$

Hence

$$P(52.5 \leq Y \leq 57.5) = P(\tfrac{1}{4} \leq S \leq \tfrac{3}{4}) = 0.175.$$

The standard normal probability table is given as Table 6.1 below. The entries in the body of the table give $P[0 \leq S \leq s]$ for s expressed to two decimal places and $0 \leq s \leq 3.09$. For example, the entry in the table corresponding to $s = 1.28$ is 0.3997. The meaning of this is

$$P(0 \leq S \leq 1.28) = 0.3997.$$

EXAMPLE 6.3.1. If S is $\eta(0, 1)$, determine

(a) $P(0 \leq S \leq 2.12)$.
(b) $P(-1.55 \leq S \leq 0)$.
(c) $P(S \geq 2.00)$.
(d) $P(|S| \geq 2.00)$.
(e) $P(-1.60 \leq S \leq -1.00)$.

Solution:

(a) This probability is given directly in the body of Table 6.1 by looking in the row headed 2.1 and the column headed 0.02. Hence,

$$P(0 \leq S \leq 2.12) = 0.4830.$$

(b) In this problem we take advantage of the fact that the standard normal distribution is symmetric about $s = 0$ and write $P(-1.55 \leq S \leq 0) = P(0 \leq S \leq 1.55)$. The desired probability is then found directly in the table by looking in the row headed 1.5 and column headed 0.05. Thus,

$$P(-1.55 \leq S \leq 0) = 0.4394.$$

(c) This probability cannot be found directly. Notice, however, that $\{s \mid 0 \leq s \leq 2.00\} \cup \{s \mid s \geq 2.00\} = \{s \mid s \geq 0\}$, and $P[S \in \{s \mid s \geq 0\}] = 0.50$ by symmetry of the distribution. Further, $\{s \mid 0 \leq s \leq 2.00\} \cap \{s \mid s \geq 2.00\} = \{2.00\}$ and $P(S = 2.00) = 0$. The latter result follows from the fact that for a continuous random variable the probability connected with any interval of length zero is zero (see Note to Chapter 3). Finally, since we find in Table 6.1 that $P(0 \leq S \leq 2.00) = 0.4772$, it follows that

$$\begin{aligned} P(S \geq 2.00) &= P(S \geq 0) - P(0 \leq S \leq 2.00) \\ &= 0.5000 - 0.4772 \\ &= 0.0228. \end{aligned}$$

(d) The event $(|S| \geq 2.00)$ is the union of two disjoint events, namely $\{S \geq 2.00\} \cup \{S \leq -2.00\}$. In (c) we found $P(S \geq 2.00) = 0.0228$ and by symmetry it must also be that $P(S \leq -2.00) = 0.0228$. Therefore

TABLE 6-1.
Standard Normal Probabilities

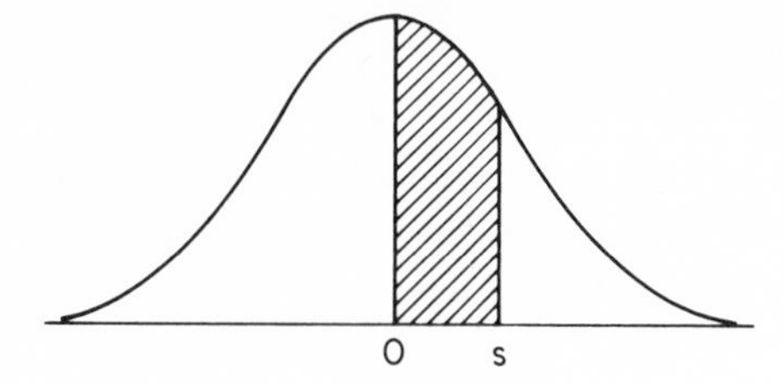

If S is distributed $\eta(0, 1)$, Prob $[0 \leq S \leq s]$ is given directly in the body of the table. Example: Prob $[0 \leq S \leq 1.65]$ appears at the intersection of the row headed 1.6 with the column headed 0.05, hence 0.4505.

s	0.00	0.01	0.02	0.03	0.04	0.05	0.06	0.07	0.08	0.09
0.0	0.0000	0.0040	0.0080	0.0120	0.0160	0.0199	0.0239	0.0279	0.0319	0.0359
0.1	0.0398	0.0438	0.0478	0.0517	0.0557	0.0596	0.0636	0.0675	0.0714	0.0753
0.2	0.0793	0.0832	0.0871	0.0910	0.0948	0.0987	0.1026	0.1064	0.1103	0.1141
0.3	0.1179	0.1217	0.1255	0.1293	0.1331	0.1368	0.1406	0.1443	0.1480	0.1517
0.4	0.1554	0.1591	0.1628	0.1664	0.1700	0.1736	0.1772	0.1808	0.1844	0.1879
0.5	0.1915	0.1950	0.1985	0.2019	0.2054	0.2088	0.2123	0.2157	0.2190	0.2224
0.6	0.2257	0.2291	0.2324	0.2357	0.2389	0.2422	0.2454	0.2486	0.2517	0.2549
0.7	0.2580	0.2611	0.2642	0.2673	0.2704	0.2734	0.2764	0.2794	0.2823	0.2852
0.8	0.2881	0.2910	0.2939	0.2967	0.2995	0.3023	0.3051	0.3078	0.3106	0.3133
0.9	0.3159	0.3186	0.3212	0.3238	0.3264	0.3289	0.3315	0.3340	0.3365	0.3389
1.0	0.3413	0.3438	0.3461	0.3485	0.3508	0.3531	0.3554	0.3577	0.3599	0.3621
1.1	0.3643	0.3665	0.3686	0.3708	0.3729	0.3749	0.3770	0.3790	0.3810	0.3830
1.2	0.3849	0.3869	0.3888	0.3907	0.3925	0.3944	0.3962	0.3980	0.3997	0.4015
1.3	0.4032	0.4049	0.4066	0.4082	0.4099	0.4115	0.4131	0.4147	0.4162	0.4177
1.4	0.4192	0.4207	0.4222	0.4236	0.4251	0.4265	0.4279	0.4292	0.4306	0.4319
1.5	0.4332	0.4345	0.4357	0.4370	0.4382	0.4394	0.4406	0.4418	0.4429	0.4441
1.6	0.4452	0.4463	0.4474	0.4484	0.4495	0.4505	0.4515	0.4525	0.4535	0.4545
1.7	0.4554	0.4564	0.4573	0.4582	0.4591	0.4599	0.4608	0.4616	0.4625	0.4633
1.8	0.4641	0.4649	0.4656	0.4664	0.4671	0.4678	0.4686	0.4693	0.4699	0.4706
1.9	0.4713	0.4719	0.4726	0.4732	0.4738	0.4744	0.4750	0.4756	0.4761	0.4767
2.0	0.4772	0.4778	0.4783	0.4788	0.4793	0.4798	0.4803	0.4808	0.4812	0.4817
2.1	0.4821	0.4826	0.4830	0.4834	0.4838	0.4842	0.4846	0.4850	0.4854	0.4857
2.2	0.4861	0.4864	0.4868	0.4871	0.4875	0.4878	0.4881	0.4884	0.4887	0.4890
2.3	0.4893	0.4896	0.4898	0.4901	0.4904	0.4906	0.4909	0.4911	0.4913	0.4916
2.4	0.4918	0.4920	0.4922	0.4925	0.4927	0.4929	0.4931	0.4932	0.4934	0.4936
2.5	0.4938	0.4940	0.4941	0.4943	0.4945	0.4946	0.4948	0.4949	0.4951	0.4952
2.6	0.4953	0.4955	0.4956	0.4957	0.4959	0.4960	0.4961	0.4962	0.4963	0.4964
2.7	0.4965	0.4966	0.4967	0.4968	0.4969	0.4970	0.4971	0.4972	0.4973	0.4974
2.8	0.4974	0.4975	0.4976	0.4977	0.4977	0.4978	0.4979	0.4979	0.4980	0.4981
2.9	0.4981	0.4982	0.4982	0.4983	0.4984	0.4984	0.4985	0.4985	0.4986	0.4986
3.0	0.4987	0.4987	0.4987	0.4988	0.4988	0.4989	0.4989	0.4989	0.4990	0.4990

$P(|S| \geq 2.00) = 2(0.0228) = 0.0456$. Since the standard deviation of S is unity while $ES = 0$, the event $\{|S| \geq 2.00\}$ is the event that S differs from its mean by at least two standard deviations. We know from Chebyschev's inequality that such an event must have a probability no greater than 0.25. Indeed, 0.0456 is substantially below 0.25, which is another indication of how weak Chebyschev's inequality can be in particular circumstances.

(e) The event $\{-1.60 \leq S \leq -1.00\}$ will, due to symmetry, have the same probability as the event $\{1.00 \leq S \leq 1.60\}$. By an argument similar to that in (c)[11], we find that

$$\begin{aligned} P\{1.00 \leq S \leq 1.60\} &= P\{0 \leq S \leq 1.60\} - P\{0 \leq S \leq 1.00\} \\ &= 0.4452 - 0.3413 \\ &= 0.1039. \end{aligned}$$

EXAMPLE 6.3.2. If X is $B(10, 0.5)$, the probability distribution of X can, by brute force calculation, be found to be as follows:

x	P(x)
0	0.001
1	0.010
2	0.044
3	0.117
4	0.205
5	0.246
6	0.205
7	0.117
8	0.044
9	0.010
10	0.001
	1.000

[11]A useful device is to draw a "picture" as follows.

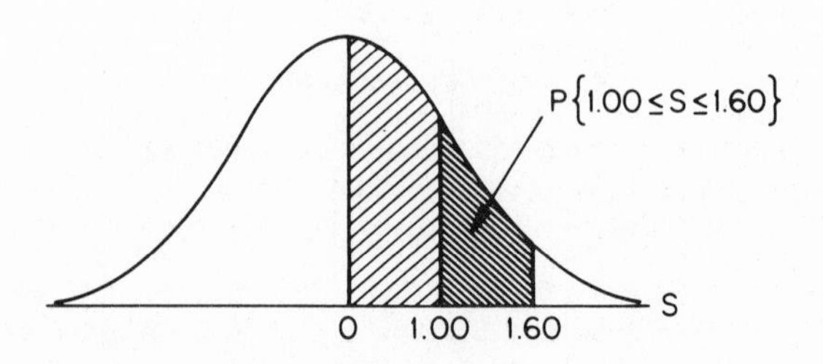

This makes it quite clear that the desired probability is

$$P(0 \leq S \leq 1.60) - P(0 \leq S \leq 1.00).$$

(a) Why is $P(x) = P(10 - x)$?

(b) Calculate the standard normal approximations for the probabilities of 0, 1, 2, 3, 4, and 5.

Solution:

(a) Since X is $B(10, 0.5)$,

$$P(X = x) = \binom{10}{x}(0.5)^x(0.5)^{10-x}$$

$$= \frac{10!}{x!(10-x)!}(0.5)^{10}.$$

Also,

$$P(X = 10 - x) = \binom{10}{10-x}(0.5)^{(10-x)}(0.5)^{10-(10-x)}$$

$$= \frac{10!}{(10-x)![10-(10-x)]!}(0.5)^{10-x}(0.5)^x$$

$$= \frac{10!}{(10-x!)x!}(0.5)^{10}$$

$$= P(X = x).$$

It is thus the symmetry of the distribution ($p = 0.5$) that results in $P(X = x) = P(X = 10 - x)$.

(b) $EX = 10(0.5) = 5$; $\sigma^2 = 10(0.5)$ as $= 2.5$.

Therefore, according to the binomial central limit theorem, we should approximate the binomial probabilities by considering

$$Z = \frac{X - 5}{\sqrt{2.5}},$$

since

$$EZ = 0 \quad \text{and} \quad \sigma_Z^2 = 1.$$

Also according to the theorem, we should not expect too much of the approximation since Z is only asymptotically $\eta(0, 1)$ and our Z variable is based only on $n = 10$. For $X = 0$, we use the interval $-0.50 \leq X \leq 0.50$. The corresponding Z interval is found by

$$\frac{-0.05 - 5.00}{\sqrt{2.5}} \cong -3.48$$

and

$$\frac{0.50 - 5.00}{\sqrt{2.5}} = -2.48.$$

The approximating probability is then found by

$$P(-3.48 \leq Z \leq -2.84) \cong P(-3.48 \leq S \leq -2.84) = 0.0023.$$

$X = 1 \rightarrow (0.50 \leq X \leq 1.50)$; then

$$\frac{1.50 - 5.00}{\sqrt{2.5}} \cong -2.22.$$

Hence,

$$P(-2.84 \leq Z \leq -2.22) \cong P(-2.84 \leq S \leq -2.22) = 0.0109.$$

$X = 2 \rightarrow (1.50 \leq X \leq 2.50)$; then

$$\frac{2.50 - 5.00}{\sqrt{2.5}} \cong -1.58.$$

Hence,

$$P(-2.22 \leq Z \leq -1.58) \cong P(-2.22 \leq S \leq -1.58) = 0.0439.$$

$X = 3 \rightarrow (2.50 \leq X \leq 3.50)$; then

$$\frac{3.50 - 5.00}{\sqrt{2.5}} \cong -0.95.$$

Hence,

$$P(-1.58 \leq Z \leq -0.95) \cong P(-1.58 \leq S \leq -0.95) = 0.1140.$$

$X = 4 \rightarrow (3.50 \leq X \leq 4.50)$; then

$$\frac{4.50 - 5.00}{\sqrt{2.5}} \cong -0.32.$$

Hence,

$$P(-0.95 \leq Z \leq -0.32) \cong P(-0.95 \leq S \leq -0.32) = 0.2034.$$

$X = 5 \rightarrow (4.50 \leq X \leq 5.50)$; then

$$\frac{5.50 - 5.00}{\sqrt{2.5}} \cong +0.32.$$

Hence,

$$P(-0.32 \leq Z \leq 0.32) \cong P(-0.32 \leq S \leq 0.32) = 0.2510.$$

Putting the results together,

x	Binomial probability	Normal approximation
0	0.001	0.0023
1	0.010	0.0109
2	0.044	0.0439
3	0.117	0.1140
4	0.205	0.2034
5	0.246	0.2510
	0.623	0.6255

The sums shown in the table above are the actual and approximate $P(X \leq 5)$.

Apparently the approximation is much better than we might have hoped with $n = 10$. The main reason for the success of this approximation is that the binomial itself is symmetric since $p = 0.5$. We saw in Section 6.2 that as n increases, the binomial distribution begins to approach symmetry since the tails become less important. But with $p = 0.5$ the distribution is *in fact* symmetric for any n and the "approach to normality" is therefore quite rapid.

The foregoing example makes it clear that the normal approximation to the binomial not only becomes more successful the larger n is, but that, for a given n, the approximation is more successful the closer p is to one-half.[12]

6.4 Generalizing the Central Limit Theorem

Up to this point, we have only considered the central limit theorem as it applied to the binomial random variable. The application of the theorem is, however, much wider. Recall that in Chapter 5 we defined the binomial variable as the *sum* of n independent Bernoulli variables, each with the same probability of success. As n increases, then, we simply sum more Bernoulli variables to get the corresponding binomial. This summing of random variables provides the key to a more general view of the central limit theorem.

Let $X_1, X_2, X_3, \ldots, X_n$ be independent random variables with means $\mu_1, \mu_2, \mu_3, \ldots, \mu_n$ respectively and variances $\sigma_1^2, \sigma_2^2, \sigma_3^2, \ldots, \sigma_n^2$ respectively and consider the sum

$$Y_n = \sum_{i=1}^{n} X_i.$$

Then,

$$EY_n = \sum_{i=1}^{n} \mu_i = \bar{\mu}$$

and

$$\text{Variance } Y_n = \sum_{i=1}^{n} \sigma_i^2 = \bar{\sigma}^2.$$

[12]Footnote 1, Chap. 6 is a rule of thumb for successful approximation of binomial probabilities by use of the standard normal variables when $n < 40$. For p near 1/10 or 9/10, n should be near 90 before a normal approximation is used; and for p near 0.05 or 0.95, n should be near 170 if a successful normal approximation is desired.

If we define

$$Z_n = \frac{Y_n - \bar{\mu}}{\bar{\sigma}},$$

we find $EZ_n = 0$ and variance $Z_n = 1$. The generalized central limit theorem than states that under rather general conditions[13] the asymptotic distribution of Z_n is $\eta(0, 1)$. Stated simply, a sum of independent random variables tends to normality as the number of variables in the sum increases.

PROBLEMS

6-1. X is $B(7, 0.3)$. Plot the graphs of X versus $P(X)$ and Y versus $P(Y)$ where $Y = X/\sigma_X$. Does the transformation Y imply a "stretching" or a "squeezing" of the graph of X?

6-2. $Y_n = X_n/\sigma_{X_n}$ where X_n is $B(n, p)$. Given the following table of values for p and n, fill in the blank spaces with the *minimum* values for n or p which will make the graph of Y_n the result of a "squeezing" of the graph of X_n.

p	n
0.10	—
0.15	—
—	20
0.40	—
—	40
—	100
0.08	—

6-3. X is $\eta(0, 1)$. Compute the following probabilities and make a rough sketch with each computation to show the corresponding area of the $\eta(0, 1)$ curve.

(a) $P(X > 0.5)$.
(b) $P(-0.7 < X < 0.7)$.
(c) $P(-1.10 < X < 1.35)$.
(d) $P(0.02 < X < 2.64)$.

[13]These conditions have to do with the X_i. All the variances σ_i^2 should be finite, for example. The conditions are usually stated fully in more advanced texts but involve concepts beyond the scope of this book. Suffice it to say that the conditions would not usually be violated in practical situations.

6-4. Y is $\eta(100, 100)$ and X is $B(50, 0.2)$. Compute the following probabilities:

(a) $P(98 < Y < 102)$.
(b) $P(110 < Y < 120)$.
(c) $P(80.4 < Y < 119.6)$.
(d) $P(X = 5)$.
(e) $P[(X = 10) \cup (X = 11)]$.
(f) $P(2 \leq X \leq 18)$.
(g) $P(15 \leq X \leq 17)$.

6-5. Find a positive number a such that $P[-a < S < a] = 0.95$ when S is distributed

(a) $\eta(0, 1)$.
(b) $\eta(\mu, \sigma^2)$.

6-6. Roll a fair die eight times.

(a) What is the exact probability of getting two 6's? more than two 6's?
(b) What are the probabilities in (a) when the normal approximation is used?

6-7. A coin is tossed 500 times. Approximate

(a) P[at least 230 heads].
(b) $P[220 <$ the number of heads $\leq 270]$.
(c) A number k such that P[at least k heads $= 0.90$].

6-8. A certain process is considered to be out of control if more than 80 in a sample of 1,200 units of its output are defective. If the process is actually producing 5.5% defectives, approximate the probability that the process will be judged out of control on any one sampling.

6-9. Suppose you wish to find the proportion of United States families with incomes between \$5,000 and \$7,500 per year. If you do this by sampling and wish your estimate to be correct within 0.03 units with probability 0.99, how large a sample should you take, given

(a) You know the true proportion is near 0.35?
(b) You have no idea of the true proportion?

6-10. An examination given to a large group of students shows a mean score of 65 and a standard deviation of 10. The instructor wants to give the top 15% a grade of A, the next 20% a grade of B, the middle 30% a grade of C, the next 25% a grade of D, and the lowest 10% a grade of F. What ranges of scores will correspond to each of these letter grades, assuming the numerical scores follow the pattern of a normal curve?

6-11. A coin is flipped 700 times. What is the probability that there will be more than 375 heads if it is known that there are more than 340?

6-12. A process for producing light bulbs is considered out of control if more than 6% of its output is defective. The firm samples 1,500 light bulbs a day and uses a 2σ control plan.

(a) In a given day 108 defectives were found. Is the process out of control?

(b) Construct the portion of this plan's OC curve for actual proportion of defectives ≤ 0.06. Interpret your results.

6-13. A large flashlight is powered by four batteries. Suppose the working life of a battery is a normally distributed random variable with a mean of 100 hours and a variance of 180 hours^{squared}. The four-battery flashlight will cease functioning if one or more of its batteries go dead. Assuming the batteries live independent lives, find the probability that a large flashlight will operate for more than 85 hours.

6-14. A ball bearing is acceptable for use in a certain type of railroad locomotive only if it has a diameter not more than 0.28 inch nor less than 0.20 inch. Every ball bearing produced for use in this type of locomotive is inspected with a measuring device which is accurate to the nearest 0.01 inch. That is, a ball bearing with true diameter between 0.205 and 0.215 inch is measured as having a diameter of 0.21 inch. Assuming that ball bearings with measured diameters of 0.20–0.28 inch, inclusive, pass inspection, find the probability that a ball bearing selected at random will be defective but pass the inspection if the true diameter of a ball bearing is a random variable distributed $\eta(0.2300, 0.0004)$.

6-15. A fair die is cast 60 times. Let X_i be the outcome of the ith trial. What is the probability that the sum of the outcomes (that is, $\sum_{i=1}^{60} X_i$) is

(a) No greater than 200?

(b) No less than 250?

6-16. The probability of hitting the jackpot on a certain Reno slot machine is 0.02. It costs $0.25 to play the machine and, in the event of a jackpot, the payoff is $5.00. Find the probability that, in 2,000 plays, the *machine* will have net earnings of

(a) More than $375.

(b) More than $280.

7 CLASSICAL ESTIMATION THEORY

7.1 Introduction

Many real world-decision problems are intimately bound up with random variables. In Chapter 5 we saw that the decision to continue operating a production process rather than to interrupt it for adjustment depended on the random variable *number of defectives produced*. Similarly, the decision whether or not to accept an order received from a supplier depended on a random variable relating to the characteristics of the received merchandise. In the quality control examples we faced situations in which we recognized the existence and importance of a random variable, but in which all the *characteristics* of the random variable were not known. Specifically, the proportion of defective items (or probability of a defective) was unknown to the decision-maker. If the proportion of defective items in a lot were known to be 0.10, there would be no interest in sampling n items and observing the resulting number of defectives. The lot would simply be rejected if the decision-maker were unwilling to have 10% defective items, and accepted otherwise. Sampling takes on importance precisely when the relevant characteristics of the random variables *cannot* be completely specified in advance. If, on the basis of an OC curve, the decision-maker decides to accept a lot if no more than 2 out of 25 items sampled are defective, then he is indirectly saying that 2 out of 25 defective in the sample is sufficient evidence that the proportion defective in the entire lot is within reason. In other words, sample evidence is being used to infer something about the unknown characteristics of a random variable. The OC curve indicates that such an inference may be incorrect. When 2 out of 25 are defective, the decision-maker may be accepting a lot which contains 10% defective items when he is willing to tolerate only 5% defectives. Alternatively, a lot with only 4% defectives may produce 3 defectives in a sample of 25, in which case rejection of the lot implies the incorrect inference that the lot contains in excess of 5% defectives. Decisions made under conditions of uncertainty always involve the possibility of error. The point of probabilistic analysis is to reveal the nature of the possible errors and to aid in the construction of a process (that is, use of an OC curve to evaluate a sampling plan) which permits some control over, and measurement of, the likelihood of various possible errors.

It is evident, therefore, that it is frequently necessary to use sample evidence to infer something about the characteristics of a random variable. Further, it is highly desirable to know something about the reliability of the inferences arrived at via sample evidence.

7.2 Parameter Estimation, I

In this section we shall introduce the notions of fixed sample estimation and corresponding estimator properties.

Consider the random variable X which has probability distribution D. Suppose further that the distribution D is not known completely. For example, X may be $B(10, p)$ with p unknown; or X may be some random variable with EX known but σ_X^2 unknown.[1] Any *constant* — known or unknown — on which the probability distribution depends is said to be a *parameter* of the distribution. n and p are parameters of the binomial distribution, EX is a parameter of the distribution of X, etc. Note that although X is a random variable, its expected value is a constant[2] and therefore a parameter.

[1]The fact that the variance is unknown means that D is not known completely. For if we knew the entire probability distribution, we could simply calculate

$$\sigma_X^2 = \sum_x (x - EX)^2 p(x).$$

Inability to calculate the variance raises the question of how EX could itself be known. Suppose, however, that X is defined as a change in some phenomenon. It may be known that the average change is zero ($EX = 0$) even if the probability distribution itself is unknown.

[2]The fact that EX is a constant does not mean that its values must be known. The important difference between X and EX is that *the* value of X is determined by a random experiment while the value of EX is the constant

$$EX = \sum_x xP(x)$$

regardless of the outcome of any random experiment.

Let $\mathcal{E}$ be a random experiment with associated random variable X, and $X \in \mathcal{S}$. Further, let θ be a parameter associated with the probability distribution of X. θ may be the mean of X, the mode of X, the probability that X will turn out to be 10, etc., depending on what is of interest for the problem at hand. We assume that the value of θ is unknown. Suppose we carry out two independent replications of the experiment $\mathcal{E}$ and call the results X_1 and X_2 respectively. Since X_1 is the outcome of a random experiment, it is a random variable. Since X_1 is the outcome of $\mathcal{E}$ and X_2 is the outcome of $\mathcal{E}$ performed independently a second time, X_1 and X_2 are independent and identically distributed random variables. In fact, the common distribution of X_1 and X_2 is the same as the distribution of the random variable X which was originally defined with respect to the experiment $\mathcal{E}$. The realized values of X_1 and X_2 are therefore said to be *random observations on* X, and the random variables X_1 and X_2 are said to constitute *a random sample corresponding to* X.[3] Suppose we focus attention on the particular case in which

$$\theta = EX.$$

Let $\hat{\theta}$ be defined by:

$$\hat{\theta} = \frac{X_1 + X_2}{2}.$$

$\hat{\theta}$ is thus defined as the average of the random variables X_1 and X_2, and it is clearly a random variable itself. That $\hat{\theta}$ is a random variable can be proven by the following argument. X is the outcome of $\mathcal{E}$ and suppose

$$X \in \mathcal{S} = \{x_1, x_2, \ldots, x_T\}.$$

It is clear then that

$$X_1 \in \mathcal{S} = \{x_1, x_2, \ldots, x_T\} \quad \text{and} \quad X_2 \in \mathcal{S} = \{x_1, x_2, \ldots, x_T\}.$$

Performing $\mathcal{E}$ twice can be looked upon as the compound experiment $\mathcal{E} \times \mathcal{E}$ with sample space

$$\mathcal{S} \times \mathcal{S} = \{(x_i, x_j) \mid x_i \in \mathcal{S} \quad \text{and} \quad x_j \in \mathcal{S}\}.$$

$\hat{\theta}$ is then defined as the random variable with sample space

$$\left\{\frac{x_i + x_j}{2} \,\middle|\, (x_i, x_j) \in \mathcal{S} \times \mathcal{S}\right\}.$$

[3]Note that the *random sample* is the set of independent and identically distributed random variables $\{X_1, X_2\}$, while the *random observations* are the respective realizations of X_1 and X_2.

EXAMPLE 7.2.1. Suppose X is a random variable with probability distribution

x	$P(x)$
1	0.40
2	0.20
3	0.40
	1.00

If $\mathcal{E}$ is the random experiment which results in X,

(a) Determine the Cartesian product sample space for the random sample X_1, X_2.

(b) Determine the sample space for the random variable $\hat{\theta} = (X_1 + X_2)/2$.

Solution:

(a) From the probability distribution above, it is clear that $X \in \mathcal{S} = \{1, 2, 3\}$. Since the random sample X_1, X_2 can be viewed as the result of the compound experiment $\mathcal{E} \times \mathcal{E}$, the corresponding sample space is

$$\mathcal{S} \times \mathcal{S} = \{(1, 1), (1, 2), (1, 3), (2, 1), (2, 2), (2, 3), (3, 1), (3, 2), (3, 3)\}.$$

(b) The sample space for $\hat{\theta}$ results from averaging the elements of each ordered pair in $\mathcal{S} \times \mathcal{S}$. Thus

Ordered pair	Average
(1, 1)	$\frac{1+1}{2} = 1$
(1, 2)	= 1.5
(1, 3)	= 2
(2, 1)	= 1.5
(2, 2)	= 2
(2, 3)	= 2.5
(3, 1)	= 2
(3, 2)	= 2.5
(3, 3)	= 3

Hence,

$$\hat{\theta} \in \{1, 1.5, 2, 2.5, 3\}.$$

EXAMPLE 7.2.2. Calculate the probability distribution and the expected value of the $\hat{\theta}$ defined in Example 7.2.1.

Solution: Since X_1 and X_2 are independent and distributed as X, the probability of any ordered pair from $\mathcal{S} \times \mathcal{S}$ is easily found by

$$\begin{aligned} P(x_i, x_j) &= P(x_i)P(x_j) \\ &= P(X_1 = x_i)\cdot P(X_2 = x_j). \end{aligned}$$

For example, the ordered pair (1, 2) results in

$$\begin{aligned} P(1, 2) &= P(X_1 = 1)P(X_2 = 2) \\ &= (0.40)(0.20) \\ &= 0.080. \end{aligned}$$

We therefore find

Ordered pair	Probability
(1, 1)	0.160
(1, 2)	0.080
(1, 3)	0.160
(2, 1)	0.080
(2, 2)	0.040
(2, 3)	0.080
(3, 1)	0.160
(3, 2)	0.080
(3, 3)	0.160
	1.000

Finally, putting the latter results together with those of Example 7.2.1, (b), the probability distribution of $\hat{\theta}$ is seen to be

$$D_{\hat{\theta}} = \{(1, 0.160), (1.5, 0.160), (2, 0.360), (2.5, 0.160), (3, 0.160)\}.$$

From the probability distribution above,

$$\begin{aligned} E_{\hat{\theta}} &= 1(0.160) + 1.5(0.160) + 2(0.360) + 2.5(0.160) + 3(0.160) \\ &= 2. \end{aligned}$$

The point of the examples above has been to demonstrate that any function of the random variables composing a random sample is itself a random variable. Suppose now that it is desired to estimate the unknown expected value of a random variable X and it is possible to obtain a random sample corresponding to X, say $X_1, X_2, X_3, \ldots, X_N$.[4] Recalling that EX is the

[4]That is to say, the random experiment which results in X can be carried out N times independently.

average of a theoretical sequence of observations on X, the natural step in attempting to estimate EX is to define the random variable $\overline{X}$, where

$$\overline{X} = \frac{X_1 + X_2 + X_3 + \cdots + X_N}{N} = \frac{1}{N}\sum_{i=1}^{N} X_i,$$

and call $\overline{X}$ an *estimator* of EX. We thus use a random variable as an estimator of a constant. Since $\overline{X}$ is a random variable, it can take on many possible values. If there is a high probability that $\overline{X}$ will be close to EX, then $\overline{X}$ will be a successful estimator of EX. In Examples 7.2.1 and 7.2.2, we calculated the probability distribution of $\hat{\theta}$, which is simply $\overline{X}$ for $N = 2$; that is,

$$\overline{X} = \hat{\theta} = \frac{X_1 + X_2}{2}.$$

Recalling that X has probability distribution

x	P(x)
1	0.40
2	0.20
3	0.40

it is clear that $EX = 2$. Further, it was shown in Example 7.2.2 that

$$E\overline{X} = 2;$$

hence

$$E\overline{X} = EX.$$

The distribution of $\overline{X}$ can be seen plotted as Figure 7.1b. The distribution of X itself is plotted as Figure 7.1a. Comparison of Figures 7.1a and 7.1b reveals that while a realization of X has high probability of being far from $EX = 2$, it is far less likely that a realization of $\overline{X}$ will be as far from $E\overline{X} = EX = 2$. Specifically, for example,

$$P(X - EX > 1.5) = P(X = 3) = 0.4,$$

while

$$P(\overline{X} - EX > 1.5) = P(\overline{X} = 3) = 0.160.$$

The difference is even more pronounced if we consider Figure 7.1c, which displays the probability distribution of $\overline{X}$ for $N = 4$. In this case we find

$$\begin{aligned} P(\overline{X} - EX > 1.5) &= P(\overline{X} = 2.75) + P(\overline{X} = 3) \\ &= 0.0512 + 0.0256 = 0.0768. \end{aligned}$$

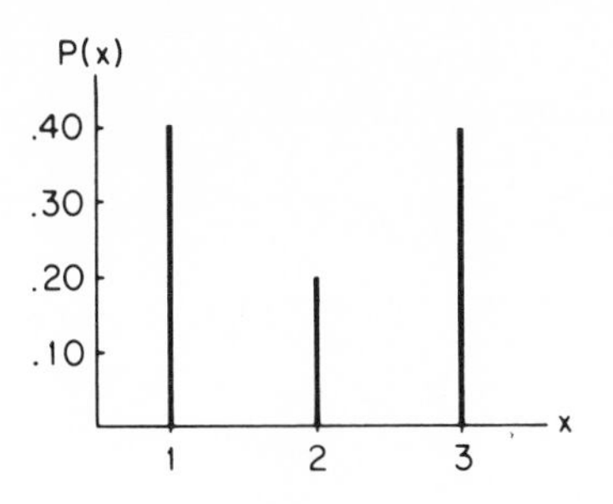

FIGURE 7.1a

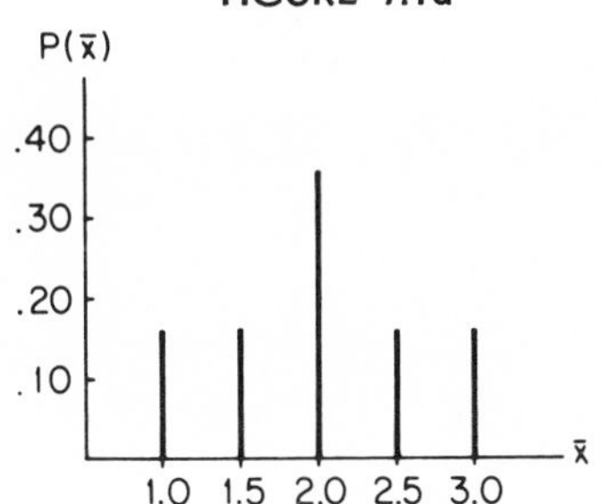

FIGURE 7.1b

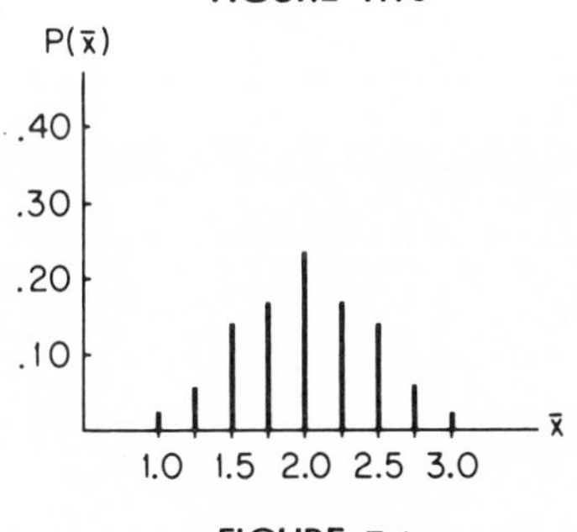

FIGURE 7.1c

All the visual impressions one receives from Figures 7.1a to 7.1c about the distribution to X relative to that of $\overline{X}$ and about the distributions of $\overline{X}$ for successively larger sample sizes are in general quite correct. We formalize these impressions in the following theorem. Since $\overline{X}$ is the "sample mean," we shall refer to

THE SAMPLE MEAN THEOREM. Let X be a random variable with variance σ_X^2 and (unknown) expected value $\mu = EX$. Let $X_1, X_2, X_3, \ldots, X_N$ be a random sample of size N corresponding to X. Define the sample mean random variable $\overline{X}$ as

$$\overline{X} = \frac{1}{N}\sum_{i=1}^{N} X_i.$$

Then

(a) $E\overline{X} = \mu$.

(b) Variance $\bar{X} = \sigma_{\bar{X}}^2 = \sigma_X^2/N$

(c) The random variable Z_N, where

$$Z_N = \frac{\overline{X} - \mu}{\sigma_{\overline{X}}}$$

is asymptotically $\eta(0, 1)$.[5]

Proof of (a):

$$\overline{X} = \frac{1}{N}(X_1 + X_2 + X_3 + \cdots + X_N),$$

$$E\overline{X} = E\left\{\frac{1}{N}(X_1 + X_2 + X_3 + \cdots + X_N)\right\},$$

$$= \frac{1}{N}E(X_1 + X_2 + X_3 + \cdots + X_N)$$

$$= \frac{1}{N}(EX_1 + EX_2 + EX_3 + \cdots + EX_N).$$

But the X_i are all distributed identically as X; hence

$$EX_i = EX = \mu \quad (i = 1, 2, \ldots, N).$$

Thus

$$E\overline{X} = \frac{1}{N}(\mu + \mu + \mu + \cdots + \mu)$$

$$= \frac{1}{N}(N\mu) = \mu. \qquad \text{Q.E.D.}$$

Proof of (b):

$$\overline{X} = \frac{1}{N}(X_1 + X_2 + X_3 + \cdots + X_N),$$

$$\text{Var}\,\overline{X} = \text{Var}\left\{\frac{1}{N}(X_1 + X_2 + X_3 + \cdots + X_N)\right\}$$

$$= \frac{1}{N^2}\text{Var}\,(X_1 + X_2 + X_3 + \cdots + X_N).$$

[5]There are pathological cases where (*c*) of the theorem does not hold. If EX and σ_X^2 are finite, the theorem is true and this covers the overwhelming majority of situations encountered in practice.

The last step follows from the fact that N is a constant, not a random variable. Further, the X_i are not only distributed identically as X so that

$$\text{Var } X_i = \text{Var } X = \sigma_X^2 \quad (i = 1, 2, \ldots, N),$$

but the X_i are also mutually independent. Thus

$$\begin{aligned}\text{Var } \overline{X} &= \frac{1}{N^2}(\text{Var } X_1 + \text{Var } X_2 + \text{Var } X_3 + \cdots + \text{Var } X_N)\\ &= \frac{1}{N^2}(\sigma_X^2 + \sigma_X^2 + \sigma_X^2 + \cdots + \sigma_X^2)\\ &= \frac{1}{N^2}(N\sigma_X^2) = \frac{1}{N}\sigma_X^2. \qquad \text{Q.E.D.}\end{aligned}$$

Comment on (a) *and* (b): (a) of the theorem indicates that regardless of the size of the sample, $E\overline{X} = \mu$. (b), however, indicates that as N increases the variance of $\overline{X}$ diminishes. Recalling Chebyschev's inequality, this means that as the sample size increases the probability that $\overline{X}$ will differ much from $E\overline{X} = \mu$ gets smaller and smaller. The variance of $\overline{X}$ can thus be taken as an indicator of the reliability of $\overline{X}$ as an estimator of μ. This notion of reliability of an estimator is often referred to as the *efficiency* of the estimator. We find then that the efficiency of $\overline{X}$ as an estimator of μ increases ($\sigma_{\overline{X}}^2$ decreases) as N increases. A sample of size $N = 20$ therefore produces a more efficient estimator of μ than a sample of size $N = 15$, in the sense of having higher probability of $\overline{X}$ being close to μ.

Proof of (c): A direct proof of the asymptotic normality of Z_N is quite beyond the level of this text. Recalling, however, the central limit theorem of Chapter 6, it is clear that the asymptotic normality of Z_N is merely a special case of the result given there.

Further comments on the theorem: It is useful to have an intuitive understanding of this important theorem which is basic to all sampling theory. Among other things, the sample mean theorem says that while it may be highly likely that a realization of X will differ substantially from EX, it is far less likely that a realization of $\overline{X}$ will differ as much from $E\overline{X}$ $(= EX)$. Suppose, for example, that

$$X \in \{1, 3, 5, 7, 9\}$$

and each of these events is equally likely. The probability is therefore $\frac{1}{5}$ that X will turn out to be four units below $EX = 5$. If we think about

$$\overline{X} = \frac{1}{N}\sum X_i,$$

however, it is clear that the *only* way $\overline{X}$ can be four units below $E\overline{X} = EX = 5$ is to have $X_1 = 1, X_2 = 1, X_3 = 1, \ldots, X_N = 1$, for only then will the realization of $\overline{X}$ be equal to unity. But this will occur with probability

$$P(\bar{X} = 1) = (\tfrac{1}{5})^N.$$

Even for $N = 4$, this turns out to be as low as 0.0016. $\overline{X}$ cannot be much below the mean unless the set of random observations is dominated by extreme realizations *all* below the mean. Similarly, $\overline{X}$ cannot be much above the mean unless the set of random observations is dominated by extreme realizations *all* above the mean. Such one-sided domination may not be too unlikely for small values of N, but it would be extremely rare even for moderate values of N.

Part (a) of the sample mean theorem defines an important property of $\overline{X}$, namely that $\overline{X}$ is an *unbiased* estimator of EX. In general, the property of unbiasedness is defined as follows:

DEFINITION. Let θ be a parameter of the distribution of the random variable X. Let $X_1, X_2, \ldots, X_N$ be a random sample corresponding to X, and let $\hat{\theta}_N$ be a function of $X_1, X_2, \ldots, X_N$, say $\hat{\theta}_N = f(X_1, X_2, \ldots, X_N)$, which is to be used as an estimator of θ. If

$$E\hat{\theta}_N = \theta,$$

then $\hat{\theta}_N$ is said to be an unbiased estimator of θ.

We can get some idea of the meaning of bias in an estimator by considering another parameter, namely the variance of X. Suppose that the variance of X is unknown. How can the random sample $X_1, X_2, \ldots, X_N$ be used to estimate σ_X^2? We know that

$$\sigma_X^2 = E[(X - EX)^2];$$

that is, the variance is the average squared discrepancy between X and EX. It seems logical to use

$$\frac{1}{N}\sum_{i=1}^{N}(X_i - EX)^2$$

as an estimator of σ_X^2. Let us call this estimator T^2 and determine whether it is unbiased.

$$T^2 = \frac{1}{N}\sum_{i=1}^{N}(X_i - EX)^2,$$

$$ET^2 = E\left[\frac{1}{N}\sum (X_i - EX)^2\right]$$

$$= \frac{1}{N}E\sum (X_i - EX)^2$$

$$= \frac{1}{N}\sum E(X_i - EX)^2.$$

But

$$E(X_i - EX)^2 = \sigma_{X_i}^2 = \sigma_X^2$$

since the X_i are all distributed identically as X.

Hence,

$$ET^2 = \frac{1}{N}\sum_{i=1}^{N} \sigma_X^2$$

$$= \frac{1}{N}(N\sigma_X^2) = \sigma_X^2.$$

Thus, T^2 is indeed an unbiased estimator of σ_X^2. Unfortunately, our search for an unbiased estimator of σ_X^2 cannot really end here. Suppose EX is itself unknown. Then even though T^2 is an unbiased estimator of σ_X^2, it is of little use for we would be unable to calculate realizations of T^2 without knowing EX. We can, however, use the sample $X_1, X_2, \ldots, X_N$ first to estimate EX and then consider the following as an estimator of σ_X^2:

$$(s^*)^2 = \frac{1}{N}\sum_{i=1}^{N} (X_i - \overline{X})^2,$$

where

$$\overline{X} = \frac{1}{N}\sum X_i.$$

Clearly, in order to determine whether $(s^*)^2$ is unbiased, we shall have to consider a term such as $E(X_i - \overline{X})^2$ which is not the same as $E(X_i - EX)^2$ and may therefore not be equal to σ_X^2. Now, it is obviously true by definition that

$$X_i - \overline{X} = (X_i - EX) - (\overline{X} - EX).$$

Hence,

$$(X_i - \overline{X})^2 = (X_i - EX)^2 + (\overline{X} - EX)^2 - 2(X_i - EX)(\overline{X} - EX),$$

and

$$\sum_i (X_i - \overline{X})^2 = \sum_i (X_i - EX)^2 + \sum_i (\overline{X} - EX)^2 - 2\sum_i (X_i - EX)(\overline{X} - EX).$$

Consider the last term in the sum:

$$\begin{aligned} -2\sum_i (X_i - EX)(\overline{X} - EX) &= -2[(X_1 - EX)(\overline{X} - EX) + (X_2 - EX)(\overline{X} - EX) + \cdots \\ &\quad + (X_N - EX)(\overline{X} - EX)] \\ &= -2(\overline{X} - EX)[(X_1 - EX) + (E_2 - EX) + \cdots + (X_N - EX)] \end{aligned}$$

$$= -2(\overline{X} - EX)[(X_1 + X_2 + \cdots + X_N) - (EX + EX + \cdots + EX)]$$
$$= -2(\overline{X} - EX)[(\sum X_i) - N(EX)]$$
$$= -2(\overline{X} - EX)\left[N\left(\frac{\sum X_i}{N}\right) - N(EX)\right]$$
$$= -2(\overline{X} - EX)[N\overline{X} - N(EX)]$$
$$= -2(\overline{X} - EX)[N(\overline{X} - EX)]$$
$$= -2N(\overline{X} - EX)^2.$$

Therefore,

$$\sum_i (X_i - \overline{X})^2 = \sum_i (X_i - EX)^2 + \sum_i (\overline{X} - EX)^2 - 2N(\overline{X} - EX)^2$$
$$= \sum_i (X_i - EX)^2 + N(\overline{X} - EX)^2 - 2N(\overline{X} - EX)^2$$
$$= \sum_i (X_i - EX)^2 - N(\overline{X} - EX)^2,$$

since

$$N(\overline{X} - EX)^2 - 2N(\overline{X} - EX)^2 = (N - 2N)(\overline{X} - EX)^2$$
$$= -N(\bar{X} - EX)^2.$$

Now,

$$(s^*)^2 = \frac{1}{N}\sum (X_i - \overline{X})^2 = \frac{1}{N}[\sum (X_i - EX)^2 - N(\overline{X} - EX)^2].$$

Recalling that

$$E\sum (X_i - EX)^2$$

has been shown to be equal to $N\sigma_X^2$, we find

$$E(s^*)^2 = \frac{1}{N}[E\sum (X_i - EX)^2 - NE(\overline{X} - EX)^2]$$
$$= \frac{1}{N}[N\sigma_X^2 - NE(\overline{X} - EX)^2]$$
$$= \sigma_X^2 - E(\overline{X} - EX)^2.$$

The last line follows from cancellation of the N's in the previous line. According to the sample mean theorem, $E\overline{X} = EX$; consequently

$$E(s^*)^2 = \sigma_X^2 - E(\overline{X} - EX)^2$$
$$= \sigma_X^2 - E(\overline{X} - E\overline{X})^2,$$

but by definition $E(\overline{X} - E\overline{X})^2 = \sigma_{\overline{X}}^2$ and by the sample mean theorem $\sigma_{\overline{X}}^2 = \sigma_X^2/N$; hence

$$E(s^*)^2 = \sigma_X^2 - E(\overline{X} - E\overline{X})^2$$
$$= \sigma_X^2 - \sigma_{\overline{X}}^2$$

$$= \sigma_X^2 - \frac{\sigma_X^2}{N}$$

$$= \sigma_X^2\left(1 - \frac{1}{N}\right)$$

$$= \sigma_X^2\left(\frac{N-1}{N}\right) \neq \sigma_X^2.$$

We conclude therefore that $(s^*)^2$ is a *biased* estimator of σ_X^2. On the average, $(s^*)^2$ underestimates $[(N-1)/N < 1]$ the variance of X. If $N = 100$, the bias is relatively unimportant for then $E(s^*)^2 = \sigma_X^2(\frac{99}{100}) = 0.99\sigma_X^2$. For a sample of size $N = 10$, however, the underestimate averages 10% of σ_X^2; that is,

$$E(s^*)^2 = 0.90\sigma_X^2.$$

There is no difficulty, though, in defining an unbiased estimator of σ_X^2. Consider s^2, defined by

$$s^2 = \frac{N}{N-1}(s^*)^2,$$

$$Es^2 = \frac{N}{N-1}E(s^*)^2$$

$$= \frac{N}{N-1}\sigma_X^2\left(\frac{N-1}{N}\right)$$

$$= \sigma_X^2.$$

But

$$s^2 = \frac{N}{N-1}(s^*)^2$$

$$= \frac{N}{N-1} \cdot \frac{1}{N}\sum_i (X_i - \overline{X})^2$$

$$= \frac{1}{N-1}\sum_i (X_i - \overline{X})^2.$$

Thus, the sum of the squared deviations from the sample mean divided by $(N-1)$[6] instead of N provides an unbiased estimator of σ_X^2. The random variable s^2 is known as the *sample variance*.

We have already commented that $\sigma_{\overline{X}}^2$, the variance of $\overline{X}$, is a measure of the efficiency of $\overline{X}$ as an estimator of EX. Since $\sigma_{\overline{X}}^2 = \sigma_X^2/N$, we are unable to measure the efficiency of $\overline{X}$ if σ_X^2 is unknown. An important question

[6]The number $(N-1)$ is termed the *degrees-of-freedom* of the sample variance s^2. In the sample $X_1, X_2, \ldots, X_N$, we start out with N degrees of freedom. Heuristically, we can regard $(N-1)$ as the degrees of freedom remaining for the estimation of σ_X^2 after the sample has already been used once to determine an estimator of EX.

which occurs is whether it would be possible to estimate the efficiency of $\overline{X}$; that is, can we estimate $\sigma_{\overline{X}}^2$? An obvious choice as an estimator of $\sigma_{\overline{X}}^2$ would be $s_{\overline{X}}^2$, defined by

$$s_{\overline{X}}^2 = \frac{s^2}{N}.$$

Then,

$$E s_{\overline{X}}^2 = E \frac{1}{N} s^2$$

$$= \frac{1}{N} E s^2.$$

But s^2 is an unbiased estimator of σ_X^2; hence

$$E s_{\overline{X}}^2 = \frac{1}{N} E s^2$$

$$= \frac{1}{N} \sigma_X^2$$

$$= \sigma_{\overline{X}}^2.$$

The sample mean $\overline{X}$ is therefore an unbiased estimator of EX and $s_{\overline{X}}^2 = s^2/N$ is an unbiased estimator of the efficiency of $\overline{X}$. Part (c) of the sample mean theorem can also be modified to read

$$Z_N^* = \frac{\overline{X} - EX}{s_{\overline{X}}} \quad \text{is asymptotically } \eta(0, 1),$$

where

$$s_{\overline{X}} = \sqrt{\frac{s^2}{N}} = \frac{s}{\sqrt{N}}.$$

We would of course regard s as an estimator of σ_X and $s_{\overline{X}}$ as an estimator of $\sigma_{\overline{X}} = \sqrt{\sigma_{\overline{X}}^2}$. Note, however, that s is *not* an unbiased estimator of σ_X.[7]

[7]While it is true that

$$E s^2 = \sigma_X^2,$$

it is simply *not* true that the expected value of s is equal to the square root of the expected value of s^2, that is,

$$E s = E \sqrt{\frac{1}{N-1} \sum (X_i - \overline{X})^2} \neq \sqrt{E \frac{1}{N-1} \sum (X_i - \overline{X})^2}.$$

EXAMPLE 7.2.3.

(a) Using the table of random numbers,[8] Table B in the back of the book, generate 10 samples, each of size $N = 5$, for the random variable

$$X \in \{0, 1, 2, 3, \ldots, 9\}$$

with equally likely elementary events. Calculate the resulting 10 realizations each of $\overline{X}$, $(s^*)^2$, and s^2.

(b) Average all the $\overline{X}$'s and compare this with EX. Average the $(s^*)^2$'s and s^2's (separately) and compare these with σ_X^2.

Solution to (a): The top row of Table B produces the following 10 samples, each of size $N = 5$. The 10 sample means are also shown along with $(s^*)^2$ and s^2.

TABLE 7-1

	Sample number									
	1	2	3	4	5	6	7	8	9	10
Observations	0	1	9	1	9	7	3	7	8	2
	3	0	3	6	8	3	9	2	2	5
	9	4	7	8	9	2	5	4	4	5
	9	6	1	9	5	3	2	8	7	9
	1	1	6	4	3	1	8	4	4	3
$\overline{X}$	4.40	2.40	5.20	5.60	6.80	3.20	5.40	5.00	5.00	4.80
$(s^*)^2$	15.04	5.04	8.16	8.24	5.76	4.16	7.44	4.80	4.80	5.76
s^2	18.80	6.30	10.20	10.30	7.20	5.20	9.30	6.00	6.00	7.20

[8]Suppose you had a 10-sided fair die with the faces numbered 0, 1, 2, . . . , 9. If you rolled the die 100 times and noted the result each time, you would have a table of 100 *random numbers*. Table B contains 2,500 random numbers and results from an electronic computer simulating the roll of a 10-sided fair die. The numbers in Table B therefore comprise a random ordering of observations on the random variable X defined in Example 7.2.3.

We illustrate the entire calculation[9] for sample No. 8:

x_i for No. 8	$x_i - \overline{X}$	$(x_i - \overline{X})^2$
7	2	4
2	−3	9
4	−1	1
8	3	9
4	−1	1
$\Sigma x_i = 25$		$\Sigma (x_i - \overline{X})^2 = 24,$
Therefore $\overline{X} = \frac{25}{5} = 5.00.$		$(s^*)^2 = \frac{24}{5} = 4.80,$
		$s^2 = \frac{24}{4} = 6.00.$

Solution to (b): Given the distribution of X, the reader should be able to show that $EX = 4.50$ and $\sigma_X^2 = 8.25$. Summing each of the last three rows in Table 7-1,

$\overline{X}$	$(s^*)^2$	s^2
4.40	15.04	18.80
2.40	5.04	6.30
5.20	8.16	10.20
5.60	8.24	10.30
6.80	5.76	7.20
3.20	4.16	5.20
5.40	7.44	9.30
5.00	4.80	6.00
5.00	4.80	6.00
4.80	5.76	7.20
47.80	69.20	86.50

we find

$$\overline{\overline{X}} = \tfrac{1}{10}\sum \overline{X} = 4.78,$$

$$\overline{(s^*)^2} = \tfrac{1}{10}\sum (s^*)^2 = 6.92,$$

$$s^2 = \tfrac{1}{10}\sum s^2 = 8.65.$$

[9]The sample variance can be calculated by its definition; or use may be made of a more efficient computing formula for

$$\sum (x_i - \overline{X})^2.$$

Namely,

$$\sum (x_i - \overline{X})^2 = \sum x_i^2 - \frac{(\sum x_i)^2}{N}.$$

The reader should be able to derive the relation above.

The 10 different $\bar{X}$ values, which are realizations of the random variable $\bar{X}$, clearly vary around $EX = 4.50$. Note that while the X realizations are frequently ≤ 2 or ≥ 7, the $\bar{X}$ values range only from 2.4 to 6.8. Further, while $P(3 \leq X \leq 6) = \frac{4}{10}$, fully 8 out of 10 $\bar{X}$ values are between 3 and 6. The average of the $\bar{X}$ values, $\bar{\bar{X}}$, is 4.78, which is close to $EX = 4.50$.

The variance of X is $\sigma_X^2 = 8.25$ and both the $(s^*)^2$ and s^2 realizations vary around 8.25. There is, however, a difference. s^2 is an unbiased estimator of σ_X^2, while $(s^*)^2$ is biased downward. Consequently, the $(s^*)^2$ realizations tend to fall short of 8.25 with greater frequency than the s^2 realizations. Thus 9 of the $(s^*)^2$ realizations are below 8.25 while only 6 of the s^2 realizations are below 8.25. The result is that the average of the $(s^*)^2$ realizations is 6.92, considerably below $\sigma_X^2 = 8.25$, which is what we would expect. The s^2 values, on the other hand, average 8.65, which is fairly close to σ_X^2.[10]

In this section we have posed two problems of estimation; namely, how would one use a random sample to estimate the mean and variance of a random variable. We found that the true mean,

$$\mu = EX,$$

[10]The average of 10 realizations of a random variable need not, of course, be equal to the expected value of the random variable. The expected value of $(s^*)^2$ is

$$\begin{aligned} E(s^*)^2 &= \frac{N-1}{N}\,\sigma_X^2 \\ &= \tfrac{4}{5}\,\sigma_X^2 \\ &= (0.8)\,(8.25) = 6.60, \end{aligned}$$

while

$$Es^2 = \sigma_X^2 = 8.25$$

and

$$E\bar{X} = EX = 4.50.$$

Thus, in *these particular sets* of 10 realizations each for $\bar{X}$, $(s^*)^2$, and s^2, the corresponding averages $\bar{\bar{X}}$, $\overline{(s^*)^2}$, and $\overline{s^2}$ *all* turned out greater than would have been expected. Nonetheless $\bar{\bar{X}}$ and $\overline{s^2}$ come close to $E\bar{X}$ and Es^2 respectively while $\overline{(s^*)^2}$ was substantially below σ_X^2.

It is particularly important to realize that the 50 numbers taken from Table B are realizations of the random variable X. The 10 calculated $\bar{X}$ values are realizations of the random variable $\bar{X}$. The 10 calculated s^2 values are realizations of the random variable s^2. The average of the s^2 values is therefore an estimate of Es^2, and so on. Hence we conclude with 10 samples of size 5 corresponding to the random variable X; 1 sample of size 10 corresponding to the random variable $\bar{X}$; 1 sample of size 10 corresponding to the random variable s^2; and so on.

could be estimated by the sample mean,

$$\overline{X} = \frac{1}{N}\sum_i X_i.$$

The true mean is the average of a *theoretical sequence,* while $\bar{X}$ is the average of a *random sample.* We found further that $\bar{X}$ had certain stochastic properties which were desirable. As an estimator of EX, $\bar{X}$ is unbiased for any size sample, N, and its efficiency increases as N increases.[11]

In order to estimate the variance of X,

$$\sigma_X^2 = E[(X - EX)^2],$$

we initially guessed at

$$(s^*)^2 = \frac{1}{N}\sum_i (X_i - \bar{X})^2.$$

While σ_X^2 is the average squared deviation in a *theoretical sequence,* $(s^*)^2$ is the average squared deviation in a *random sample.* We found, however, that $(s^*)^2$ did not provide an unbiased estimator of σ^2. Rather, the sample variance,

$$s^2 = \frac{1}{N-1}\sum_i (X_i - \bar{X})^2,$$

which is a simple modification of $(s^*)^2$, did provide an unbiased estimator of σ_X^2. We saw directly that the bias introduced by using $(s^*)^2$ would be serious only for small sample sizes, for

$$E(s^*)^2 = \frac{N-1}{N}\sigma_{\bar{X}}^2$$

so that as N increases, $(N - 1)/N$ approaches unity and the bias therefore approaches zero. Although we have not shown it directly, it is true that s^2 and $(s^*)^2$ both increase in efficiency as N increases. We know that $Es^2 = \sigma_X^2$ regardless of the size of the sample. The probability distribution of s^2 is therefore "centered" on σ_X^2. Yet as N increases, the variance of the random variable s^2 diminishes, so that the probability that s^2 will be "far" from σ_X^2 decreases. This is portrayed in Figure 7.2, which illustrates that $Es^2 = \sigma_X^2$ regardless of N, but that as N increases, the probability of a large discrepancy between s^2 and σ_X^2 diminishes. With $(s^*)^2$ two results occur as N in-

[11]It can be shown by more advanced methods that $\overline{X}$ is the most efficient unbiased estimator of EX. That is, any other estimator which is a linear function of the elements of the random sample $X_1, X_2, \ldots, X_N$ and an unbiased estimator of EX will have a variance which is greater than $\sigma_{\bar{X}}^2$.

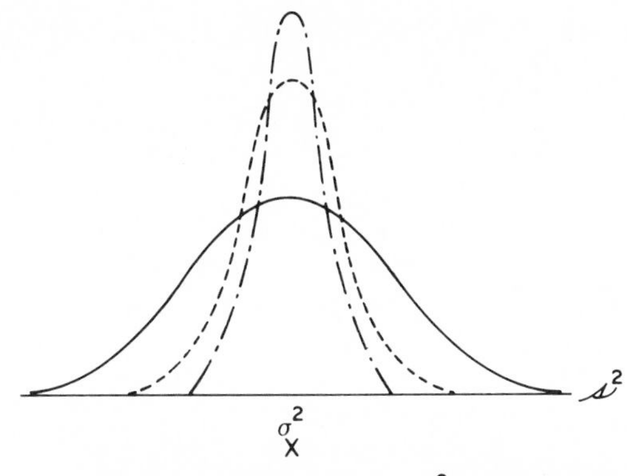

FIGURE 7.2

creases. For small N, the expected value of $(s^*)^2$ is quite far from σ_X^2; as N increases, this bias diminishes. In addition, the variance of $(s^*)^2$ declines as N increases so that the probability of a large discrepancy between $(s^*)^2$ and σ_X^2 also diminishes. If, therefore, a large sample is available, it matters little whether one uses $(s^*)^2$ or s^2 to estimate σ_X^2, for the bias involved with $(s^*)^2$ is negligible and $(s^*)^2$ and s^2 are of comparable efficiency.

The question now remaining is whether we found useful estimators of EX and σ_X^2 merely "by luck," or whether the method we used to find estimators of EX and σ_X^2 illustrates a general principle which will be of use in other estimation problems. Fortunately, the latter is indeed the case, and we shall formalize the principle in the next section.

7.3 Parameter Estimation, II

Briefly, to estimate the mean and variance of the random variable X, we began by considering the mean and variance of a random sample $X_1, X_2, \ldots, X_N$ corresponding to X. More formally, suppose it is desired to estimate $E(X^k)$, where k is a positive constant. Since $E(X^k)$ is the average value of X^k in a *theoretical sequence*, we shall use the corresponding average in a *random sample* as the estimator. Thus the parameter $E(X^k)$ would be estimated by the random variable

$$\frac{1}{N}\sum_i X_i^k = \overline{(X^k)}.$$

The following table illustrates the principle for several values of k:

Parameter	Estimator based on $X_1, X_2, \ldots, X_N$
EX	$\frac{1}{N}\sum_i X_i = \overline{X}$
$E(X^2)$	$\frac{1}{N}\sum_i (X_i^2) = \overline{(X^2)}$
$E(X^3)$	$\frac{1}{N}\sum_i (X_i^3) = \overline{(X^3)}$
$E(X^{10})$	$\frac{1}{N}\sum_i (X_i^{10}) = \overline{(X^{10})}$

This method of estimation, known as the *method of moments*[12] or the *analogue method*, frequently provides estimators with desirable stochastic properties. It is obvious that this principle was employed directly to yield our estimator of EX. Let us now use the method of moments to estimate the variance of X. Recall first that

$$\sigma_X^2 = E[(X - EX)^2] = EX^2 - (EX)^2.$$

According to the method of moments, EX^2 should be estimated by

$$\frac{1}{N}\sum_i X_i^2.$$

and EX should be estimated by

$$\frac{1}{N}\sum_i X_i,$$

Consequently, a method of moments estimator of σ_X^2 would be, say M^2 where

$$\begin{aligned} M^2 &= \frac{1}{N}\sum X_i^2 - \left(\frac{1}{N}\sum X_i\right)^2 \\ &= \frac{1}{N}\sum X_i^2 - \frac{1}{N^2}\left(\sum X_i\right)^2 \\ &= \frac{1}{N}\left[\sum X_i^2 - \frac{(\sum X_i)^2}{N}\right]. \end{aligned}$$

It can easily be shown,[13] however, that

$$\sum (X_i - \overline{X})^2 = \sum X_i^2 - \frac{(\sum X_i)^2}{N}.$$

[12]This estimation method is due to Karl Pearson.
[13]See Footnote 9 p. 190.

Consequently,

$$M^2 = \frac{1}{N}\left[\sum X_i^2 - \frac{(\sum X_i)^2}{N}\right]$$
$$= \frac{1}{N}\sum (X_i - \overline{X})^2$$
$$= (s^*)^2.$$

The estimator $(s^*)^2$ is thus seen to be a methods of moments estimator of the variance σ_X^2. Since we know that

$$E(s^*)^2 \neq \sigma_X^2,$$

it is clear that the method of moments procedure does not always provide unbiased estimators. Yet use of the method of moments procedure will nearly always result in estimators which increase in efficiency [precisely as in the case of $(s^*)^2$] as N increases.[14] Further, if the method of moments estimator is biased, the bias generally becomes negligible as N increases. Finally, consideration of the method of moments estimator often points the way to an unbiased estimator with an efficiency property similar to that of the method of moments estimator.

Apparently, then, if one can obtain a large enough sample, the method of moments procedure is an attractive device for obtaining estimators which are reasonably efficient and are either unbiased or nearly so. The practical question is how large a sample is large enough. There is no unambiguous answer to this question but — as so often happens — Chebyschev's inequality provides some insight.

Suppose we use the method of moments procedure to estimate $E(X)$. The estimator is

$$\overline{X} = \frac{1}{N}\sum_i X_i.$$

Chebyschev's inequality states that

$$P(|\overline{X} - E\overline{X}| \geq \delta] \leq \frac{\text{Var }(\overline{X})}{\delta^2},$$

where δ is positive but may be as close to zero as one wishes. Since

$$E\overline{X} = EX \quad \text{and} \quad \text{Var }(\overline{X}) = \sigma_{\overline{X}}^2 = \frac{\sigma_X^2}{N},$$

the inequality above becomes

$$P[|\overline{X} - EX| \geq \delta] \leq \frac{1}{N}\frac{\sigma_X^2}{\delta^2}.$$

[14]In general, the method of moments estimator of $E(X^k)$ increases in efficiency as N increases if $E\ (X^{2k})$ is not infinite. Since the majority of practical applications involve estimating EX and $E(X^2)$, we require that $E(X^4)$ be finite. This condition is fulfilled in most cases which are of practical interest.

Suppose that δ has been chosen such that if $|\overline{X} - EX| \geq \delta$, we would then say that $\overline{X}$ is "far" from EX. Chebyschev's inequality can be interpreted as stating that $\overline{X}$ will be "far" from EX with a probability no greater than $(1/N)(\sigma_X^2/\delta^2)$. It is clear that the latter probability is smaller the larger is the sample size (N) on which the estimator $\overline{X}$ is based. In the limit, as N approaches infinity (written: $N \to \infty$), $1/N$ approaches zero so that the maximum probability that $\overline{X}$ will be "far" from EX must also approach zero. We have, then, that

(i) $P[|\bar{X} - EX| \geq \delta] \leq \dfrac{1}{N}\dfrac{\sigma_X^2}{\delta^2}$.

(ii) As $N \to \infty$, $\dfrac{1}{N}\dfrac{\sigma_X^2}{\delta^2} \to 0$.

(iii) Consequently, as $N \to \infty$, $P[|\overline{X} - EX| \geq \delta] \to 0$,

In simplest terms, the last result states that the larger the sample size used to determine $\overline{X}$, the smaller the probability that $\overline{X}$ will be "far" from EX. This is nothing other than the increasing efficiency of $\overline{X}$ as an estimator of EX. An estimator which never ceases to increase in efficiency as N increases is said to be a *consistent estimator*. The formal definition of consistency is therefore the following.

DEFINITION. Let θ be a parameter to be estimated, and let $\hat{\theta}_N$ be a (random variable) estimator based on a random sample of size N. If

$$P[|\hat{\theta}_N - \theta| \geq \delta] \to 0 \quad \text{as } N \to \infty$$

then $\hat{\theta}_N$ is said to be a *consistent estimator* of θ.

We shall now prove the following.

METHOD OF MOMENTS THEOREM. Let X be a random variable with $E(X^{2k})$ finite, where k is any finite positive integer. Then the method of moments estimator of $E(X^k)$ is *unbiased* and *consistent.*

Proof: The method of moments estimator of $E(X^k)$ is

$$(\overline{X^k}) = \frac{1}{N}\sum_i (X_i^k),$$

where $X_1, X_2, \ldots, X_N$ is a random sample of size N corresponding to X.

(a) To show that $(\overline{X^k})$ is unbiased,

$$E(\overline{X^k}) = E\frac{1}{N}\sum_i (X_i^k)$$

$$= \frac{1}{N} E \sum_i (X_i^k)$$

$$= \frac{1}{N} \sum_i E(X_i^k).$$

But each X_i is distributed exactly as X; hence

$$E(X_i^k) = E(X^k) \quad (i = 1, 2, \ldots, N).$$

Thus,

$$E(\overline{X^k}) = \frac{1}{N} \sum_i E(X_i^k)$$

$$= \frac{1}{N} \sum_i E(X^k)$$

$$= \frac{1}{N} \{N[E(X^k)]\}$$

$$= E(X^k). \qquad \text{Q.E.D}$$

(b) To show that $(\overline{X^k})$ is consistent;

$$P[|(\overline{X^k}) - E(\overline{X^k})| \geq \delta] \leq \frac{\text{Var }(\overline{X^k})}{\delta^2},$$

which follows from Chebyschev's inequality. But it has been shown that $E(\overline{X^k}) = E(X^k)$; hence

$$P[|(\overline{X^k}) - E(X^k)| \geq \delta] \leq \frac{\text{Var }(\overline{X^k})}{\delta^2}.$$

Now

$$\text{Var }(\overline{X^k}) = \text{Var}\left\{\frac{1}{N} \sum_i (X_i^k)\right\}$$

$$= \frac{1}{N^2} \text{Var} \sum_i (X_i^k).$$

Since the X_i are mutually independent, the variance of the sum above is the sum of the variances; that is,

$$\text{Var }(\overline{X^k}) = \frac{1}{N^2} \text{Var} \sum_i (X_i^k)$$

$$= \frac{1}{N^2} \sum_i \text{Var }(X_i^k).$$

But each X_i is distributed exactly as X; hence[15]

$$\text{Var }(X_i^k) = \text{Var }(X^k) \quad (i = 1, 2, \ldots, N).$$

[15]It is at this point that we require $E(X^{2k})$ to be finite, for then $\text{Var }(X^k) = E(X^{2k}) - [E(X^k)]^2$ is finite.

Thus,

$$\begin{aligned}\operatorname{Var}(\overline{X^k}) &= \frac{1}{N^2}\sum_i \operatorname{Var}(X_i^k)\\ &= \frac{1}{N^2}\sum_i \operatorname{Var}(X^k)\\ &= \frac{1}{N^2}\{N \operatorname{Var}(X^k)\}\\ &= \frac{\operatorname{Var}(X^k)}{N}.\end{aligned}$$

Substituting the latter result into the Chebyschev inequality,

$$P[|(\overline{X^k}) - E(X^k)| \geq \delta] \leq \frac{\operatorname{Var}(\overline{X^k})}{\delta^2} = \frac{1}{N}\frac{\operatorname{Var}(X^k)}{\delta^2}.$$

As $N \to \infty$, $\frac{1}{N}\frac{\operatorname{Var}(X^k)}{\delta^2} \to 0$;

consequently,

$$P[|(\overline{X^k}) - E(X^k)| \geq \delta] \to 0 \text{ as } N \to \infty \qquad \text{Q.E.D.}$$

Comment on the theorem: It is important to recognize the distinction between unbiasedness and consistency. The former simply means that *on the average* the estimator $(\overline{X^k})$ will be equal to $E(X^k)$. That is, if we averaged many $(\overline{X^k})$ realizations, each based on a sample of size N,[16] the result would be $E(X^k)$. The one $(\overline{X^k})$ realization available from one sample of size N may, of course, be quite far from $E(X^k)$. It is at this point that the consistency property enters and states that the probability of an $(\overline{X^k})$ being far from $E(X^k)$ is smaller the larger N is.

We turn now to the question of how large must N be in order that $\overline{X}$ be reasonably efficient as an estimator of EX. Suppose we consider that $\overline{X}$ is "far" from EX if

$$|\overline{X} - EX| \geq \tfrac{1}{3}\sigma_X.$$

We are saying, then, that "closeness" to EX depends on how variable X itself is. If $\sigma_X = 9$, then $\overline{X}$ is "far" from EX if they differ by 3 units or more. If, on the other hand, $\sigma_X = 30$, then $\overline{X}$ is not considered to be "far" from EX unless they differ by at least 10 units. In light of these facts, we take $\delta = \frac{1}{3}\sigma_X$ in Chebyschev's inequality and find

$$P[|\overline{X} - EX| \geq \tfrac{1}{3}\sigma_X] \leq \frac{1}{N}\frac{\sigma_X^2}{\sigma_X^2/9} = \frac{9}{N}.$$

[16]We did this for $\overline{X}$ corresponding to 10 samples of size $N = 5$ in Example 7.2.3.

Suppose $N = 36$, then

$$P[|\overline{X} - EX| \geq \tfrac{1}{3}\sigma_X] \leq \tfrac{1}{4}.$$

Thus with a sample of size 36, the probability of $\overline{X}$ being "far" from EX is at most 0.25. We have enough experience now, however, to know that Chebyschev's inequality gives quite conservative upper-limit probabilities in most cases. We can sharpen the result by using the sample mean theorem, which states that

$$Z_N = \frac{\overline{X} - EX}{\sigma_{\overline{X}}}$$

is asymptotically $\eta(0, 1)$. Suppose we calculate for $N = 36$ the normal approximation to the probability that $|\overline{X} - EX| \geq \frac{1}{3}\sigma_X$; that is, $(\overline{X} - EX) \geq \frac{1}{3}\sigma_X$ or $(\bar{X} - EX) \leq -\frac{1}{3}\sigma_X$. First consider $\bar{X} - EX \geq \frac{1}{3}\sigma_X$. This implies

$$Z_{36} = \frac{\bar{X} - EX}{\sigma_{\overline{X}}} \geq \frac{\frac{1}{3}\sigma_X}{\sigma_{\overline{X}}}.$$

But

$$\sigma_{\overline{X}} = \sqrt{\sigma^2_{\overline{X}}} = \sqrt{\frac{\sigma^2_X}{N}} = \sqrt{\frac{\sigma^2_X}{36}} = \frac{\sigma_X}{6};$$

hence

$$Z_{36} = \frac{\overline{X} - EX}{\sigma_{\overline{X}}} \geq \frac{\frac{1}{3}\sigma_X}{\frac{\sigma_X}{6}} = 2.$$

According to Table 6.1, if Z_{36} is $\eta(0, 1)$,

$$P(Z_{36} \geq 2) = \tfrac{1}{2} - P(0 \leq Z_{36} \leq 2) = 0.0228.$$

Clearly, $P[(\overline{X} - EX) \leq -\frac{1}{3}\sigma_X]$ will be approximated by $P(Z_{36} \leq -2) = P(Z_{36} \geq 2)$, by symmetry of the normal distribution. Hence

$$P[|\overline{X} - EX| \geq \tfrac{1}{3}\sigma_X] \cong 2(0.0228) = 0.0456.$$

The sample mean theorem therefore indicates that $\overline{X}$ is indeed highly efficient if $N = 36$, for the probability is then only about 0.05 that $\overline{X}$ will be "far" from EX.[17] Even for $N = 25$, the probability of $\bar{X}$ being at least $\frac{1}{3}\sigma_X$

[17]This measure of efficiency is only approximate. Its accuracy depends on how well the normal distribution approximates

$$P[|\overline{X} - EX| \geq \tfrac{1}{3}\sigma_X].$$

Experiments with various distributions of the random variable X indicate that for $N = 36$, the normal approximation is indeed quite satisfactory.

away from EX is only about 0.10,[18] indicating that reasonable levels of efficiency in estimating EX can be attained with fairly modest sample sizes.

In general, larger sample sizes are usually required for estimating EX_2 with the same level of efficiency as EX. In most practical situations, however, a sample of size 30 or so does provide an $(\overline{X^2})$ which has reasonable[19] efficiency as an estimator of $E(X^2)$. Consequently either

$$(s^*)^2 = \frac{\sum X_i^2}{N} - \frac{(\sum X_i)^2}{N}$$

or

$$s^2 = \frac{N}{N-1}(s^*)^2$$

should provide reasonable efficiency as estimators of σ_X^2 if $N \geq 30$. Finally, the fact that $(\overline{X^2})$ and $\overline{X}$ are consistent estimators of $E(X^2)$ and EX respectively implies that *both* $(s^*)^2$ and s^2 are consistent estimators of σ_X^2. Although a proof of the consistency of $(s^*)^2$ and s^2 would be beyond the level of this text, the result should be intuitively acceptable to the reader.

7.4 Interval Estimation

It is clear that a random sample can be used to estimate an unknown parameter. Suppose the random sample X_1, X_2, X_3 produces the set of realizations $X_1 = 5$, $X_2 = 1$, $X_3 = 6$. We would then calculate the realized sample mean as $(5 + 1 + 6)/3 = 4$ and this would be our *point estimate* of EX. It is reasonable to ask, however, whether this point estimate really exhausts all the information about EX which is contained in the random sample. Suppose, for example, that prior to obtaining the random sample it was thought — perhaps on the basis of theory or earlier investigations — that $EX = 5$. Does the sample mean of 4 contradict this belief, confirm it, or what? The answer clearly depends on the efficiency of $\overline{X}$ as an estimator of EX. If $\overline{X}$ were so efficient that by no stretch of the imagination could it differ from EX by more than 0.25, then an $\overline{X}$ realization of 4 would surely contradict the prior belief that $EX = 5$. On the other hand, if the efficiency of $\overline{X}$ were such that $\overline{X}$ might very likely differ from EX by as much as 1.5, then an $\overline{X}$ realization of 4 would *not* contradict the hypothesis $EX = 5$. Indeed it would not confirm the hypothesis either. Statistical evidence can

[18]The reader should be able to show this by using the normal approximation.

[19]The term *reasonable* must be judged in the context of what is to be done with the resulting estimate. The statement in the text is an empirical rule of thumb which will serve most investigators well in most practical applications.

never confirm any hypothesis; the evidence (that is, the sample mean) either contradicts the hypothesis or is consistent with the hypothesis.[20] Evidence which is consistent with some hypothesis does not, of course, prove that the hypothesis is correct, for the same evidence will in general also be consistent with other (similar) hypotheses.

This additional use of efficiency can be harnessed to provide further information in the following way. In order to estimate EX, we use

$$\overline{X} = \frac{1}{N}\sum_i X_i,$$

which has variance $\sigma_{\overline{X}}^2 = \sigma_X^2/N$. According to Chebyschev's inequality,

$$P[|\overline{X} - EX| \geq \delta] \leq \frac{\sigma_{\overline{X}}^2}{\delta^2}.$$

Suppose we let $\delta = 2\sigma_{\overline{X}}$, then

$$P[|\overline{X} - EX| \geq 2\sigma_{\overline{X}}] \leq \frac{\sigma_{\overline{X}}^2}{4\sigma_{\overline{X}}^2} = \frac{1}{4},$$

or

$$P[|\overline{X} - EX| \leq 2\sigma_{\overline{X}}] \geq \tfrac{3}{4},$$

or

$$P[-2\sigma_{\overline{X}} \leq (\overline{X} - EX) \leq 2\sigma_{\overline{X}}] \geq \tfrac{3}{4};$$

thus with probability at least $\frac{3}{4}$, $\overline{X}$ will differ from EX by no more than $2\sigma_{\overline{X}}$. Consider the last set of inequalities inside the square brackets:

$$-2\sigma_{\overline{X}} \leq (\overline{X} - EX) \leq 2\sigma_{\overline{X}}.$$

Multiplying the entire set of inequalities by (-1) results in[21]

$$2\sigma_{\overline{X}} \geq (-\overline{X} + EX) \geq -2\sigma_{\overline{X}} \quad \text{or} \quad -2\sigma_{\overline{X}} \leq (-\overline{X} + EX) \leq 2\sigma_{\overline{X}}.$$

[20]A warning is in order. Even if it were true that

$$P\,[|\overline{X} - EX| \geq 0.25] = 0.001,$$

an $\overline{X}$ realization of 4 would not contradict $EX = 5$ in any absolute sense. The evidence would be overwhelmingly against the hypothesis that $EX = 5$, but there would still be that probability of 0.001 to worry about; and there is no absolute guarantee that the realized $\overline{X}$ is not the one in a thousand that differs from EX by more than 0.25. Absolute contradiction of $EX = 5$ would require

$$P[|\overline{X} - EX| \geq 0.25] = 0,$$

and, as noted in Section 7.3, the probability is not zero for any finite sample size.

[21]While $2 < 3$, upon multiplication by (-1) the inequality must be reversed for $-2 > -3$.

Adding $\overline{X}$ to each part results in

$$\overline{X} - 2\sigma_{\overline{X}} \leq EX \leq \overline{X} + 2\sigma_{\overline{X}}.$$

The latter set of inequalities is mathematically equivalent to the original set so that

$$P[-2\sigma_{\overline{X}} \leq (\overline{X} - EX) \leq 2\sigma_{\overline{X}}] \geq \tfrac{3}{4}$$

implies

$$P[\overline{X} - 2\sigma_{\overline{X}} \leq EX \leq \overline{X} + 2\sigma_{\overline{X}}] \geq \tfrac{3}{4},$$

which is known as a *confidence interval statement*[22] about EX with *confidence coefficient* $\geq \frac{3}{4}$. The interpretation of the confidence interval is extremely important. First, note that the confidence interval statement is actually a probability statement and must therefore be a statement about one or more random variables. A close look reveals that a statement is being made about two random variables, namely $(\overline{X} - 2\sigma_{\overline{X}})$ and $(\overline{X} + 2\sigma_{\overline{X}})$. The term EX is a parameter (unknown), not a random variable. The statement then says that with probability at least $\frac{3}{4}$ the random variable $(\overline{X} - 2\sigma_{\overline{X}})$ will be less than or equal to EX *and simultaneously*[23] the random variable $(\overline{X} + 2\sigma_{\overline{X}})$ will be greater than or equal to EX. The interval from $(\overline{X} - 2\sigma_{\overline{X}})$ to $(\overline{X} + 2\sigma_{\overline{X}})$ is a random interval; this is so since $\overline{X}$ is a random variable and therefore the position of the interval depends on the random experiment which generates $\overline{X}$. If we denote this random interval by I_N,[24] the confidence interval statement can be rewritten as

$$P[I_N \text{ contains } EX] \geq \tfrac{3}{4}.$$

Suppose it is known that $2\sigma_{\overline{X}} = 1$ and a particular random sample of size N results in a sample mean of 4. The realization of I_N is then the interval from $(4 - 1 = 3)$ to $(4 + 1 = 5)$. This does *not*, however, mean that the interval from 3 to 5 will contain EX with probability $\geq \frac{3}{4}$. Indeed, EX is some number and either is or is not contained in the interval from 3 to 5. Suppose that we obtain another random sample of size N and the sample mean this

[22]*The confidence interval statement* is often referred to as a *confidence interval.* Actually

$$\overline{X} - 2\sigma_{\overline{X}} \leq EX \leq \overline{X} + 2\sigma_{\overline{X}}$$

is the confidence interval while

$$P[\overline{X} - 2\sigma_{\overline{X}} \leq EX \leq \overline{X} + 2\sigma_{\overline{X}}] \geq \tfrac{3}{4}$$

is the confidence interval statement.

[23]This is in the set-theoretic sense of intersection.

[24]The subscript N indicates that the interval depends on $\overline{X}$, which is the sample mean for a sample of size N.

time turns out to be 4.5. The realization of I_N would be the interval from $(4.5 - 1 = 3.5)$ to $(4.5 + 1 = 5.5)$. In general, 100 random samples (each of size N) would produce 100 $\overline{X}$ realizations and therefore 100 I_N realizations. We would then have 100 statements such as

$$3 \leq EX \leq 5,$$

$$3.5 \leq EX \leq 5.5,$$

$$\text{etc.},$$

some of which would be true statements and some of which would be false statements. Since these are all based on a probability statement with confidence coefficient $\geq \frac{3}{4}$, however, we would expect that at least 75 of the 100 statements would be true.[25]

It is not difficult to see how we could construct a confidence interval statement such that

$$P[I_N \text{ contains } EX] \geq \tfrac{8}{9}.$$

According to Chebyschev's inequality,

$$P[|\overline{X} - EX| \geq 3\sigma_{\overline{X}}] \leq \tfrac{1}{9};$$

therefore

$$P[|\overline{X} - EX| \leq 3\sigma_{\overline{X}}] \geq \tfrac{8}{9}$$

which implies

$$P[\overline{X} - 3\sigma_{\overline{X}} \leq EX \leq \overline{X} + 3\sigma_{\overline{X}}] \geq \tfrac{8}{9} \cong 0.89$$

as desired. In this case we would expect at least 89 out of 100 statements constructed according to $\overline{X} \pm 3\sigma_{\overline{X}}$ to be true statements. Note, however, that the increased degree of confidence in the truth of the statements being made is obtained at a cost of having wider intervals for $3\sigma_{\overline{X}} > 2\sigma_{\overline{X}}$ if N is fixed. In general the wider the interval the greater the probability that it will contain the parameter. Yet, the wider the interval the less useful the information it is providing. Usually it is possible to increase the confidence coefficient without increasing the width of the resulting intervals only by increasing the sample size. Suppose that $N = 10$ provides small enough intervals when the intervals are defined by $\overline{X} \pm 2\sigma_{\overline{X}}$. The confidence coefficient would then be $\geq \frac{3}{4}$. If it were desired to increase the confidence coefficient to $\geq \frac{8}{9}$, the intervals would be defined by $\overline{X} \pm 3\sigma_{\overline{X}}$. To increase

[25]The game of horseshoes provides a useful analogy. The spike is fixed in the ground and corresponds to EX. The horseshoe corresponds to I_N and after the horseshoe is thrown, it either contains the spike (a ringer) or does not contain the spike. If an individual has probability $\geq \frac{3}{4}$ of getting a ringer, then we would expect that in 100 tosses at least 75 would have contained the spike.

the confidence coefficient without increasing the width of the interval would require that the sample size be increased from $N = 10$ to $N = N^*$ such that

$$2\frac{\sigma_X}{\sqrt{10}} = 3\frac{\sigma_X}{\sqrt{N^*}}.$$

Solving this for N^*,

$$\frac{2}{3}\frac{\sqrt{N^*}}{\sqrt{10}} = \frac{\sigma_X}{\sigma_X} = 1,$$

$$\sqrt{N^*} = \frac{3\sqrt{10}}{2},$$

$$N^* = \frac{9(10)}{4} = \frac{90}{4} = 22.5.$$

We would thus require 22 or 23 observations in order to increase the confidence coefficient to the level desired without increasing the width of the confidence intervals.

In most practical applications of confidence intervals, one encounters an additional problem, namely an unknown $\sigma_{\overline{X}}$. We do, however, have available an estimate of $\sigma_{\overline{X}}$ which could be used as a substitute. Recalling that s^2 is an unbiased estimator of σ_X^2, it follows that $s_{\overline{X}}^2 = s^2/N$ is an unbiased estimator of $\sigma_{\overline{X}}^2$ and that $s_{\overline{X}} = s/\sqrt{N}$ should therefore be used in place of $\sigma_{\overline{X}}$ to obtain

$$\overline{X} - 2s_{\overline{X}} \leq EX \leq \overline{X} + 2s_{\overline{X}}.$$

The true confidence coefficient would not be as great as if $\sigma_{\overline{X}}$ were used, but as a practical matter if $N \geq 30$, little error would be introduced by simply constructing the confidence interval as though $s_{\overline{X}}$ were $\sigma_{\overline{X}}$. The general form for the confidence interval statement with $\sigma_{\overline{X}}$ unknown can be given as

$$P[\overline{X} - ks_{\overline{X}} \leq EX \leq \overline{X} + ks_{\overline{X}}] \geq 1 - \frac{1}{k^2},$$

which follows from the approximate Chebyschev inequality (with $N \geq 30$)[26]

$$P[|\overline{X} - EX| \geq ks_{\overline{X}}] \leq \frac{1}{k^2}.$$

Finally, the confidence interval statement would be used as follows in comparison with some prior hypothesis about the value of EX. If the interval

$$3.5 \leq EX \leq 4.5$$

has been derived from a random sample on the basis of a confidence coefficient $\geq \frac{3}{4}$, it would be said that any hypothesis about EX which con-

[26]For $N < 30$ and σ_X unknown, there are no really satisfactory ways to construct a confidence interval for EX unless the form of the probability distribution of X happens to be known. In that case no new principles are introduced, but the matter does become more complicated and is probably better left out of this account.

jectured that EX was either > 4.5 or < 3.5 would be rejected (contradicted by the statistical evidence) with a degree of confidence $\geq \frac{3}{4}$. When a hypothesis is rejected with a degree of confidence $\geq \frac{3}{4}$, this implies that there is a probability perhaps as high as $\frac{1}{4}$ that the hypothesis is being rejected falsely.

PROBLEMS

7-1. As shown below, corporate profits as a percent of gross national product varied from a low of 4.2% to a high of 5.8% during the years 1953–62. Using these data, estimate the expected value of the random variable *corporate profits as a percent of GNP*. Is your estimate unbiased? Comment.

Year	(100% X corporate profit)/GNP
1953	5.0%
1954	4.6
1955	5.8
1956	5.6
1957	5.0
1958	4.2
1959	5.1
1960	4.6
1961	4.5
1962	4.7

Source: *Survey of Current Business, Sept. 1963.*

7-2. Suppose that a sample of families with incomes between \$4,000 and \$4,500 yields the following set of consumption data.

Family number	Income	Consumption
1	\$4,200	\$3,710
2	4,450	4,300
3	4,100	4,250
4	4,025	3,980
5	4,400	4,200
6	4,375	4,350
7	4,350	3,975
8	4,120	4,400
9	4,010	5,230
10	4,460	5,000

Estimate the expected value of

(a) Consumption of families with incomes between \$4,000 and \$4,500.

(b) The average propensity to consume (= consumption ÷ income) of families with incomes between $4,000 and $4,500.

7-3. X is $B(10, p)$, where p is the unknown probability of a success. Let X_1 denote the number of successes in a single trial of the experiment, X_2 denote the number of successes in a second trial, and so on up to X_N. Show that

(a) $\overline{X} = (\sum_{i=1}^{N} X_i)/N$ is an unbiased estimator of EX.

(b) $\overline{X}/10$ is an unbiased estimator of p.

7-4. Each month the Bureau of the Census draws a sample of 35,000 families from 357 different regions of the United States. The results of this sample are used to calculate a national unemployment rate u, where u is defined as $u = X/Y$. X = the number of persons in the sample who are members of the labor force but are unemployed at the time of the sample and Y = the number of persons in the sample who are members of the labor force. It is obvious that both X and Y are random variables.

(a) Under the assumption that each of the 35,000 families sampled contains only one individual of working age, explain why Y must be distributed as $B(35{,}000, p)$ and X distributed as $B(Y, p^*)$. To what do p and p^* refer?

(b) Suppose each of the 35,000 families sampled contains exactly one member of the labor force (that is, the supposition is equivalent to assuming $Y = 35{,}000$ and is not a random variable). Show that, under these conditions, u is an unbiased estimator of p^*.

7-5. The table below shows the proportion of United States families which purchased new automobiles during any year for the period 1954–63, inclusive. Estimate the expected value and variance of the random variable X = the proportion of United States families purchasing new automobiles during a year. Also estimate the variance of your estimator of EX.

Year	1954	1955	1956	1957	1958	1959	1960	1961	1962	1963
Proportion of United States families purchasing new automobiles	0.09	0.12	0.12	0.09	0.08	0.10	0.10	0.08	0.10	0.11

Source: *Survey of Consumer Finances, 1964.*

7-6. From the random number table (Appendix Table B, p. 326) generate five samples each of size $N = 6$ for the random variable $X \in \{0, 1, 2, 3, \ldots, 9\}$ and $P(X = x) = \frac{1}{10}$.

(a) Calculate the five realizations of $\overline{X}, (s^*)^2$, and s^2.

(b) Average all the $\overline{X}$'s and show that this produces the same estimate of EX as would be produced by the estimator $\overline{\overline{X}}$ = the average of all 30 observations on X. (That is, $\overline{\overline{X}}$ is the estimator $\overline{X}$ when the five samples of size 6 are considered one sample of size 30.)

(c) Average all the $(s^*)^2$'s. This average is a realization of the estimator $\overline{(s^*)^2}$. What does $\overline{(s^*)^2}$ estimate? Is it an unbiased estimator?

(d) Repeat (c) for the (s^2)'s.

7-7. Consider the random variables $\overline{X}_3, \overline{X}_4, \overline{X}_5$ which denote sample means for samples of sizes $N = 3, N = 4, N = 5$, respectively, drawn on the random variable X.

(a) What are the respective expected values and variances of the random variables $\overline{X}_3, \overline{X}_4, \overline{X}_5$?

(b) Using the random number table, generate one realization each of the random variables $\overline{X}_3, \overline{X}_4, \overline{X}_5$ for the random variable X defined in Problem 7-6. Compute the realizations of

$$\overline{\overline{X}} = \frac{\overline{X}_3 + \overline{X}_4 + \overline{X}_5}{3} \quad \text{and}$$

$$\overline{X}_{12} = \frac{\sum (12\ X \text{ realizations used in computing } \overline{X}_3, \overline{X}_4, \overline{X}_5)}{12}.$$

Are $\overline{\overline{X}}$ and $\overline{X}_{12}$ both unbiased estimators of EX? Why, then, are the calculated realizations of $\overline{\overline{X}}$ and $\overline{X}_{12}$ not identical?

(c) Which of the estimators $\overline{\overline{X}}$ and $\overline{X}_{12}$ is the more efficient?

(d) Find a set of constants a_3, a_4, a_5 which, when used in calculating a weighted average of $\overline{X}_3, \overline{X}_4$, and $\overline{X}_5$, eliminates the discrepancy between $\overline{\overline{X}}$ and $\overline{X}_{12}$. That is, find a_3, a_4, a_5 such that

$$\frac{a_3\overline{X}_3 + a_4\overline{X}_4 + a_5\overline{X}_5}{a_3 + a_4 + a_5} = \overline{X}_{12}.$$

7-8. Suppose that the Bureau of the Census (see Problem 7-4) wants not only an estimate of the national unemployment rate but also a set of four regional estimates — one for the Far West, the Midwest, the Southeast, and the Northeast. Treating membership in the labor force as nonrandom, a typical sample of 35,000 members of the labor force might produce the following results:

Region	Regional sample size	Estimated regional unemployment rate	Estimated variance of regional estimates
Far West	6,500	0.044	0.000065
Midwest	14,000	0.047	0.000032
Southeast	6,000	0.043	0.000068
Northeast	8,500	0.051	0.000057
	35,000		

(The estimates of variances of regional unemployment rates were derived from the following: Estimated unemployment for region i is $u_i = X_i/N_i$ where N_i = the number of labor force members in the region i sample and X_i = the random variable number of the N_i labor force members who were unemployed at the time of the sample. Thus,

$$\begin{aligned} \text{var}\,(u_i) &= \text{var}\left(\frac{X_i}{N_i}\right) \\ &= \frac{1}{N_i^2}\,\text{var}\,(X_i) \\ &= \frac{1}{N_i^2}\,[N_i p_i(1 - p_i)] = \frac{1}{N_i}\,p_i(1 - p_i), \end{aligned}$$

where p_i = true unemployment rate. A biased but consistent estimator of var (u_i) is

$$\frac{1}{N_i}\,u_i(1 - u_i).)$$

Use the weighted average method of Problem 7-7(d) to estimate the national unemployment rate. Also compute an estimate of the variance of this "large sample" estimate by using

$$\hat{\sigma}_u^2 = \frac{1}{35{,}000}u(1 - u),$$

where u is the estimated *national* unemployment rate.

7-9. A crucial assumption of classical estimation theory is that the random variables comprising a random sample be independently and identically distributed. With many economic variables, particularly where the sample realizations take the form of a time series (that is, the realizations are values of the same economic variable at different points in time), the classical assumption is violated. Consider the time series realizations on the *Consumer's Price Index* below. With the exception of 1955, this price index shows an increase in its value over the previous year. It is obvious, for example, that the random variable P_{1951} (= *Consumer's Price Index* in 1951) has a different expected value from P_{1960}. It is also obvious that the *expected value* of P_t is closely related to the *realization* of P_{t-1}. That is to say, not only do P_t and P_{t-1} have different probability distributions, they also are not stochastically independent. We can, however, make a pair of *reasonable* assumptions which will restore to classical estimation techniques the power to be used with time series or similarly "trended" random variables. The time path of realizations of the *Consumer's Price Index* may be said to imply that $P_t = P_{t-1} + X$, where X is a random variable with unknown distribution. Let us formally assume

(a) Given the realization of P_{t-1}, P_t is distributed as $P_{t-1} + X$ (that is, $[P_t = P_{t-1} + X \mid P_{t-1}]$).
(b) $EX = a$, var $X = \sigma_X^2$ where a and σ_X^2 are constants.

Under these assumptions, we can estimate EP_t merely by adding an estimate of EX to the realization P_{t-1}. That is, $E[P_t \mid P_{t-1}] = P_{t-1} + EX = P_{t-1} + a$, and var $[P_t \mid P_{t-1}] = \sigma_X^2$. We can use classical techniques to find estimators of $EX = a$ and σ_X^2 since $X = P_t - P_{t-1}$. Using the series on *Consumer's Price Index* below,

(i) Estimate EX, σ_X^2, var $\overline{X}$.
(ii) Make a forecast of $E(P_{1964})$.

(It will interest you to know that the actual realization P_{1964} turned out to be 108.1.)

t	P_t = Consumer's Price Index
1951	90.5
1952	92.5
1953	93.2
1954	93.6
1955	93.3
1956	94.7
1957	98.0
1958	100.7
1959	101.5
1960	103.1
1961	104.2
1962	105.4
1963	106.7

Source: *Economic Indicators, June 1965.*

7-10. From the random number table (p. 326) generate a sample of size $N = 10$ for the random variable X^2 where $X \in \{0, 1, 2, \ldots, 9\}$ and $P(X = x) = \frac{1}{10}$. Calculate the method of moments estimators of $E[X^2]$ and var $[X^2]$ and compare these with the true values. Comment on the properties (bias, efficiency, consistency) of this general class of estimators.

7-11. Suppose you have been hired to estimate some parameter of a random variable. Your employer offers you the choice between

(a) Generating your own sample of size N.
(b) Using the results of two previous samples of size N_1 and N_2 respectively. $N_1 = N_2 = \frac{1}{2}N$, but the individual observations have been lost. All that remains are the respective estimates of the desired parameter and variances of these estimates.

Which would you choose, and why, if

(i) Usual estimating techniques yield unbiased estimators?
(ii) Usual estimating techniques are only capable of producing biased but consistent estimators?

7-12. Use Chebyschev's inequality to find an upper limit to the probability that an estimate of $E[X^2]$ (where $X \in \{0, 1, 2, \ldots, 9\}$ as in Problem 7-10) will differ from the true $E[X^2]$ by eight units or more when the estimator is based on a sample of size $N = 20$.

7-13. Use Chebyschev's inequality to find an upper limit for the probability that your estimate of $E[C/Y]$ in Problem 7-2(b) differs from the true value by at least $\frac{1}{2}$ of the true standard deviation of C/Y.

7-14. For many economic decisions it is vital that an estimated parameter have a small probability of being "far" from the true value of that parameter.

(a) Use the sample mean theorem to approximate the probability that $\overline{X}$, from a sample of size $N = 1{,}200$, will differ from EX by more than $\frac{1}{50}\sigma_X$.
(b) With what sample size will the approximate probability that $|\overline{X} - EX| \geq \frac{1}{250}\sigma_X$ be the same as in (a)?

7-15. Use the following data on monthly *changes* in the average hourly earnings of manufacturing workers to find an estimate of the expected monthly change. With what probability would an estimator of $E\{$monthly change in average hourly earnings$\}$, based on a sample of this size, be at least as large as yours if the true expected change is equal to zero?

Hint: Use the sample mean theorem and assume

$$\sigma_{\bar{X}}|_{EX=0} = \sqrt{\hat{\sigma}^2_{\bar{X}}|_{EX=0}}.$$

Month	Change in average hourly earnings over the previous month
January, 1963	+1¢
February	0
March	+1
April	0
May	+1
June	+1
July	−1
August	−2
September	+4
October	0
November	+2
December	+2
January, 1964	+1
February	0
March	+2
April	0
May	0
June	0
July	0
August	−1
September	+5
October	−4
November	+3

Source: *Economic Indicators*, Dec. 1964.

7-16. A manufacturer has kept records of the percent defective output from a certain process. The records of the past 10 weeks are listed below. Use these data to find:

(a) A point estimate of the true percent defective.
(b) An interval estimate of the true percent defective with confidence coefficient of $\frac{8}{9}$.

What are the differences between a point estimate and an interval estimate?

Week number	% defective
1	11.0
2	8.4
3	8.9
4	13.1
5	12.6
6	8.0
7	7.6
8	11.4
9	10.8
10	6.9

7-17. Suppose a state legislature, which is contemplating passing a tax of 4¢ per pack on the sale of cigarettes, effective beginning next year, has hired you to estimate the revenue that such a tax would yield next year. You are given the following data on cigarette sales for the current year and the past 13 years. Since cigarette sales have been increasing over time, you plan to make your revenue forecast conditional on the level of this year's sales and treat the annual change in sales as a random variable with constant mean and variance (see Problem 7-9). Disregard the possible effects on sales that a tax of 4¢ per pack might have and forecast next year's expected tax revenue in the form of a confidence interval statement with degree of confidence $\geq \frac{3}{4}$.

Year (0 = current year)	Statewide sales of cigarettes in millions of packs
0	25.7
−1	25.4
−2	23.8
−3	23.5
−4	22.5
−5	22.0
−6	21.1
−7	20.9
−8	20.3
−9	20.4
−10	18.9
−11	18.5
−12	17.9
−13	17.2

7-18. The U.S. Department of Commerce compiles the gross national product (GNP) figures of the United States by two different methods. On the one hand an estimate of GNP is arrived at by summing flows of final output. On the other hand an estimate of GNP is the result of summing total claims against final product. According to accounting conventions, both estimates should yield the same GNP figure. But measurements of aggregates are rarely perfect and there generally results a discrepancy between the product estimate of GNP and the claims estimate. For cases in which such a discrepancy arises, the Department of Commerce has instituted the convention of adding the difference between product estimate and claims estimate to the claims estimate. This difference is called the *statistical discrepancy* and the convention of adding it to the claims estimate of GNP is nothing more than a method of equating the two estimates. The statistical discrepancy is a random variable and realizations of this random variable for the years 1948–64 are given below.

(a) With confidence coefficient 0.75, "test" the hypothesis that the true expected value of the statistical discrepancy equals 0.

(b) What would an expected value $\neq 0$ imply and why would it be a matter of concern to the Department of Commerce?

Year	Statistical discrepancy (in millions of dollars)
1948	−2,043
1949	309
1950	1,488
1951	3,348
1952	2,172
1953	2,996
1954	2,885
1955	2,093
1956	−1,136
1957	4
1958	1,552
1959	−806
1960	−1,010
1961	−738
1962	503
1963	−670
1964	−542

Source: *Survey of Current Business, Aug. 1965.*

8 ELEMENTS OF ECONOMETRICS

8.1 Introduction

Most economists would probably agree that econometrics is the application of the tools of probability and statistics to economic problems and phenomena. Such a broad definition would encompass not only the material to be presented in this chapter, but also the material on decision theory to be presented in the next chapter. It is more in keeping with the actual development of the subject of econometrics over the last 25 years, however, to separate the material of this chapter from that of the next. Despite the lofty ambitions of the initial definition, the subject matter considered under the title of econometrics has by and large been limited to one specific area, namely the estimation and application of linear stochastic equations. The area of decision theory, which would be encompassed by a broad definition of econometrics, has developed alongside econometrics (in the narrow sense) but has been embraced by economists far more slowly and continues even now to be regarded as a "different" field of study.

8.2 Motivating the Linear Stochastic Equation

Let us begin the discussion of the linear stochastic equation by defining three sets of variables.

Let $\mathcal{Y}$ = the set of *dependent* variables,

$\mathcal{X}$ = the set of *first-order independent* variables,

$\mathcal{Z}$ = the set of *second-order independent* variables.

It is assumed that the set $\mathcal{Y}$ is determined by (hence is dependent upon) the sets $\mathcal{X}$ and $\mathcal{Z}$. The sets $\mathcal{X}$ and $\mathcal{Z}$ are sets of independent variables in the sense that they are not determined by (do not depend on) the set $\mathcal{Y}$. The distinction between $\mathcal{X}$ and $\mathcal{Z}$ is that the elements of the $\mathcal{X}$ set are the main determinants of $\mathcal{Y}$, while the elements of the $\mathcal{Z}$ set are of relatively minor importance in determining $\mathcal{Y}$. In other words, a statement such as *$\mathcal{Y}$ is determined by $\mathcal{X}$ alone* would be false, but still a satisfactory approximation to reality; while *$\mathcal{Y}$ is determined by $\mathcal{Z}$ alone* would be not only false but a poor approximation to reality.

Suppose we simplify the situation such that

$$\mathcal{Y} = \{Y\},$$
$$\mathcal{X} = \{X\},$$
$$\mathcal{Z} = \{Z_1, Z_2, \ldots, Z_n\};$$

that is, we consider one dependent variable determined by one first-order independent variable and n second-order independent variables. The relation between $Y, X, Z_1, Z_2, \ldots, Z_n$ can be written

$$Y = f(X, Z_1, Z_2, \ldots, Z_n),$$

which is read *the variable Y depends on (or is a function of) the variables $X, Z_1, Z_2, \ldots, Z_n$*. The relation indicates that if the values of X and the Z's are known, then the (unique) value of Y corresponding to these values of X and the Z's is also known.[1] Suppose further that X and the Z's have separate, independent influences on Y and that these influences are additive. This implies the relation between Y, X, and the Z's can be written[2]

$$Y = g(X) + g^*(Z_1, Z_2, \ldots, Z_n),$$

[1]If, for example,

$$Y = f(X, Z_1, Z_2) \quad \text{and} \quad f(X, Z_1, Z_2) = 2X + Z_1 - Z_2$$

then

$$X = 2, Z_1 = 3 \quad \text{and} \quad Z_2 = 0.5$$

imply

$$Y = 2(2) + 3 - 0.5 = 6.5.$$

[2]This was assumed in the example of Footnote 1, where

$$f(X, Z_1, Z_2) = 2X + Z_1 - Z_2$$

implies

$$g(X) = 2X,$$
$$g^*(Z_1, Z_2) = (Z_1 - Z_2).$$

If, on the contrary,

$$f(X, Z_1, Z_2) = 2X + Z_1 - (Z_2X),$$

then the function f cannot be written as the sum of a function of X plus a function of the Z's.

which means that the original function f is the sum of two functions: g (which involves only X) and g^* (which involves only the Z's). If the value of X is known, this determines a value $g(X)$ and the dependent variable Y will be equal to $g(X)$ *if* it should happen that the net effect of all the Z's "washes out" to zero; that is, if the Z values are such that $g^* = 0$.[3] In general, of course, this need not happen so that a given value of X results not in one value for Y, but rather in a *set* of possible values depending on the Z's.

Consider an example in which

Y = pounds of output per man-hour.

X = pounds of raw material used per man-hour.

Z_1 = temperature in degrees Fahrenheit in the factory.

Z_2 = age, in months, of raw material used.

Suppose $g(X) = 0.9X$,

and

$$g^*(Z_1, Z_2) = -0.05(Z_1 - 72) - 0.1(Z_2 - 2),$$

so that

$$Y = 0.9X + [-0.05(Z_1 - 72) - 0.1(Z_2 - 2)].$$

A relation of this sort is known as a *production function;* that is, it indicates how output per man-hour depends on input per man-hour (the main determinant of output), temperature, and age of raw material used. The function indicates that with temperature and age of material held constant, an increase of input by 1 pound per man-hour will increase output by $\frac{9}{10}$ pound per man-hour. It is also seen that the higher the temperature rises above 72° the lower the output, and the older the material used the lower the output. Suppose now that inputs are applied in production at the rate of 50 pounds per man-hour ($X = 50$). This alone would result in output at a rate of

$$0.9X = 0.9(50) = 45 \text{ pounds per man-hour.}$$

The actual output rate, however, will not be 45 pounds per man-hour unless $g^* = 0$. If, for example, $Z_1 = 72$ and $Z_2 = 2$, then $g^* = 0$ and $Y = 45$. If, on the other hand, 2 month old material is used while the temperature is 74°, then

$$g^* = -0.05(74 - 72) - 0.1(2-2)$$
$$= -0.05(2) = -0.10$$

[3]Suppose $g^*(Z_1, Z_2) = Z_1 - Z_2$ as in Footnote 2, p. 215. Then if the values of Z_1 and Z_2 are the same, $g^* = 0$ and Y will turn out to be $g(X) = 2X$.

and output will be

$$Y = g(X) + g^*(Z_1, Z_2)$$
$$= 45 - 0.10 = 44.9.$$

The following table indicates some of the possible output rates with input fixed at a rate of 50 pounds per man-hour ($Z_2 = 0$ means brand new raw material):

TABLE 8-1

X	Z_1	Z_2	$g(X)$	$g^*(Z_1, Z_2)$	Y
50	72	2	45	0	45.00
50	74	2	45	−0.10	44.90
50	76	2	45	−0.20	44.80
50	80	2	45	−0.40	44.60
50	72	0	45	+0.20	45.20
50	72	1	45	+0.10	45.10
50	72	3	45	−0.10	44.90
50	72	4	45	−0.20	44.80
50	74	3	45	−0.20	44.80
50	80	4	45	−0.60	44.40
50	86	6	45	−1.10	43.90

Table 8-1 should make clear the distinction between the $\mathfrak{X}$ and $\mathcal{Z}$ sets. While temperature varied all the way from 72 to 86° and age of material varied from brand new to 6 months old, the rate of output varied only between 43.9 and 45.2 pounds per man-hour. Thus even with substantial variation in the values of the elements of the $\mathcal{Z}$ set, output never strayed very far from the 45 pounds per man-hour resulting from the input rate alone. On the other hand, if the input rate should be reduced by only 2 pounds, this alone would imply a reduction of output amounting to 1.8 pounds per man-hour which is considerably more than any reduction observed above due to age and temperature variation. To cause output to decline by as much as 1.8 pounds, the temperature would have to rise to 108° with brand new material; or 20 month old material would have to be used at a temperature of 72°; or some combination such as 92° temperature and 10 month old material. It is clear, then, that if the factory temperature is fairly well controlled by heating and air-conditioning units, and raw material is ordered with some care so that it does not usually lie unused for very many months, any substantial variations in the rate of output per man-hour must be largely the result of variations in the input rate.

Let us return now to the general relation

$$Y = g(X) + g^*(Z_1, Z_2, \ldots, Z_n).$$

It is often the case that some of the variables in the $\mathcal{Z}$ set cannot be specified very well. The investigator may know, for example, that one of the elements of the $\mathcal{Z}$ set is the decision-maker's expectations about the future, but there may be no satisfactory way to measure these expectations. In the output example, the investigator who wishes to know what output rate will result from an input rate of 60 pounds per man-hour next Tuesday may have no way of knowing *exactly* what the temperature in the factory will be next Tuesday. In some circumstances the investigator may simply have no idea of what variables actually belong in the $\mathcal{Z}$ set. In many instances theory and empirical investigation can do no more than reveal the elements which belong in the $\mathcal{X}$ set so that the investigator must carry out his work with little if any knowledge of the $\mathcal{Z}$ set. Let us suppose, then, that we have no knowledge at all about the $\mathcal{Z}$ set except to know that its net impact on Y is relatively small. We denote this by writing

$$Y = g(X) + \epsilon^*,$$

where the one "catchall" variable ϵ^* has replaced the function

$$g^*(Z_1, Z_2, \ldots, Z_n).$$

Suppose it were not known that temperature and age of material affected output, and we used the relation

$$Y = 0.9X + \epsilon^*.$$

Suppose that on 11 consecutive days inputs were applied at the rate of 50 pounds per man-hour and the daily outputs were given by

Day number	1	2	3	4	5	6	7	8	9	10	11
Y	45.0	44.9	44.8	44.6	45.2	45.1	44.9	44.8	44.8	44.4	43.9

If we subtract 45 from each day's output, we find the implied ϵ^* values:

Day number	1	2	3	4	5	6	7	8	9	10	11
ϵ^*	0	−0.1	−0.2	−0.4	+0.2	+0.1	−0.1	−0.2	−0.2	−0.6	−1.1

which are, of course, precisely the g^* values we used before. Now, however, we have no idea of the origin of the ϵ^* values since the elements of the $\mathcal{Z}$ set are unknown to us. From the current point of view, ϵ^* plays the role of a random variable[4] — its value cannot be predicted with certainty prior to observing the actual output rate at the end of the day.

Once we regard ϵ^* as a random variable, it is clear that Y must also be a random variable since even if X is known, the resulting Y cannot be predicted with certainty because of the inability to set or predict ϵ^*. With respect to the X variable, the situation is not as clear. Depending on the situation, the X variable may or may not be a random variable. This is true even in the output example. One may think that the rate of input could be set prior to the production taking place. If this were the case, X would be a controlled nonrandom variable. Suppose, though, that the raw material is stored in sacks, each of which has a capacity of 10 pounds. If the machinery which fills the sacks is imperfect and if some sacks contain a small amount of defective raw material, then the amount of usable raw material per sack is a random variable. Use of five sacks per man-hour may then not result in an input rate of 50 pounds per man-hour, though one would not expect any substantial deviation from 50 pounds per man-hour. Note that knowledge of the realization of X would offer no clues as to the likely value of ϵ^*.[5] In what follows we shall always proceed on the assumption that X is a random variable. This is more general than the opposite assumption and no difficulties are introduced if in fact X is a controlled rather than random variable.

Our final assumption is that $g(X)$ can be represented in the linear form

$$g(X) = \alpha^* + \beta X,$$

[4]A word is in order about the clause ϵ^* *plays the role of a random variable.* Suppose temperature had no effect on the output rate and the only element of the Z set were age of material. Prior to starting production, all one has to do is check the inventory to find out how old the material is; hence Z_2 = age of material is not a random variable. Still, ϵ^* would *play the role of a random variable* in the sense of our being unable to predict its value with certainty if we simply did not known that Z_2 was the relevant variable. If temperature is important, however, the situation is somewhat different, for temperature itself can be regarded as a random variable. That is, even with the thermostat set at 72°, the possibilities of varying outside temperatures, varying humidity levels, varying efficiency of the heating plant, etc., result in an inability to predict the inside temperature with certainty. Now if it were unknown that temperature influenced output, ϵ^* would not only *play the role of a random variable* due to our ignorance about the elements of the Z set, it would indeed *be* a random variable because the Z set itself contains one or more random variables.

[5]That is, X and the Z set are not only independent in the sense that

$$f(X, Z_1, Z_2, \ldots, Z_n) = g(X) + g^*(Z_1, Z_2, \ldots, Z_n),$$

but X is also stochastically independent of the Z's. This is a key assumption to which we shall return later in the chapter.

where α^* and β are constants.[6] The equation for Y is now transformed from

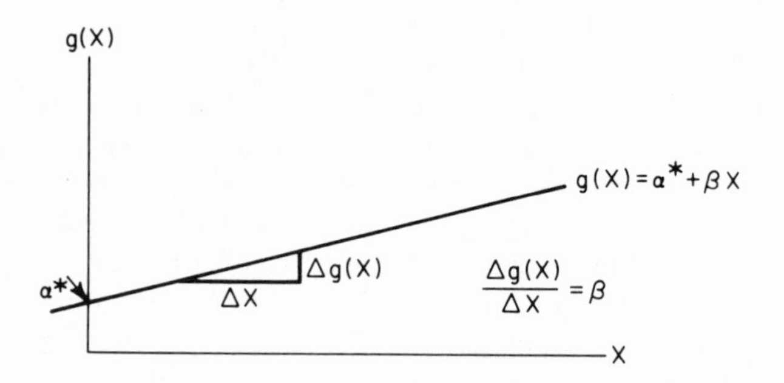

the general

$$Y = g(X) + g^*(Z_1, Z_2, \ldots, Z_n)$$

into the linear stochastic form[7]

$$Y = \alpha^* + \beta X + \epsilon^*.$$

One final point is that it is convenient to have the average effect of the Z set be equal to zero. The average effect is the expected value of ϵ^* and suppose

$$E\epsilon^* = \mu^*.$$

We can then write

$$\begin{aligned} Y &= \alpha^* + \beta X + \epsilon^* \\ &= \alpha^* + \beta X + \epsilon^* + \mu^* - \mu^* \\ &= (\alpha^* + \mu^*) + \beta X + (\epsilon^* - \mu^*) \\ &= \alpha + \beta X + \epsilon, \end{aligned}$$

where $\alpha = (\alpha^* + \mu^*)$, $\epsilon = (\epsilon^* - \mu^*)$, and $E\epsilon = 0$ since

$$\begin{aligned} E\epsilon &= E(\epsilon^* - \mu^*) \\ &= \mu^* - \mu^* = 0. \end{aligned}$$

[6]In the output example, $\alpha^* = 0$, $\beta = 0.9$. The equation $g(X) = \alpha^* + \beta X$ is said to be *linear* because its graph is a straight line with α^* the intercept on the $g(X)$ axis and β, the slope, measuring the change in $g(X)$ per unit change in X.

[7]Assuming $g(X)$ is linear is not as restrictive as it may appear. Suppose, for example, that output depends on the square of input. Then if input is I, we can use

$$X = I^2$$

as the independent variable and the linear function $\alpha^* + \beta X$ is really $\alpha^* + \beta I^2$. What is restrictive is the assumption that we *know* the form of the g function.

8.3 Estimation in the Linear Stochastic Model

The results of the preceding section can be summarized as follows. The dependent variable Y is determined by the independent variable X and all other (minor) influences according to the linear stochastic equation

$$Y = \alpha + \beta X + \epsilon, \tag{8.1}$$

where

(i) Y, X, and ϵ are all random variables.
(ii) X and ϵ are stochastically independent.
(iii) $E\epsilon = 0$ and $\text{Var}(\epsilon) = \sigma^2$.
(iv) α, β, and σ^2 are constants (parameters).

This is the complete specification of the (classical) linear stochastic equation — generally referred to as a *regression model.*[8]

Several properties of the equation are of interest:

(i)
$$\begin{aligned} EY &= E(\alpha + \beta X + \epsilon) \\ &= \alpha + \beta EX + E\epsilon \\ &= \alpha + \beta EX. \end{aligned} \tag{8.2}$$

(ii)
$$\begin{aligned} \text{Var}(Y) &= \text{Var}(\alpha + \beta X + \epsilon) \\ &= \text{Var}(\alpha + \beta X) + \text{Var}(\epsilon) \quad (X \text{ and } \epsilon \text{ independent}) \\ &= \beta^2 \text{Var}(X) + \sigma^2. \end{aligned} \tag{8.3}$$

The expected value of Y seems to depend only on the expected value of the main determinant X. Recalling, however, that

$$\alpha = \alpha^* + E\epsilon^*,$$

it is clear that the expected value of Y depends also on the expected net impact of the Z set. Similarly, two factors contribute to any discrepancy between Y and its expected value, namely variations in $X[\beta^2 \text{Var}(X)]$ and in the net impact of the Z set (σ^2). It is implicitly assumed that

$$\beta^2 \text{Var}(X) > \sigma^2;$$

that is, most of the variation in Y results from variation of X. The variance σ^2 is often termed the *true error variance* in the sense that it is the error involved in ascribing variation in Y to X alone.

[8]The term *regression* comes from one of the earliest studies which used a model of this sort. This early study found that the height of sons could be well predicted by the use of the linear stochastic model $Y = \alpha + \beta X + \epsilon$, where Y = height of son and X = height of father. In general, Y is termed the *regressand* and X the *regressor*.

The relationship of the parameter β to the random variables X and Y can be investigated as follows. If we multiply the linear stochastic equation (8.1) by X, we arrive at

$$XY = \alpha X + \beta X^2 + \epsilon X,$$

which implies

$$\begin{aligned} E(XY) &= \alpha EX + \beta EX^2 + E(\epsilon X) \\ &= \alpha EX + \beta EX^2 \end{aligned} \tag{8.4}$$

since, with ϵ and X independent, $E(\epsilon X) = (E\epsilon)(EX) = 0(EX) = 0$. Equation (8.2) implies $\alpha = EY - \beta EX$, which can be substituted for α in (8.4) yielding

$$E(XY) = (EY - \beta EX)EX + \beta EX^2,$$

$$E(XY) = (EY)(EX) - \beta(EX)^2 + \beta EX^2,$$

$$E(XY) - (EX)(EY) = \beta[EX^2 - (EX)^2];$$

therefore

$$\beta = \frac{E(XY) - (EX)(EY)}{EX^2 - (EX)^2}. \tag{8.5}$$

Now

$$EX^2 - (EX)^2 = \text{Var}\,(X)$$

by definition and

$$E(XY) - (EX)(EY) = \text{Cov}\,(X, Y)$$

by definition,[9] so that

$$\beta = \frac{\text{Cov}\,(X, Y)}{\text{Var}\,(X)}.$$

Since Var (X) must be positive, the sign of β and the sign of Cov (X, Y) must be the same. Thus if $\beta > 0$, the Cov (X, Y) must be > 0, indicating that increases in X are likely to lead to increases in Y and decreases in X to decreases in Y. If $\beta < 0$, the Cov (X, Y) must also be < 0, indicating that increases in X are likely to lead to reductions in Y and reductions in X to increases in Y.

The major problem connected with the linear stochastic equation is that the theory which leads to the specification of the equation does not generally reveal the values of α, β, and σ^2. Thus the theory involved may reveal that X is the main determinant of Y, but it may not specify by how much Y changes per unit change in X. If an investigator wishes to forecast the value of Y, he must not only know what X will be, he must also know the values of α and β. If the investigator wishes to make some statement as to how much Y is apt to differ from the forecast which depends on X alone, he

[9]See Section 4.4.

must know something about the error variance σ^2. The problem, then, is seen to be one of obtaining estimators of the unknown parameters α, β, and σ^2.

In Chapter 7 we saw that parameters could be estimated on the basis of a random sample. In the case of the linear stochastic equation, there are three random variables Y, X, and ϵ. Suppose we can obtain a random sample $X_1, X_2, \ldots, X_N$ corresponding to the independent variable X. Now X_1 and a corresponding ϵ_1 generate the random variable Y_1 according to

$$Y_1 = \alpha + \beta X_1 + \epsilon_1.$$

Y_1, of course, is the directly observable random variable. Suppose for example that the realized value of X_1 is 50 and the corresponding realized value of Y_1 is 45. Since α and β are unknown, the X_1 and Y_1 realizations cannot be used to infer the realized value of ϵ_1. The investigator therefore obtains a random sample of X's and a random sample of corresponding Y's, but the ϵ's are never observable, precisely for the reason that α and β are unknown parameters. We write the two random samples as a set of ordered pairs

$$\{(X_1, Y_1), (X_2, Y_2), (X_3, Y_3), \ldots, (X_N, Y_N)\}$$

in order to indicate that Y_1 corresponds to X_1, Y_2 corresponds to X_2, and so on.

Returning to the output example in Section 8.2, suppose we observed the production process on 10 randomly chosen days over the next 6 months[10] and found

TABLE 8-2

Day number	X	Y
14	45	39.0
102	40	35.4
87	51	46.2
·	53	46.4
·	48	43.5
·	57	51.6
·	52	45.5
·	42	35.7
·	50	43.9
·	53	45.5

[10]Since we require a random sample, we could proceed as follows. Number each day of the next 6 months consecutively: 001, 002, 003, 004, . . . , 132. (The total of 132 days assumes 6(30) = 180 days during a 6 month period, minus 6(8) = 48 days to eliminate 4 Saturdays and 4 Sundays each month. Now turn to the random number table, read 3-digit numbers starting at the upper left. Continue until 10 numbers between 001 and 132 have been obtained. If the 3-digit numbers which fell in the required interval were 014, 102, 087, etc., we would observe the input-output results on days 14, 102, 87, etc.

The set of ordered pairs

$$\{(45, 39.0), (40, 35.4), (51, 46.2), \ldots, (53, 45.5)\}$$

would be the set of realizations of the random variables $X_1, X_2, \ldots, X_{10}$ and the corresponding random variables $Y_1, Y_2, \ldots, Y_{10}$.

We can now state that the fundamental problem of regression analysis is to determine estimators of the parameters α, β, and σ^2 by the use of the available random samples $\{(X_1, Y_1,), (X_2, Y_2), \ldots, (X_N, Y_N)\}$.

Actually, estimators of α and β can be defined quite readily by means of the method of moments procedure. According to (8.5),

$$\beta = \frac{E(XY) - (EX)(EY)}{EX^2 - (EX)^2}$$

and the method of moments estimator of each component of β is

$$E(XY) \text{ estimated by } \frac{1}{N}\sum_i X_iY_i,$$

$$EX \text{ estimated by } \frac{1}{N}\sum_i X_i,$$

$$EY \text{ estimated by } \frac{1}{N}\sum_i Y_i,$$

$$EX^2 \text{ estimated by } \frac{1}{N}\sum_i X_i^2,$$

$$(EX)^2 \text{ estimated by } \left(\frac{1}{N}\sum_i X_i\right)^2.$$

Consequently, the method of moments estimator of β, denoted by $\hat{\beta}$, is

$$\hat{\beta} = \frac{\frac{1}{N}\sum X_iY_i - \left(\frac{1}{N}\sum Y_i\right)}{\frac{1}{N}\sum X_i^2 - \left(\frac{1}{N}\sum X_i\right)^2}.$$

Multiplying numerator and denominator by N^2, we arrive at

$$\hat{\beta} = \frac{N\sum X_iY_i - (\sum X_i)(\sum Y_i)}{N\sum X_i^2 - (\sum X_i)^2}, \tag{8.6}$$

which is a convenient form for computing the realized value of the random variable $\hat{\beta}$[11] from the realizations of the X_i and the Y_i.

Equation (8.2) implies

$$\alpha = EY - \beta EX$$

[11] $\hat{\beta}$ is a random variable for precisely the same reasons that $\bar{X}$ and s^2 are random variables.

so that the method of moments estimator of α, say $\hat{\alpha}$, is given by

$$\hat{\alpha} = \frac{1}{N}\sum Y_i - \hat{\beta}\left(\frac{1}{N}\sum X_i\right)$$

or

$$\hat{\alpha} = \bar{Y} - \hat{\beta}\bar{X}. \tag{8.7}$$

EXAMPLE 8.3.1. Using the X_i, Y_i realizations given in Table 8.2, compute realizations of $\hat{\beta}$ and $\hat{\alpha}$ for the model

$$Y_i = \alpha + \beta X_i + \epsilon_i \quad (i = 1, 2, \ldots, 10),$$

where X_i = pounds of raw material per man-hour on day i and Y_i = pounds of output per man-hour on day i.

Solution: First repeat Table 8-2 and add the additional columns required by the estimating formulas given in (8.6) and (8.7).

x_i	y_i	$x_i y_i$	x_i^2
45	39.0	1755.0	2025
40	35.4	1416.0	1600
51	46.2	2356.2	2601
53	46.4	2459.2	2809
48	43.5	2088.0	2304
57	51.6	2941.2	3249
52	45.5	2366.0	2704
42	35.7	1499.4	1764
50	43.9	2195.0	2500
53	45.5	2411.5	2809
$\sum x_i = 491$	$\sum y_i = 432.7$	$\sum x_i y_i = 21{,}487.5$	$\sum x_i^2 = 24{,}365$

We therefore find ($N = 10$)

$$\hat{\beta} = \frac{10\sum x_i y_i - (\sum x_i)(\sum y_i)}{10\sum x_i^2 - (\sum x_i)^2} = \frac{10(21{,}487.5) - 491(432.7)}{10(24{,}365) - (491)^2}$$

$$= \frac{2{,}419.3}{2{,}569.0} = 0.94,$$

$$\hat{\alpha} = \frac{\sum y_i}{N} - \hat{\beta}\frac{\sum x_i}{N} = \frac{432.7}{10} - (0.94)\,\frac{491}{10}$$

$$= 43.27 - (0.94)(49.1) = 43.27 - 46.15$$

$$= -2.88.$$

At this point it would be useful to comment on the origin of the X, Y observations in Table 8-2. It was assumed that the true relation was given by

$$Y = -1 + 0.9X + \epsilon.$$

The β value of 0.9 is the same as that used in the production function example of Section 8.2. The α value of -1 is $E\epsilon^*$, which is the assumed average net effect of temperature and age variation; α^* is assumed equal to zero. The 10 values of X which appeared in Table 8-2 were chosen arbitrarily. For each X value,

$$-1 + 0.9X$$

was calculated and this represented the output which would result if ϵ were zero. Next a table of random numbers with a mean of zero and a variance of unity[12] was used to obtain 10 ϵ values. This resulted in the following table.

X	$-1 + 0.9X$	ϵ	$Y = -1 + 0.9X + \epsilon$
45	39.5	−0.46	39.04
40	35.0	0.42	35.42
51	44.9	1.30	46.20
53	46.7	−0.34	46.36
48	42.2	1.30	43.50
57	50.3	1.29	51.59
52	45.8	−0.31	45.49
42	36.8	−1.11	35.69
50	44.0	−0.10	43.90
53	46.7	−1.20	45.50

The final column (rounded to one decimal place) was used as the set of realized Y values.

We see, therefore, that the realized $\hat{\beta}$ of 0.94 is quite close to the true β of 0.90. The realized $\hat{\alpha}$ of -2.88 is really quite far from the true α of -1. Some of the reasons for this will be considered later in the chapter. In practice, of course, the investigator never knows the true α and β[13] so that a comparison such as we have made here is a luxury never available in an applied situation.

The remaining problem is that of determining an estimator of σ^2, the variance of ϵ, but no observations on ϵ are available. We proceed as follows. Equation (8.1) implies

$$\epsilon = Y - \alpha - \beta X$$

[12]This is not Appendix Table B, but another table constructed to approximate random observations on the random variable which is distributed η (0, 1).

[13]Indeed, if α and β were known, there would be no reason to estimate them.

and since $E\epsilon = 0$,

$$\text{Var}(\epsilon) = E[(\epsilon - E\epsilon)^2] = E\epsilon^2.$$

but

$$\epsilon^2 = (Y - \alpha - \beta X)^2.$$

Consequently,

$$\sigma^2 = E\epsilon^2 = E[(Y - \alpha - \beta X)^2].$$

The obvious method of moments estimator of $E[(Y - \alpha - \beta X)^2]$ would be

$$\frac{1}{N}\sum_i (Y_i - \alpha - \beta X_i)^2,$$

if α and β were known. Since α and β are unknown, we use instead their method of moments estimators $\hat{\alpha}$ and $\hat{\beta}$. The resulting estimator of σ^2, say $\hat{\sigma}^2$, is then given by

$$\hat{\sigma}^2 = \frac{1}{N-2}\sum_i (Y_i - \hat{\alpha} - \hat{\beta} X_i)^2, \tag{8.8}$$

where the division by $(N - 2)$ rather than N is a degrees of freedom correction precisely analogous to that made in the case of the sample variance in Chapter 7. It can be shown that this is the appropriate correction for obtaining an unbiased estimator of σ^2.

Equation (8.8) is not the most convenient for computation purposes. Rather, consider

$$(N-2)\hat{\sigma}^2 = \sum_i (Y_i - \hat{\alpha} - \hat{\beta} X_i)^2,$$

and since $\hat{\alpha} = \bar{Y} - \hat{\beta}\bar{X}$,

$$\begin{aligned}
(N-2)\hat{\sigma}^2 &= \sum_i [Y_i - (\bar{Y} - \hat{\beta}\bar{X}) - \hat{\beta}X_i]^2 \\
&= \sum_i [(Y_i - \bar{Y}) - \hat{\beta}(X_i - \bar{X})]^2 \\
&= \sum_i [(Y_i - \bar{Y})^2 + \hat{\beta}^2(X_i - \bar{X})^2 - 2\hat{\beta}(Y_i - Y)(X_i - \bar{X})] \\
&= \sum_i (Y_i - \bar{Y})^2 + \hat{\beta}^2\sum_i (X_i - \bar{X})^2 - 2\hat{\beta}\sum_i (Y_i - \bar{Y})(X_i - \bar{X}).
\end{aligned}$$

Now

$$\begin{aligned}
\hat{\beta} &= \frac{N\sum_i X_iY_i - (\sum_i X_i)(\sum_i Y_i)}{N\sum_i (X_i^2) - (\sum_i X_i)^2} \\
&= \frac{\sum_i X_iY_i - \frac{1}{N}\sum_i X_i\sum_i Y_i}{\sum_i X_i^2 - \frac{1}{N}(\sum X_i)^2} \\
&= \frac{\sum_i X_iY_i - \bar{X}\sum Y_i}{\sum (X_i - \bar{X})^2};
\end{aligned}$$

therefore

$$\hat{\beta} \sum (X_i - \overline{X})^2 = \sum X_i Y_i - \overline{X} \sum Y_i. \tag{8.9}$$

Also,

$$\begin{aligned}
\sum_i (Y_i - \overline{Y})(X_i - \overline{X}) &= \sum_i (Y_i)(X_i - \overline{X}) - \sum_i \overline{Y}(X_i - \overline{X}) \\
&= \sum_i Y_i X_i - \overline{X} \sum_i Y_i - \overline{Y} \sum_i (X_i - \overline{X}) \\
&= \sum_i Y_i X_i - \overline{X} \sum_i Y_i,
\end{aligned}$$

since

$$\sum_i (X_i - \overline{X}) = \sum_i X_i - N\overline{X} = \sum_i X_i - N \frac{\sum X_i}{N} = 0.$$

Consequently

$$\begin{aligned}
-2\hat{\beta} \sum_i (Y_i - \overline{Y})(X_i - \overline{X}) &= -2\hat{\beta}(\sum_i Y_i X_i - \overline{X} \sum_i Y_i) \\
&= -2\hat{\beta}[\hat{\beta} \sum_i (X_i - \overline{X})^2]
\end{aligned}$$

by substituting from (8.9); therefore

$$\begin{aligned}
(N - 2)\hat{\sigma}^2 &= \sum_i (Y_i - \overline{Y})^2 + \hat{\beta}^2 \sum_i (X_i - \overline{X})^2 - 2\hat{\beta} \sum_i (Y_i - \overline{Y})(X_i - \overline{X}) \\
&= \sum_i (Y_i - \overline{Y})^2 + \hat{\beta}^2 \sum_i (X_i - \overline{X})^2 - 2\hat{\beta}^2 \sum_i (X_i - \overline{X})^2 \\
&= \sum_i (Y_i - \overline{Y})^2 - \hat{\beta}^2 \sum_i (X_i - \overline{X})^2.
\end{aligned}$$

Finally,

$$(N - 2)\hat{\sigma}^2 = [\sum_i Y_i^2 - N^2\overline{Y}] - \hat{\beta}^2[\sum_i X_i^2 - N\overline{X}^2] \tag{8.10}$$

is the most convenient computing form for $\hat{\sigma}^2$.

EXAMPLE 8.3.2. Compute the realization of $\hat{\sigma}^2$ for the data of Example 8.3.1.

Solution: In Example 8.3.1 we found $\hat{\beta} = 0.94$, $\sum x_i^2 = 24{,}365$, $\overline{X} = 49.1$, $\overline{Y} = 43.27$, and $N = 10$. All that remains is to compute

$$\sum y_i^2,$$

which is easily found to be

$$\sum y_i^2 = 18{,}958.57.$$

Therefore

$$(N-2)\hat{\sigma}^2 = [18{,}958.57 - 10(43.27)^2] - (0.94)^2[24{,}365 - 10(49.1)^2]$$
$$= (235.64) - (0.8836)(256.90)$$
$$= 235.64 - 227.00$$
$$= 8.64.$$

Hence

$$\hat{\sigma}^2 = \frac{8.64}{N-2} = \frac{8.64}{8}$$
$$= 1.08.$$

Recalling that the data were constructed such that $\sigma^2 = 1.00$, the estimate 1.08 is indeed quite close to the true error variance.

8.4 Scatter Diagrams and Least-Squares Estimation

Suppose we begin with the linear stochastic equation

$$Y = \alpha + \beta X + \epsilon$$

and obtain a random sample of X, Y values

$$\{(X_1, Y_1), (X_2, Y_2), \ldots, (X_N, Y_N)\}.$$

On the basis of the realized X, Y values, we calculate estimates of α and β. In the examples of Section 8.3 we found $\hat{\alpha} = -2.88$ and $\hat{\beta} = 0.94$. This is usually represented by writing the equation

$$\hat{Y} = -2.88 + 0.94X,$$

where the "hat," or caret, over the Y indicates that this equation produces *estimates* of Y values. For example, our estimate of the output that would result from an input rate of $X = 60$ is

$$\hat{Y} = -2.88 + 0.94(60) = 53.52.$$

The value $\hat{Y} = 53.52$ is merely an estimate of the output rate and is subject to two sources of error:

(i) The first error source arises from the fact that output is being forecast on the basis of input (X) alone; no account can be taken of the factors contained in the ϵ term since the ϵ value cannot be predicted with certainty.

(ii) The second error source arises from the fact that we are using estimates of α and β instead of the true parameters themselves.

It is clear that the first error source cannot be eliminated[14] but the better we succeed in estimating α and β the more the second source of error is reduced.[15]

In order to minimize the second error source, we must attempt to approximate the equation

$$Y = \alpha + \beta X$$

as closely as possible by using a random sample

$$\{(X_1, Y_1), (X_2, Y_2), \ldots, (X_N, Y_N)\}.$$

A useful visual device is to construct a *scatter diagram* on the basis of the realized X, Y values. The scatter diagram simply plots the X, Y values on a graph with the dependent variable Y measured on the vertical axis and the independent variable X measured on the horizontal axis. Figure 8.1 contains the scatter diagram corresponding to the observed sample for Example 8.3.1. The circled point corresponds to the first observation and has coordinates $X = 45$, $Y = 39$. The dashed line in Figure 8.1 represents the equation

$$Y = -1 + 0.9X,$$

which is the line we used to generate the data and which we now wish to estimate solely on the basis of the sample of X, Y realizations. In practice, of course, the position of this "true" line is unknown. The reason that the observations do not lie on the true line is that the equation $Y = -1 + 0.9X$ does not take the ϵ term into account; that is, it assumes $\epsilon = 0$ and it was seen in Example 8.3.1 that none of the ϵ realizations was zero for this particular set of 10 observations. Note, however, that all the points in the scatter diagram cluster about the true line. If the points are spread rather uniformly about the true line, the pattern of points essentially traces out the line. Indeed, the assumptions

(i) $E\epsilon = 0$.

(ii) $\text{Var } \epsilon = \sigma^2$.

(iii) ϵ and X are stochastically independent.

[14]This cannot occur unless all the elements of the Z set are specified and taken into account directly.

[15]In our case the true values of α and β are known: $\alpha = -1$, $\beta = 0.9$. We can therefore predict that an input rate of $X = 60$ will result in an output rate of

$$-1 + 0.9\ (60) = 53$$

if $\epsilon = 0$. Hence the value $Y = 53.52$ involves a net error of $+0.52$ due to the use of estimates of α and β instead of the true parameter values.

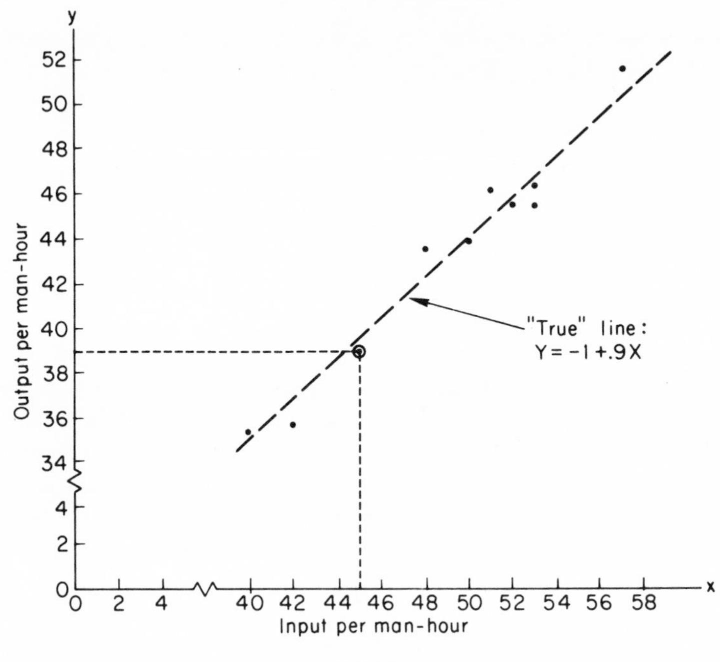

FIGURE 8.1

imply that one should expect the observations to cluster uniformly about the true line. Consider Figures 8.2a–8.2c which contain three scatter diagrams with the "true" line shown dashed. In none of the three cases do

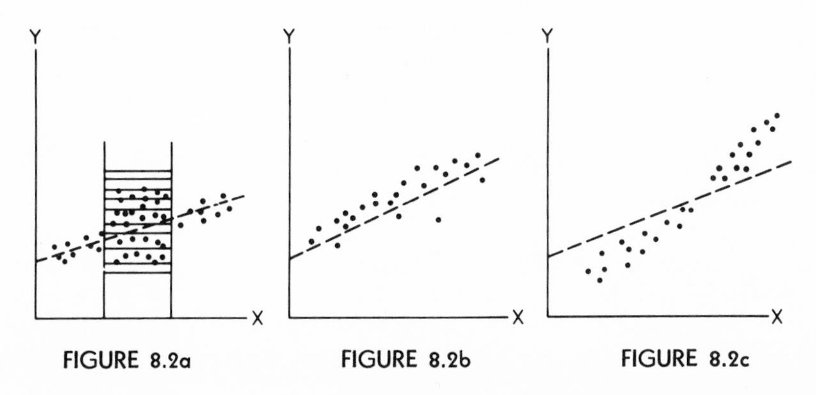

FIGURE 8.2a FIGURE 8.2b FIGURE 8.2c

the points scatter uniformly about the true line. Clearly, the cluster of points in Figure 8.2a violates the assumption that ϵ has constant variance σ^2. The vertical distance between any given point and the true line measures the realized value of ϵ for that observation. Obviously the ϵ's were much more variable within the shaded vertical band of Figure 8.2a than outside that band. Figure 8.2b shows a scatter diagram which contradicts the assumption $E\epsilon = 0$, because all but four of the many points shown lie above the true line, thereby indicating $E\epsilon > 0$. A possible pattern which illustrates violation of the assumption that ϵ and X are independent is shown in Figure 8.2c. In this case we clearly have the result

$$\text{Cov}\ (\epsilon, X) > 0,$$

since low values of X are associated with low (that is, negative) values of ϵ and high values of X are associated with high values of ϵ.

It is an implication of the assumptions (i) to (iii), therefore, that one should expect the cluster of points to be spread uniformly about the true line.[16] This is, however, only an expectation and might not be fulfilled, especially in a small sample. The scatter diagram of Figure 8.3, for example, cannot be interpreted as a violation of the rule of uniform spreading even though three out of four ϵ values are positive. If $P(\epsilon > 0) = \frac{1}{2}$, the proba-

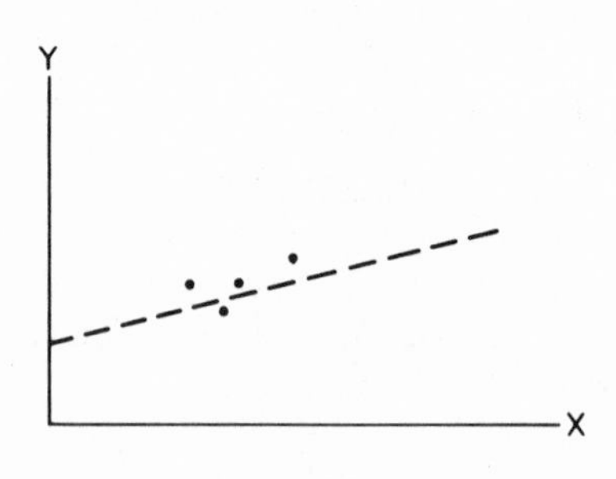

FIGURE 8.3

bility that three out of four independent ϵ values will be positive is $4!/3!1!$ $(1/2)^3(1/2)^1 = 1/4$. Thus even if all the assumptions are correct, a small sample of observations could easily display a pattern of nonuniform spreading. This is merely another indication that the efficiency of an estimator is generally greater the larger the sample size on which it is based.

The uniform spreading rule can be used to define another estimation method, namely the *method of least squares*. Essentially, the method of least squares estimates the parameters α and β in such a way that the observed scatter and the resulting estimate of the line $Y = \alpha + \beta X$ satisfy the uniform spreading rule. The least squares method can be motivated as follows.

[16]If one of the assumptions is false, then the points will not spread uniformly about the "true" line. This, however, is an entirely different matter which will be discussed in Section 8.6.

We know that if $a \neq 0$,

$$E[(\epsilon - a)^2] > E[(\epsilon - 0)^2] = \sigma^2. \tag{8.11}$$

In other words, a random variable varies less[17] around its mean than around any other constant. Suppose we somehow obtain estimates of α and β, say $\bar{\alpha}$ and $\bar{\beta}$. For a particular value of X, say X_i, we would then estimate that Y would be equal to

$$\bar{\alpha} + \bar{\beta}X_i$$

if $\epsilon_i = 0$. Now the actual value of Y corresponding to X_i is Y_i, and the difference

$$Y_i - (\bar{\alpha} + \bar{\beta}X_i)$$

is the ϵ_i realization *implied* by the estimates $\alpha = \bar{\alpha}$ and $\beta = \bar{\beta}$. By this device we arrive at

$$Y_1 - (\bar{\alpha} + \bar{\beta}X_1) \text{ as the implied } \epsilon_1.$$
$$Y_2 - (\bar{\alpha} + \bar{\beta}X_2) \text{ as the implied } \epsilon_2.$$
$$\vdots$$
$$Y_N - (\bar{\alpha} + \bar{\beta}X_N) \text{ as the implied } \epsilon_N.$$

Since $E\epsilon = 0$, it is natural to require that we choose $\bar{\alpha}$ and $\bar{\beta}$ such that

$$\frac{1}{N}\sum_i [Y_i - (\bar{\alpha} + \bar{\beta}X_i)] = 0;$$

that is, the average of the implied ϵ values should be zero. Solving the equation above, we find

$$\frac{1}{N}\sum_i [Y_i - (\bar{\alpha} + \bar{\beta}X_i)] = 0,$$

$$\frac{1}{N}\sum Y_i - \frac{1}{N}\sum \bar{\alpha} - \frac{1}{N}\sum \bar{\beta}X_i = 0,$$

$$\bar{Y} - \frac{1}{N}(N\bar{\alpha}) - \frac{1}{N}\bar{\beta}\sum X_i = 0,$$

$$\bar{Y} - \bar{\alpha} - \bar{\beta}\bar{X} = 0;$$

therefore

$$\bar{\alpha} = \bar{Y} - \bar{\beta}\bar{X}. \tag{8.12}$$

[17]It varies less in the sense of expected squared deviation.

Recalling (8.7), it is clear that the method of moments estimators satisfy the property that the average of the implied ϵ values is zero. This requirement alone, however, is insufficient to insure that the points of the scatter diagram will cluster uniformly about the resulting line. Consider the scatter diagram of Figure 8.4. The solid line in Figure 8.4 has been drawn such that the

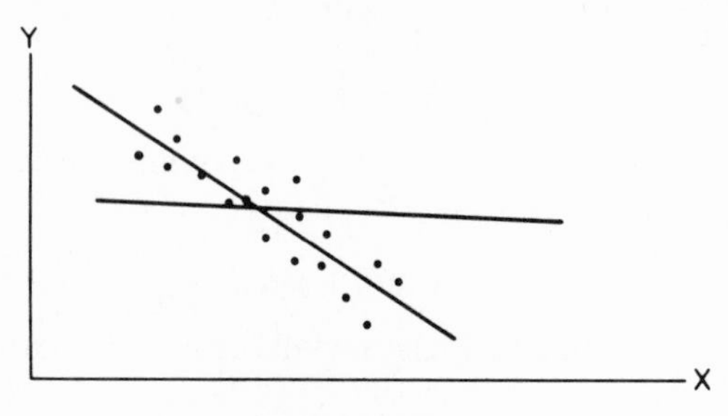

FIGURE 8.4

implied ϵ values average zero,[18] but the solid line would be a poor estimate of the "true" line (shown dashed in Figure 8.4). If (8.12) is satisfied, the implied ϵ values do indeed average zero, but it is natural to require that *in addition*

$$S^* = \frac{1}{N} \sum_i [Y_i - (\bar{\alpha} + \bar{\beta} X_i)]^2,$$

or equivalently

$$NS^* = S = \sum_i [Y_i - (\bar{\alpha} + \bar{\beta} X_i)]^2$$

be as small as possible. This requirement states that the variance of the implied ϵ values should be as small as possible; a requirement which is perfectly consistent with the relation in (8.11). It is clear that the variance requirement will be satisfied by a line such as that shown dashed in Figure 8.4; that is, by a line which goes through the "middle" of the cluster in such a way as to satisfy the uniform spreading rule. This amounts to requiring that the line be such that the sum of the squared deviations S about the line be as small as possible; hence the name least squares estimators for estimators which satisfy this property.

The least squares estimators therefore satisfy both (8.12) and minimization of

$$S = \sum_i [Y_i - (\bar{\alpha} + \bar{\beta} X_i)]^2.$$

[18]The positive ϵ's associated with low values of X cancel the negative ϵ's associated with large values of X.

Since (8.12) must be satisfied, we can write

$$\begin{aligned} S &= \sum_i [Y_i - \bar{\alpha} - \bar{\beta} X_i]^2 \\ &= \sum_i [Y_i - (\bar{Y} - \bar{\beta}\bar{X}) - \bar{\beta} X_i]^2 \\ &= \sum_i [(Y_i - \bar{Y}) - \bar{\beta}(X_i - \bar{X})]^2 \\ &= \sum_i [(Y_i - \bar{Y})^2 + \bar{\beta}^2 (X_i - \bar{X})^2 - 2\bar{\beta}(X_i - \bar{X})(Y_i - \bar{Y})] \\ &= \sum_i (Y_i - \bar{Y})^2 + \bar{\beta}^2 \sum (X_i - \bar{X})^2 - 2\bar{\beta} \sum (X_i - \bar{X})(Y_i - \bar{Y}). \end{aligned}$$

It is clear, then, that to minimize S we must first choose $\bar{\beta}$ such that

$$\bar{\beta}^2 \sum (X_i - \bar{X})^2 - 2\bar{\beta} \sum (X_i - \bar{X})(Y_i - \bar{Y})$$

is as small as possible and then choose $\bar{\alpha}$ to satisfy (8.12). Let

$$T = a\bar{\beta}^2 - 2b\bar{\beta},$$

where

$$a = \sum (X_i - \bar{X})^2 > 0$$

(we assume the X_i are not all equal), and

$$b = \sum (X_i - \bar{X})(Y_i - \bar{Y}).$$

Since $a > 0$, minimizing T is the same as minimizing

$$\frac{T}{a} = \bar{\beta}^2 - 2\frac{b}{a}\bar{\beta}.$$

Now if $\bar{\beta} = b/a$,

$$\frac{T}{a} = \left(\frac{b}{a}\right)^2 - 2\left(\frac{b}{a}\right)^2 = -\left(\frac{b}{a}\right)^2.$$

If $\bar{\beta} = (b/a) + u$, where $u \neq 0$, then

$$\begin{aligned} \frac{T}{a} &= \left(\frac{b}{a} + u\right)^2 - 2\left(\frac{b}{a}\right)\left(\frac{b}{a} + u\right) \\ &= \left(\frac{b}{a}\right)^2 + 2u\frac{b}{a} + u^2 - 2\left(\frac{b}{a}\right)^2 - 2u\frac{b}{a} \\ &= -\left(\frac{b}{a}\right)^2 + u^2 > -\left(\frac{b}{a}\right)^2 \end{aligned}$$

since $u^2 > 0$. Thus T/a, hence T and S, are all minimized if $\bar{\beta} = b/a$. We conclude therefore that $\bar{\beta}$ should be chosen such that

$$\bar{\beta} = \frac{b}{a} = \frac{\sum (X_i - \bar{X})(Y_i - \bar{Y})}{\sum (X_i - \bar{X})^2},$$

but in the derivation of (8.10) it was shown that

$$\frac{\sum (X_i - \bar{X})(Y_i - \bar{Y})}{\sum (X_i - \bar{X})^2} = \frac{N \sum X_i Y_i - (\sum X_i)(\sum Y_i)}{N \sum X_i^2 - (\sum X_i)^2};$$

hence $\bar{\beta} = \hat{\beta}$; whereupon (8.12) implies $\bar{\alpha} = \hat{\alpha}$.

We began by trying to fit to the scatter diagram a line which would closely approximate the "true" line $Y = \alpha + \beta X$. We found that the assumptions inherent in the linear stochastic model implied that the observed scatter of points should spread uniformly about the true line. This, in turn, implied that the fitted line should result in implied ϵ values with an average of zero and a variance as small as possible, that is, that the estimated values of α and β should be least squares estimates. Having derived the least squares estimators, we found them to be identical to the method of moments estimators, $\hat{\alpha}$ and $\hat{\beta}$. The estimators $\hat{\alpha}$ and $\hat{\beta}$, in addition to having the desirable properties of method of moments estimators, result in the line,

$$\hat{Y} = \hat{\alpha} + \hat{\beta} X,$$

which provides the *best* fit to the observed scatter diagram. The line

$$\hat{Y} = \hat{\alpha} + \hat{\beta} X$$

is described as the line of best fit in the sense that

$$\sum (Y_i - \hat{\alpha} - \hat{\beta} X_i)^2 = \sum (Y_i - \hat{Y}_i)^2,$$

which measures the extent to which the observed Y values differ from the estimated Y values, is as small as possible. We know already that

$$\hat{\sigma}^2 = \frac{1}{N-2} \sum (Y_i - \hat{\alpha} - \hat{\beta} X_i)^2$$

is an unbiased estimator of the error variance $\sigma^2 = E\epsilon^2$. The estimators $\hat{\alpha}$ and $\hat{\beta}$ minimize this estimated error variance.

8.5 Stochastic Properties and "Goodness-of-Fit"

Since the least squares and method of moments estimators are identical, the properties to be considered apply equally to both. First consider $\hat{\beta}$.

$$\begin{aligned}\hat{\beta} &= \frac{\sum (X_i - \bar{X})(Y_i - \bar{Y})}{\sum (X_i - \bar{X})^2} \\ &= \frac{\sum (X_i - \bar{X}) Y_i}{\sum (X_i - \bar{X})^2} - \frac{\bar{Y} \sum (X_i - \bar{X})}{\sum (X_i - \bar{X})^2} \\ &= \frac{\sum (X_i - \bar{X}) Y_i}{\sum (X_i - \bar{X})^2},\end{aligned}$$

since

$$\sum (X_i - \overline{X}) = 0.$$

For each Y_i it is true that $Y_i = \alpha + \beta X_i + \epsilon_i$; therefore

$$\begin{aligned}\hat{\beta} &= \frac{\sum (X_i - \overline{X})(\alpha + \beta X_i + \epsilon_i)}{\sum (X_i - \overline{X})^2} \\ &= \frac{\alpha \sum (X_i - \overline{X}) + \beta \sum (X_i - \overline{X})X_i + \sum (X_i - \overline{X})\epsilon_i}{\sum (X_i - \overline{X})^2}\end{aligned}$$

Now

$$\alpha \sum (X_i - \overline{X}) = \alpha(0) = 0;$$

and since

$$\beta \overline{X} \sum (X_i - \overline{X}) = \beta \overline{X}(0) = 0,$$

$$\begin{aligned}\beta \sum (X_i - \overline{X})X_i &= \beta \sum (X_i - \overline{X})X_i - \beta \overline{X} \sum (X_i - \overline{X}) \\ &= \beta \sum (X_i - \overline{X})X_i - \beta \sum (X_i - \overline{X})\overline{X} \\ &= \beta \sum (X_i - \overline{X})(X_i - \overline{X}) \\ &= \beta \sum (X_i - \overline{X})^2.\end{aligned}$$

Consequently,

$$\begin{aligned}\hat{\beta} &= \frac{\alpha \sum (X_i - \overline{X}) + \beta \sum (X_i - \overline{X})X_i + \sum (X_i - \overline{X})\epsilon_i}{\sum (X_i - \overline{X})^2} \\ &= \frac{\beta \sum (X_i - \overline{X})^2 + \sum (X_i - \overline{X})\epsilon_i}{\sum (X_i - \overline{X})^2} \\ &= \beta + \frac{\sum (X_i - \overline{X})\epsilon_i}{\sum (X_i - \overline{X})^2}.\end{aligned}$$

Now the term

$$\sum (X_i - \overline{X})^2 = (N - 1)s_X^2,$$

where s_X^2 is an unbiased estimator of the variance of X. We can therefore write

$$\begin{aligned}\hat{\beta} &= \beta + \frac{\sum (X_i - \overline{X})\epsilon_i}{(N-1)s_X^2} \\ &= \beta + \sum \frac{(X_i - \overline{X})}{(N-1)s_X^2}\,\epsilon_i \\ &= \beta + \sum f_i(X)\epsilon_i,\end{aligned}$$

where

$$f_i(X) = \frac{(X_i - \overline{X})}{(N-1)s_X^2}.$$

With $\hat{\beta}$ written in this form we can easily determine that it is an unbiased estimator of β, for

$$\begin{aligned} E\hat{\beta} &= E[\beta + \sum f_i(X)\epsilon_i] \\ &= \beta + E\sum f_i(X)\epsilon_i \\ &= \beta + \sum Ef_i(X)\epsilon_i. \end{aligned}$$

Consider the term $Ef_i(X)\epsilon_i$. Since the set $\{(X_i, Y_i)\}$ comprises a random sample, the independence of ϵ_i and X_i implies that ϵ_i is independent of all the X_i variables for $i = 1, 2, \ldots, N$. As a result, ϵ_i and $f_i(X)$ are stochastically independent and the term $Ef_i(X)\epsilon_i$ can be written as a product of expectations,

$$\begin{aligned} Ef_i(X)\epsilon_i &= [Ef_i(X)][E\epsilon_i] \\ &= [Ef_i(X)][0] \\ &= 0. \end{aligned}$$

Therefore

$$\begin{aligned} E\hat{\beta} &= \beta + \sum Ef_i(X)\epsilon_i \\ &= \beta + \sum (0) \\ &= \beta, \end{aligned}$$

which proves that $\hat{\beta}$ is an unbiased estimator of β. The efficiency of $\hat{\beta}$ as an estimator of β depends on the variance of $\hat{\beta}$, σ^2. By definition, $\sigma_{\hat{\beta}}^2 = E[(\hat{\beta} - E\hat{\beta})^2] = E[(\hat{\beta} - \beta)^2]$ since $E\hat{\beta} = \beta$. It is shown in Section 8.5 of the appendix that

$$\sigma_{\hat{\beta}}^2 = \frac{\sigma^2}{N-1} E\left(\frac{1}{s_X^2}\right)$$

where

$$\frac{\sum (X_i - \overline{X})^2}{N-1} = s_X^2,$$

and σ^2 is the variance of ϵ. Notice that as the sample size N increases, s_X^2 approaches σ_X^2 with a probability of unity since the sample variance s_X^2 is a consistent estimator of σ_X^2. Consequently, as N increases,

$$E\left(\frac{1}{s_X^2}\right) \to E\left(\frac{1}{\sigma_X^2}\right) = \frac{1}{\sigma_X^2}.$$

As a result, as $N \to \infty$,

$$\sigma_{\hat{\beta}}^2 \to \frac{\sigma^2}{N-1} \cdot \frac{1}{\sigma_X^2} = \frac{1}{N-1}\left(\frac{\sigma^2}{\sigma_X^2}\right).$$

But as $N \to \infty$, $1/(N-1) \to 0$ so that we have an unbiased estimator $\hat{\beta}$, whose variance approaches zero as N increases. This means that the efficiency of $\hat{\beta}$ continues to increase as N increases; that is, $\hat{\beta}$ is a consistent estimator of β. For a given sample size N, the efficiency of $\hat{\beta}$ is given by

$$\sigma_{\hat{\beta}}^2 = \frac{\sigma^2}{N-1} E\left(\frac{1}{s_X^2}\right),$$

which of course cannot be calculated since σ^2 and $E(1/s_X^2)$ are both unknown. If, however, we replace σ^2 by its unbiased estimator

$$\hat{\sigma}^2 = \frac{1}{N-2} \sum (Y_i - \hat{\alpha} - \hat{\beta}X_i)^2$$

and estimate $E(1/s_X^2)$ by $(1/s_X^2)$,[19] we obtain an estimator of $\sigma_{\hat{\beta}}^2$, say $s_{\hat{\beta}}^2$, given by

$$\begin{aligned} s_{\hat{\beta}}^2 &= \frac{\hat{\sigma}^2}{N-1}\left(\frac{1}{s_X^2}\right) \\ &= \frac{\hat{\sigma}^2}{N-1}\left(\frac{N-1}{\sum (X_i - \overline{X})^2}\right) \\ &= \frac{\hat{\sigma}^2}{\sum (X_i - \overline{X})^2}. \end{aligned} \tag{8.13}$$

Turning to $\hat{\alpha}$,

$$\begin{aligned} \hat{\alpha} &= \overline{Y} - \hat{\beta}\overline{X} \\ &= \frac{1}{N}\sum (\alpha + \beta X_i + \epsilon_i) - \hat{\beta}\frac{1}{N}\sum X_i \\ &= \frac{1}{N}\sum \alpha + \beta\frac{1}{N}\sum X_i + \frac{1}{N}\sum \epsilon_i - \hat{\beta}\frac{1}{N}\sum X_i \\ &= \alpha + \beta\overline{X} + \frac{1}{N}\sum \epsilon_i - \hat{\beta}\overline{X} \\ &= \alpha + \beta\overline{X} + \frac{1}{N}\sum \epsilon_i - [\beta + \sum f_i(X)\epsilon_i]\overline{X} \\ &= \alpha + \beta\overline{X} + \frac{1}{N}\sum \epsilon_i - \beta\overline{X} - \sum \overline{X}f_i(X)\epsilon_i \\ &= \alpha + \frac{1}{N}\sum \epsilon_i - \sum [\overline{X}f_i(X)]\epsilon_i. \end{aligned}$$

Therefore

$$\begin{aligned} E\hat{\alpha} &= \alpha + \frac{1}{N}E\sum \epsilon_i - E\sum [\overline{X}f_i(X)]\epsilon_i \\ &= \alpha + \frac{1}{N}\sum E\,\epsilon_i - \sum E[\overline{X}f_i(X)]E\,\epsilon_i \\ &= \alpha, \end{aligned}$$

[19]Obviously, $E(1/s_X^2) = E(1/s_X^2)$ so that $(1/s_X^2)$ is an unbiased estimator of $E(1/s_X^2)$.

since ϵ_i is independent of the X's and $E\epsilon_i = 0$. The estimator $\hat{\alpha}$ is thus seen to be unbiased. It can also be shown that $\hat{\alpha}$ is a consistent estimator of α, and an estimator, say $s_{\hat{\alpha}}^2$, of the variance of $\hat{\alpha}$ is given by

$$s_{\hat{\alpha}}^2 = \frac{\hat{\sigma}^2 \sum X_i^2}{N \sum (X_i - \overline{X})^2}. \tag{8.14}$$

The expressions for $s_{\hat{\alpha}}^2$ and $s_{\hat{\beta}}^2$ reveal a good deal about the estimators $\hat{\alpha}$ and $\hat{\beta}$. Taking

$$s_{\hat{\beta}}^2 = \frac{\hat{\sigma}^2}{\sum (X_i - \overline{X})^2},$$

it is clear that

(i) The smaller the variance of ϵ (which is estimated by $\hat{\sigma}^2$), the more efficient the resulting estimator of β. If the variance of ϵ is small, the random observations not only cluster uniformly about the "true" line, they also cluster very tightly about the line, thus making it substantially easier to "see" the slope β.

(ii) The wider the range of X values, the larger is

$$\sum (X_i - \overline{X})^2,$$

the more efficient is the resulting estimator of β. If the X's are restricted to a very small range, very little of the "true" line can be "seen" and it becomes difficult to estimate the line with very much precision.

Turning to

$$s_{\hat{\alpha}}^2 = \frac{\hat{\sigma}^2 \sum X_i^2}{N \sum (X_i - \overline{X})^2},$$

both remarks made about $s_{\hat{\beta}}^2$ are seen to hold again with respect to efficiency in estimating α, and in addition

(iii) The smaller is

$$\frac{\sum X_i^2}{N},$$

the more efficient is the resulting estimator of α. We thus want

$$\sum (X_i - \overline{X})^2 = \sum X_i^2 - (N\overline{X}^2)$$

to be large while

$$\sum X_i^2$$

is to be small. This can be accomplished by having X's which are moderate in absolute value and evenly balanced around zero so that $\overline{X}$ is close to zero. In this event the scatter of points would cross the Y axis making it substantially easier to "see" the value of α.

The foregoing discussion of $s_{\hat{\alpha}}^2$ and $s_{\hat{\beta}}^2$ sheds a good deal of light on the production function estimation of Examples 8.3.1 and 8.3.2. We found there that

$$\hat{Y} = -2.88 + 0.94X, \quad \text{and} \quad \hat{\sigma}^2 = 1.08,$$

$$\sum x_i^2 = 24{,}365 \quad \text{and} \quad \sum (x_i - \overline{X})^2 = \sum x_i^2 - N\overline{X}^2 = 256.90.$$

Consequently,

$$s_{\hat{\beta}}^2 = \frac{1.08}{256.90} = 0.0042;$$

therefore

$$s_{\hat{\beta}} = \sqrt{0.0042} \cong 0.065$$

and

$$s_{\hat{\alpha}}^2 = \frac{(1.08)(24{,}365)}{10(256.90)} = 10.2430;$$

therefore

$$s_{\hat{\alpha}} = \sqrt{10.2430} \cong 3.201.$$

An approximate confidence interval[20] for β with confidence coefficient ≥ 0.75 would be

$$\hat{\beta} - 2s_{\hat{\beta}} \leq \beta \leq \hat{\beta} + 2s_{\hat{\beta}},$$

$$0.94 - 0.13 \leq \beta \leq 0.94 + 0.13,$$

$$0.81 \leq \beta \leq 1.07.$$

A similarly constructed interval for α, however, would yield

$$\hat{\alpha} - 2s_{\hat{\alpha}} \leq \alpha \leq \hat{\alpha} + 2s_{\hat{\alpha}},$$

$$-2.88 - 6.40 \leq \alpha \leq -2.88 + 6.40,$$

$$-9.28 \leq \alpha \leq 3.52.$$

In the case of β, the width of the interval is 0.26 (1.07 − 0.81), which is less than $\frac{3}{10}$ of the true value of β $\left(\text{that is, } \frac{0.26}{0.90} < \frac{3}{10}\right)$. In the case of α, which has a true value of $\alpha = -1.0$, the width of the interval is 12.80, which clearly fails to provide any useful information. That is, the α interval would fail to contradict a hypothesis such as $\alpha = -9$ which would clearly be quite far from the truth. The substantial imprecision of the estimator of α results

[20]It is only approximate since $s_{\hat{\beta}}$ is merely an estimator of $\sigma_{\hat{\beta}} = \sqrt{\sigma_{\hat{\beta}}^2}$.

from the fact that the X values obtained (see Figure 8.1) were all positive and quite far from zero. The scatter diagram provided no very clear view of where the "true" line would cross the Y axis, and the result was a rather inefficient estimate of α.

In order to facilitate judgments about the efficiency of the parameter estimates, the estimated standard errors[21] of $\hat{\alpha}$ and $\hat{\beta}$, are usually presented along with the fitted equation as follows:

$$\hat{Y} = \underset{(s\hat{\alpha})}{\hat{\alpha}} + \underset{(s\hat{\beta})}{\hat{\beta}}X\,,$$

or in the production function example

$$\hat{Y} = \underset{(3.201)}{-2.88} + \underset{(0.065)}{0.94}\,X.$$

One final point to be made concerns the notion of "goodness-of-fit" of the estimated linear stochastic equation. Recall that in discussing the properties of the linear stochastic equation it was found via (8.3) that

$$\text{Var}\,(Y) = \beta^2\,\text{Var}\,(X) + \sigma^2.$$

An implicit assumption was that most of the variation of Y was due to the $\mathfrak{X}$ set $[\beta^2\,\text{Var}\,(X)]$ rather than the $\mathfrak{Z}$ set (σ^2). Equation (8.10) shows that

$$(N-2)\hat{\sigma}^2 = \sum (Y_i - \overline{Y})^2 - \hat{\beta}^2 \sum (X_i - \overline{X})^2$$

or

$$\sum (Y_i - \overline{Y})^2 = \hat{\beta}^2 \sum (X_i - \overline{X})^2 + (N-2)\hat{\sigma}^2,$$

which is the sample analogue of the relation in (8.3). The sample relation states that the total variation of the observed Y's about their sample mean is due to

(i) Variation in the observed X's; that is,

$$\hat{\beta}^2 \sum (X_i - \overline{X})^2.$$

plus

(ii) Variation of the implied ϵ values; that is, $(N-2)\hat{\sigma}^2$.

The estimators $\hat{\alpha}$ and $\hat{\beta}$ made $(N-2)\hat{\sigma}^2$ as small as possible and therefore the ratio of

$$\hat{\beta}^2 \sum (X_i - \overline{X})^2 \quad \text{to} \quad \sum (Y_i - \overline{Y})^2$$

[21] $s_{\hat{\alpha}}$ and $s_{\hat{\beta}}$ are estimates of the standard deviation of $\hat{\alpha}$ and $\hat{\beta}$. In the context of linear stochastic equations, however, the term *standard error* is almost universally used rather than standard deviation.

indicates the maximum proportion of the variation in Y which can be accounted for (or "explained") by variation in X. This proportion is known as the *coefficient of determination* and is denoted by r^2, where

$$r^2 = \frac{\hat{\beta}^2 \sum (X_i -)\overline{X}^2}{\sum (Y_i - \overline{Y})^2}. \tag{8.15}$$

Using the relation implied by (8.10) again, we find[22]

$$\sum (Y_i - \overline{Y})^2 = \hat{\beta}^2 \sum (X_i - \overline{X})^2 + (N - 2)\hat{\sigma}^2,$$

$$1 = \frac{\hat{\beta}^2 \sum (X_i - \overline{X})^2}{\sum (Y_i - \overline{Y})^2} + \frac{(N - 2)\hat{\sigma}^2}{\sum (Y_i - \overline{Y})^2},$$

$$\frac{\hat{\beta}^2 \sum (X_i - \overline{X})^2}{\sum (Y_i - \overline{Y})^2} = 1 - \frac{(N - 2)\hat{\sigma}^2}{\sum (Y_i - \overline{Y})^2},$$

$$r^2 = 1 - \frac{(N - 2)\hat{\sigma}^2}{\sum (Y_i - \overline{Y})^2}. \tag{8.16}$$

$$\left(\begin{array}{l}\text{Proportion of variation} \\ \text{``explained'' by } \mathfrak{X} \text{ set}\end{array}\right) = 1 - \left(\begin{array}{l}\text{Proportion of variation} \\ \text{``explained'' by } \mathcal{Z} \text{ set}\end{array}\right)$$

In Example 8.3.1 it was found that

$$(n - 2)\hat{\sigma}^2 = 8.64 \quad \text{and} \quad \sum (y_i - \overline{Y})^2 = 235.64,$$

so that

$$r^2 = 1 - \frac{8.64}{235.64} = 0.963,$$

indicating that 96.3% of the output variation is due to input variation alone. The complete summary of the production function "study" would then be given as

$$\hat{Y} = \underset{(3.201)}{-2.88} + \underset{(0.065)}{0.94X} \qquad r^2 = 0.963.$$

EXAMPLE 8.5.1. The main determinant of the liquid asset holdings (Y^*) of a spending unit[23] is undoubtedly the income level (X^*) enjoyed by the spending unit.

[22]It is clear from (8.16) that $0 \leq r^2 \leq 1$.

[23]Liquid asset holdings are composed of checking accounts, savings accounts, and nonmarketable U.S. government bonds. A *family unit* is a set of persons residing together and related by blood, marriage, or adoption. A *family unit* is a *spending unit* if it contains only husband, wife and dependent children. If the *family unit* contains another member who is financially independent (for example an adult, unmarried son), then the latter would be counted separately and the *family unit* would contain two *spending units.*

A 1963 study by the Survey Research Center of the University of Michigan resulted in the following data.

Y^* = average liquid asset holdings per spending unit	X^* = spending unit income[24]
$ 0	$1,500
75	2,500
160	3,500
330	4,500
255	5,500
465	6,750
880	8,750
1,485	12,500

Apply the linear stochastic equation $Y^* = \alpha + \beta X^* + \epsilon$ and estimate α and β using the data above. How important is income X^* in determining liquid asset holdings Y^*?

Solution: Given the orders of magnitude of the date above, computations will be made easier if all data are measured in hundreds of dollars rather than dollars. We define

$$Y = \frac{Y^*}{100} \quad \text{and} \quad X = \frac{X^*}{100},$$

which results in

y	x	xy	x^2	y^2
0	15.0	0	225.00	0.000
0.75	25.0	18.75	625.00	0.563
1.60	35.0	56.00	1,225.00	2.560
3.30	45.0	148.50	2,025.00	10.890
2.55	55.0	140.25	3,025.00	6.503
4.65	67.5	313.88	4,556.25	21.623
8.80	87.5	770.00	7,656.25	77.440
14.85	125.0	1,856.25	15,625.00	220.523
36.50	455.0	3,303.63	34,962.50	340.102

[24]The income levels are the midpoints of a range of income levels. Thus the income level $1,500 is used to represent the range $1,000–1,999.

Since $N = 8$,

$$\hat{\beta} = \frac{8(3{,}303.63) - 455(36.5)}{8(34{,}962.50) - (455)^2} = \frac{9{,}821.54}{72{,}675.00} = 0.135,$$

$$\hat{\alpha} = \frac{36.50}{8} - (0.135)\,\frac{455}{8} = 4.5625 - (0.135)(56.875) = -3.116,$$

$$\sum y^2 - N\bar{Y}^2 = 340.102 - 8(4.5625)^2 = 173.571,$$

$$\sum x^2 - N\bar{X}^2 = 34{,}962.50 - 8(56.875)^2 = 9{,}084.375,$$

$$\begin{aligned}(N - 2)\hat{\sigma}^2 &= 173.571 - (0.135)^2(9{,}084.375)\\ &= 173.571 - 165.563\\ &= 8.008,\end{aligned}$$

$$\hat{\sigma}^2 = \frac{8.008}{N - 2} = \frac{8.008}{6} = 1.335,$$

$$r^2 = \frac{\hat{\beta}^2 \sum (x_i - \bar{X})^2}{\sum (y_i - \bar{Y})^2} = \frac{165.563}{173.571} = 0.954,$$

$$s_{\hat{\beta}}^2 = \frac{\hat{\sigma}^2}{\sum (x_i - \bar{X})^2} = \frac{1.335}{9{,}084.375} = 0.000147,$$

$$s_{\hat{\beta}} = \sqrt{0.000147} \cong 0.012,$$

$$s_{\hat{\alpha}}^2 = \frac{\hat{\sigma}^2 \sum x_i^2}{N \sum (x_i - \bar{X})^2} = \frac{1.335(34{,}962.50)}{8(9{,}084.375)} = 0.6422,$$

$$s_{\hat{\alpha}} = \sqrt{0.6422} \cong 0.801;$$

therefore

$$\left(\frac{\hat{Y}^*}{100}\right) = \underset{(0.801)}{-3.116} + \underset{(0.012)}{0.135}\left(\frac{X^*}{100}\right) \qquad r^2 = 0.954.$$

This can be converted back to dollars by multiplying the equation by 100 to yield

$$\hat{Y}^* = \underset{(80.1)}{-311.6} + \underset{(0.012)}{0.135}\, X^* \qquad r^2 = 0.954.$$

The standard error of $\hat{\alpha}$ must also be multiplied by 100, of course, since the standard error is measured in the same units (dollars) as Y^*. Since liquid asset holding can never be negative, the -311.6 should be taken as indicating that the line crosses the income axis at a positive income. Thus income must be above a certain "threshold" level before a spending unit can afford to hold any liquid assets.

The r^2 of 0.954 indicates that income is indeed an important determinant of liquid asset holdings and in fact accounts for about 95% of the variation in holdings of liquid assets. Alternatively, the standard error of $\hat{\beta}$ implies the following approximate confidence interval for β with confidence coefficient ≥ 0.75:

$$\hat{\beta} - 2s_{\hat{\beta}} < \beta < \hat{\beta} + 2s_{\hat{\beta}}$$
$$0.135 - 0.024 \leq \beta \leq 0.135 + 0.024$$
$$0.111 \leq \beta \leq 0.159.$$

If this confidence interval had contained the value zero, the data would have been consistent with the hypothesis $\beta = 0$; that is, income has no effect on liquid asset holdings. On the contrary, we have instead the indication that for every $1,000 increase in income, liquid asset holdings should, on the average, be expected to rise by somewhere between $111 and $159.

8.6 Elements of Specification Analysis

It is an unfortunate fact of life that economic behavior and economic phenomena do not always comply with the assumptions made about them. That is to say, the assumptions underlying the linear stochastic model may be poor approximations to economic reality with the result that methods derived in this chapter may not accomplish all that we expect of them. In this section we shall discuss several of the complications which often arise when the theory of linear stochastic models is applied in real economic problems. The treatment will necessarily be brief and selective, but it will offer the reader some of the flavor of econometric analysis without introducing matters far beyond the scope of this book.

Nonlinearity

It has been quite well established that the demand for many commodities is subject to a *saturation level*. For example, no matter how wealthy an individual may be, there is a limit to how much butter he will want to consume. Suppose that a researcher wished to estimate how the demand for butter varies with income[25] and the "true" relation (neglecting ϵ) is as shown

[25]Assume that the prices of butter and its substitutes (for example, margarine) are being held constant so that variation in butter consumption would be due primarily to variation in income. This can be approximately accomplished in practice by observing the income and butter consumption of many individuals *all* in the same area during a given short interval of time. A study carried out in this way is known as a *cross section* study.

by the solid line in Figure 8.5. The "reality" is that no butter is consumed unless income is at least A_1 and no matter how high income rises, no one consumes more than B (pounds per month) of butter. The true relation is

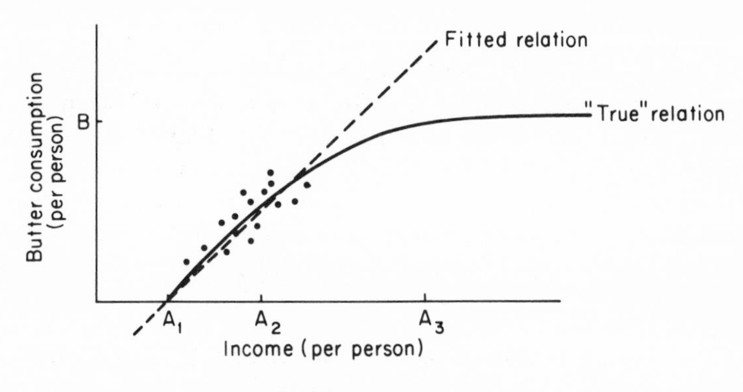

FIGURE 8.5

clearly not a straight line. Suppose, however, that the researcher observes the scatter of points indicated in Figure 8.5 and proceeds to fit the relation shown as the dashed line in the figure. It is clear that the fitted relation will yield a high r^2 value and will even approximate the true relation quite well within the range of the *observed data.* If, for example, it were desired to forecast expected butter consumption corresponding to income level A_2, the fitted relation would do quite well. On the other hand, a forecast corresponding to income level A_3 would seriously overstate the actual expected butter consumption.

The most serious aspect of nonlinearity of the true relation is thus seen to arise in the context of attempting to forecast outside the range of the observed data. This is referred to as the problem of *extrapolation.*

The further the true relation is from a straight line and the wider the range of observed X values, the easier it is to detect the nonlinearity. A scatter diagram such as Figure 8.6 would quickly reveal that the model

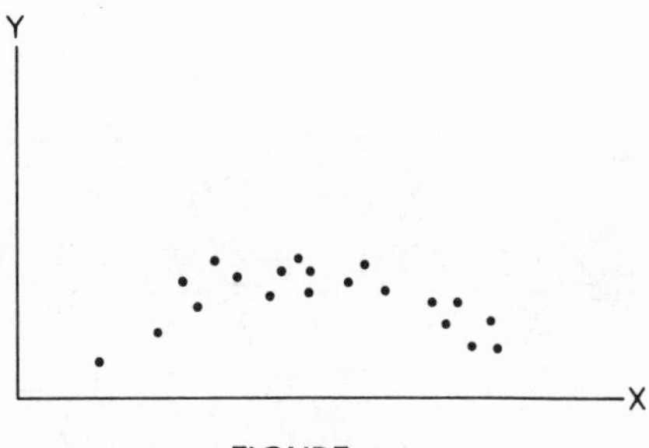

FIGURE 8.6

$Y = \alpha + \beta X + \epsilon$ is a poor approximation to reality. What to do in such a situation can be discussed in the context of the next problem to be investigated.

Omitted Variables

The United States imports a good deal of South American coffee and the amount imported in a given year surely depends upon the price of imported coffee beans. It is likely also true, however, that the level of personal income in the United States influences the amount of coffee imported. That is, for a given price of coffee beans, more will be imported the higher personal income is in the United States. Suppose, then, that the true relation is

$$Y = \alpha + \beta X^I + \gamma X^{II} + \epsilon,$$

where

$$Y = \text{amount of coffee imported into United States.}$$

$$X^I = \text{price of imported coffee beans.}$$

$$X^{II} = \text{personal income in the United States.}$$

All other influences are truly minor and are summarized in ϵ. Let us further suppose, however, that the researcher mistakenly omits the income variable X^{II} and fits the equation

$$\hat{Y} = \hat{\alpha} + \hat{\beta} X^I$$

by the standard least squares technique. Will $\hat{\beta}$ still serve the purpose of estimating β, the effect of coffee bean prices on coffee imports? If so, then the omission of X^{II} may result in "explaining" the variation of coffee imports less completely than is possible, but it may not seriously affect the ability to judge how variation in coffee bean prices alone would affect the importation of coffee. It is easy to see that this hopeful state of affairs will generally not materialize. We saw in Section 8.5 that $\hat{\beta}$ could be written (substituting X^I for X)

$$\hat{\beta} = \frac{\sum (X_i^I - \overline{X}^I) Y_i}{\sum (X_i^I - \overline{X}^I)^2}.$$

If we substitute for Y_i the relation $Y_i = \alpha + \beta X_i^I + \gamma X_i^{II} + \epsilon_i$, we find

$$\begin{aligned}\hat{\beta} &= \frac{\sum (X_i^I - \overline{X}^I)(\alpha + \beta X_i^I + \gamma X_i^{II} + \epsilon_i)}{\sum (X_i^I - \overline{X}^I)^2} \\ &= \frac{\alpha \sum (X_i^I - \overline{X}^I)}{\sum (X_i^I - \overline{X}^I)^2} + \frac{\beta \sum (X_i^I - \overline{X}^I) X_i^I}{\sum (X_i^I - \overline{X}^I)^2} \\ &\quad + \frac{\gamma \sum (X_i^I - \overline{X}^I) X_i^{II}}{\sum (X_i^I - \overline{X}^I)^2} + \frac{\sum (X_i^I - \overline{X}^I)\epsilon_i}{\sum (X_i^I - \overline{X}^I)^2}.\end{aligned}$$

As before,

$$\sum (X_i^I - \overline{X}^I) = 0,$$

and

$$\sum (X_i^I - \overline{X}^I)X_i^I = \sum (X_i^I - \overline{X}^I)^2,$$

so that

$$\begin{aligned}\hat{\beta} &= \beta + \frac{\gamma \sum (X_i^I - \overline{X}^I)X_i^{II}}{\sum (X_i^I - \overline{X}^I)^2} + \frac{\sum (X_i^I - \overline{X}^I)\epsilon_i}{\sum (X_i^I - \overline{X}^I)^2} \\ &= \beta + \gamma \frac{\sum (X_i^I - \overline{X}^I)X_i^{II}}{\sum (X_i^I - \overline{X}^I)^2} + \sum f_i(X^I)\epsilon_i,\end{aligned}$$

which is the same as the result achieved in Section 8.5 except for the additional term

$$\frac{\gamma \sum (X_i^I - \overline{X}^I)X_i^{II}}{\sum (X_i^I - \overline{X}^I)^2}.$$

Suppose that we consider the "auxiliary relation"

$$(\widehat{X^{II}}) = \hat{a} + \hat{b}X^I$$

with the coefficients $\hat{a}$ and $\hat{b}$ determined by least squares just *as though* we had started with the model[26]

$$X^{II} = a + bX^I + \epsilon.$$

We would find that

$$\hat{b} = \frac{\sum (X_i^I - \overline{X}^I)X_i^{II}}{\sum (X_i^I - \overline{X}^I)^2},$$

which is precisely the term multiplying γ in the expression above for $\hat{\beta}$. Although the relation between X^{II} and X^I may be nearly devoid of economic meaning, it is still unlikely that $\hat{b}$ will turn out to be zero either for a particular set of N observations on X^I and X^{II} or even on the average over many sets of N observations. Consequently we find

$$\hat{\beta} = \beta + \gamma\hat{b} + \sum f_i(X^I)\epsilon_i$$

and

$$E\hat{\beta} = \beta + \gamma(E\hat{b}).$$

[26]In this context, the model is nonsense since it states that United States personal income depends primarily on the price of imported coffee beans.

In general, therefore, $\hat{\beta}$ will not be an unbiased estimator of β and in any particular calculation, $\hat{\beta}$ will differ from β not only because of the ϵ effect but also because income was erroneously neglected. If, for example, the observations on Y and X^I had been taken during a period when both income and coffee bean prices were rising, we would have $\hat{b} > 0$. Then since increases in income can be expected to increase the importation of coffee, γ is also positive so that

$$\gamma\hat{b} > 0,$$

and we can expect an upward bias in the estimation of β. The term $\hat{\beta}$ would in a real sense be "confounding" the effects of both price and income on coffee imports and the value of $\hat{\beta}$ would give a misleading indication of the pure price effect.[27] There is, therefore, a clear danger involved in omitting a variable which is relevant to the $\mathfrak{X}$ set. It is generally far better to include in the analysis a variable whose membership in the $\mathfrak{X}$ set may be somewhat doubtful than to omit such a variable. If it turns out to have been included unnecessarily, this will generally be revealed by the corresponding estimated coefficient being close to zero.[28]

False omission, on the other hand, will not be easily detected and instead will severely reduce the usefulness of the coefficients which are estimated.

The actual process of fitting an equation with several independent variables (known as a *multiple regression equation*) involves no new stochastic principles or results, merely more difficult arithmetic, and will not be treated here.[29]

Independence of X and ϵ

The independence of X and ϵ turns out to be perhaps the most critical assumption of the linear stochastic model. In fact, the nonlinearity and omission of variables problems can be viewed as violations of the assumption of independence of X and ϵ. Suppose the "true" relation is

$$Y = \alpha + \beta X^I + \gamma X^{II} + \epsilon.$$

[27]If an abnormally poor coffee harvest led to a short supply of coffee beans and consequently a high price for imported coffee beans, the use of $\hat{\beta}$ would seriously underestimate the resulting decline in imports if $\gamma\hat{b}$ were positive. This is so because β is negative (a price *increase* leads to a *reduction* in imports) and a positive γb term will result in $\hat{\beta}$ being larger than β, that is, closer to zero; hence $\hat{\beta}$ underestimates the price effect.

[28]This is in the sense that a calculated confidence interval will be consistent with the hypothesis that the true coefficient of the variable in question is zero.

[29]The nonlinearity problem as given in Figure 8.5 can be viewed as having omitted a term in X^2. The model to be fitted would be

$$Y = \alpha + \beta X + \gamma X^2 + \epsilon.$$

If the variable[30] X^{II} is omitted, then the researcher — whether he realizes it or not — is working with the relation

$$Y + \alpha + \beta X^{I} + u,$$

where u is a composite error term; that is,

$$u = \gamma X^{II} + \epsilon.$$

Now although ϵ may be independent of X^{I}, the composite error term $(\gamma X^{II} + \epsilon)$ will not be independent of X^{I} unless X^{II} and X^{I} are stochastically independent random variables. The term $\hat{\gamma}b$ which we encountered in discussing omitted variables was actually the X^{II} component of the composite error term.

The problem of lack of independence of X and ϵ can arise in econometric situations even in the absence of omitted variables. We refer here to a problem which stems from economic interdependence, or what might be called the "omitted relations" problem. The nature of the difficulty can be illustrated by the following highly simplified abstraction. Let

I = total income in the economy.

S = total private spending in the economy.

G = government spending.

Suppose that total income I is the only important determinant of private spending and that the linear stochastic relation

$$S = \alpha + \beta I + \epsilon$$

is a reasonable approximation to reality. The "innocence" of the relation above is strictly illusory. Suppose government spending G depends on the perceived needs for public services and that the latter do not depend on economic conditions. If this is true, then G is surely independent of ϵ, but our concern is with whether I is independent of ϵ. Indeed, I is not independent of ϵ, a fact which is clearly brought out by the accounting relation which states that the total income of the economy must be equal to the total spending which occurs in the economy; that is,

$$I = S + G.$$

The dependence of I and ϵ results from the relation $I = S + G$, which had been omitted — and naturally so — when the only desire of the researcher was to consider how income affected private spending. In combination, however, the two relations imply

$$I = S + G,$$
$$I = (\alpha + \beta I + \epsilon) + G,$$

[30] X^{II} may be, say, $(X^{I})^2$ or an entirely different variable.

$$I = \alpha + \beta I + \epsilon + G,$$
$$I - \beta I = \alpha + G + \epsilon,$$
$$I(1 - \beta) = \alpha + G + \epsilon,$$
$$I = \frac{\alpha}{1 - \beta} + \left(\frac{1}{1 - \beta}\right)G + \left(\frac{\epsilon}{1 - \beta}\right);$$

whence it is clear that ϵ and I are not independent since in fact I is, in part, determined by ϵ. *The gist of the difficulty is that if income and private spending are simultaneously determined by a complex process of economic interdependence, then if S is dependent on ϵ so must I be dependent on ϵ.* Recall that one of our early assumptions was that the $\mathcal{Y}$ set was determined, in part, by the $\mathcal{X}$ set but not vice versa. It is this basic assumption which has been violated with the result that I (an element of $\mathcal{X}$) is not independent of ϵ.

The independence of G and ϵ, however, does permit estimation of α and β, for the relation

$$I = \left(\frac{\alpha}{1 - \beta}\right) + \left(\frac{1}{1 - \beta}\right)G + \frac{\epsilon}{1 - \beta}$$

does satisfy the assumptions of the linear stochastic model. Suppose we use least squares on the relation above and denote the estimator of $(\alpha/1 - \beta)$ by $(\hat{\alpha}/1 - \hat{\beta})$ and the estimator of $(1/1 - \beta)$ by $(1/1 - \hat{\beta})$.

If we find

$$\frac{\hat{\alpha}}{1 - \hat{\beta}} = 500 \quad \text{and} \quad \frac{1}{1 - \hat{\beta}} = 10,$$

these two equations can be "solved back" to yield the results

$$\hat{\alpha} = 50,$$
$$\hat{\beta} = 0.90.$$

In general, the results obtained in this manner would yield consistent estimators of α and β respectively. Direct use of the relation $S = \alpha + \beta I + \epsilon$ would yield biased estimators due to the dependence of I and ϵ. In fact it can be shown that the bias would not become negligible as the sample size increased so that the estimators would be both biased and inconsistent.

Note that the ability to obtain useful estimators — and they are only consistent, not unbiased — of α and β depended on our being able to specify all relevant relations even though the only one of direct interest was the private spending equation. It is easy to envision two additional difficulties:

(i) In a realistic situation the relations may turn out to be such that one cannot "solve back" for the desired coefficients as we did for $\hat{\alpha}$ and $\hat{\beta}$.

(ii) In a realistic situation there may be many additional relations that must be specified, but not enough may be known about them to be able to specify them correctly.

If such difficulties should arise — and they do all too frequently in practice — the researcher is forced into approximations and into accepting estimators with lower efficiency than he would like.

Although further discussion of such problems would carry us far afield of our elementary survey of econometrics, it is useful to be aware of these complications even at this level and to recognize the frequent necessity of accepting second or third best in order to come up with any answer at all. The values of a careful analysis of the stochastic model are

(i) The researcher is able to judge which techniques are most appropriate to the real problem at hand.
(ii) The researcher is afforded insight into the possible shortcomings of the procedures being employed and is thereby enabled to make more capable use of his results.
(iii) The path to improved techniques is more easily seen.

PROBLEMS

8-1. Suppose the main determinant of personal consumption expenditures (C) to be gross natural product (Y). This may be expressed as $C = \alpha + \beta Y + \epsilon$. Assume:

(a) $E\epsilon = 0$.

(b) $E\epsilon_i\epsilon_j = 0$, for $i \neq j$; σ^2, for $i = j$.

(c) ϵ and Y are stochastically independent.

Use the following data to find method of moments estimates of α, β, and σ^2. Give economic and statistical interpretations to your results.

Year	C (in billions of 1958 dollars)	Y (in billions of 1958 dollars)
1955	274.2	438.0
1956	281.4	446.1
1957	288.2	452.5
1958	290.1	447.3
1959	307.3	475.9
1960	316.2	487.8
1961	322.6	497.3
1962	338.6	530.0
1963	352.4	550.0
1964	372.1	577.6
	$\sum C = 3{,}143.1$	$\sum Y = 4{,}902.5$
	$\sum C^2 = 997{,}369.47$	$\sum Y^2 = 2{,}424{,}441.45$
	$\sum CY = 1{,}554{,}922.74$	

Source: *Survey of Current Business*, Aug., 1965.

8-2. Make the usual stochastic assumptions and estimate α, β, and σ^2 from the regression model

$$G = \alpha + \beta A + \epsilon \qquad (\text{var}(\epsilon) = \sigma^2),$$

where G = personal consumption expenditures for gasoline and oil, and A = the number of automobiles registered in the United States. Give an economic interpretation to your estimate of β.

Year	G (in billions of 1954 dollars)	A (in millions)
1950	6.0	36.1
1951	6.6	38.0
1952	7.1	39.7
1953	7.7	42.2
1954	8.0	44.6
1955	8.7	48.0
1956	9.2	49.9
1957	9.5	51.8
1958	9.7	53.5
1959	10.2	55.5
1960	10.5	57.8
1961	10.7	59.3
1962	11.1	61.4
1963	11.5	63.4
	$\sum G = 126.5$	$\sum A = 701.2$
	$\sum G^2 = 1,182.17$	$\sum A^2 = 36,159.90$
	$\sum GA = 6,536.89$	

Source: *Survey of Current Business, July, 1964; Oct., 1965.*

8-3. Suppose a random sample of incomes is taken in a certain city. The 10 respondents with highest incomes are interviewed again next year as are the 10 with lowest incomes. In the second interview it is found that the incomes of the top 10 tend to be lower than they were in the first sample while the incomes of the bottom 10 are generally higher. Why is it not valid to conclude from this that inequality in the distribution of income has lessened? (Those who would argue in this way are guilty of a type of faulty reasoning which has become known as *regression fallacy*.)

8-4. Using the following data, estimate α, β, the standard errors of your estimates, and compute r^2 for the regression model $D = \alpha + \beta C + \epsilon$, where D = the number of deaths due to cancer per 100,000 of population in the United States and C = the number of cigarettes produced in the United States (measured in billions). What objections could be made to the assertion *these results are evidence that cigarette smoking causes cancer?*

Year	D	C
1941	120.1	217.9
1942	122.1	257.5
1943	124.3	296.2
1944	128.8	323.6
1945	134.0	332.2
1946	130.0	350.0
1947	132.3	369.9
1948	134.9	386.8
1949	138.8	385.0
1950	139.8	392.0
	$\sum D = 1{,}305.1$	$\sum C = 3{,}311.1$
	$\sum D^2 = 170{,}739.0$	$\sum C^2 = 1{,}127{,}424.0$
	$\sum CD = 435{,}479.0$	

Source: *Historical Statistics of the United States.*

8-5. Two random variables X and Y are said to be *correlated* if they have a nonzero covariance. X and Y are *causally* related if one is cause and the other is effect. Random variables which are causally related will also be correlated; but random variables which are correlated are not necessarily causally related. Suppose we think that a random variable X is the primary determinant of Y (that is, X is the most important cause of Y). The effect on Y of all other determining factors (which are of secondary importance) we lump together as ϵ^*. Suppose we envision the relationship as $Y = \beta X + \epsilon^*$. Statistical evidence of correlation between Y and X would be consistent with our hypothesis that Y and X are causally related.

(a) How might we use the least-squares estimate of β and its standard error to test our hypothesis?

(b) With a finite sample size, could we ever be 100% sure our hypothesis was true?

8-6. Suppose we want to estimate β in the relationship $Y = \beta X + \epsilon^*$ where we know $E\epsilon^* = 0$. That is, we know that the effect on Y of all secondary determinants averages zero. To estimate β from the usual regression model $Y = \alpha + \beta X + \epsilon$ is not to take account of all *a priori* knowledge. The estimate of β thus obtained, while it would be unbiased, would not be very efficient. On efficiency grounds we would do better to derive an estimation technique which takes account of our *a priori* knowledge. To say that we know $E\epsilon^* = 0$ is to say that we already know one point on the regression line. Specifically we know that the point ($X = 0$, $Y = 0$) lies on the regression line.

Since a line is determined by two points, we need determine only one other point on the regression line. In general when we constrain the regression line to pass through the point ($X = 0$, $Y = 0$), it is not possible to find an estimator of β which both minimizes the sum of squared residuals and, at the same time, makes the implied ϵ^*'s average zero. Instead there will be one estimator $\hat{\beta}_c = \sum XY/\sum X^2$ (the constrained least-squares estimator) which minimizes the sum of squared residuals and another estimator $\tilde{\beta}$ which makes the implied ϵ^*'s average zero.

(a) What is $\tilde{\beta}$?

(b) Under the usual stochastic assumptions about X and ϵ^*, $\hat{\beta}_c$ is an unbiased estimator of β. Show that $\tilde{\beta}$ is also unbiased under these conditions.

(c) var $\hat{\beta}_c = \sigma^2/\sum X^2$. Show that var $\tilde{\beta} = n\sigma^2/(\sum X)^2$.

(d) Using the relationship

$$n \sum (X - \bar{X})^2 = n \sum X^2 - (\sum X)^2 \geq 0,$$

prove that $\hat{\beta}_c$ is always at least as efficient as $\tilde{\beta}$. (That is, prove var $\hat{\beta}_c \leq$ var $\tilde{\beta}$.)

8-7. The primary determinant of the amount of green peppers grown (G) in any year is the number of acres that were seeded (A). That is, $G = \beta A + \epsilon^*$. Suppose that, on the average, all other factors (ϵ^*) affecting the green pepper crop exert a zero influence (that is, $E\epsilon^* = 0$).

(a) Make the usual stochastic assumptions concerning A and ϵ^* and calculate $\hat{\beta}_c = \sum AG/\sum A^2$, the constrained least-squares estimator (see Problem 8-6) of β from the data below.

(b) Calculate an estimate of the standard error of $\hat{\beta}_c = \hat{\sigma}\sqrt{1/\sum A^2}$. (Note that the degrees of freedom correction for $\hat{\sigma}^2$ is $n - 1$.)

(c) r^2 is defined as 1 − (proportion of variation "explained" by the Z set). In this problem we assume that the average influence of the Z set is zero. Thus it is the variation of Y about zero $= \sum Y^2$ that we are trying to "explain." In the constrained regression case, therefore, the proportion of variation "explained" by the Z set $= (n - 1)\hat{\sigma}^2/\sum Y^2$. Compute r^2 for the green pepper regression and plot the regression line on a scatter diagram of actual observations.

(d) Do you think we really know enough about the G determinants to assume $E\epsilon^* = 0$? Discuss the dangers of this assumption.

Year	G = Green pepper output in millions of cwt.	A = Acreage planted in thousands of acres
1944	1.43	26.6
1945	1.69	29.2
1946	1.99	35.4
1947	1.60	33.7
1948	2.05	36.6
1949	2.37	41.2
1950	2.42	41.5
1951	2.33	38.4
1952	2.36	37.0
1953	2.51	41.0
1954	2.78	48.0
1955	2.94	45.0
1956	2.72	40.2
1957	2.81	43.9
1958	2.41	40.0

Source: *Agricultural Statistics, 1960.*

8-8. In the derivation of least-squares estimators, we considered X, ϵ, and hence Y as random variables. The problem in forecasting is somewhat different as we would like to say what value, Y_0, of Y is most likely to occur *given* that X takes on the value X_0. Here we treat X_0 as a controlled (nonstochastic) variable. But Y_0 is still a random variable since we cannot control ϵ_0. We define $\hat{Y}_0 = \hat{\alpha} + \hat{\beta}X_0$ as the least-squares forecast of Y_0 conditional on X_0. $e_0 = Y_0 - \hat{Y}_0$ is the least-squares forecast error. Using the information that $\hat{\alpha}$ and $\hat{\beta}$ are unbiased estimators of α and β and that X_0 is nonstochastic,

(a) Prove $Ee_0 = 0$, which implies $\hat{Y}_0$ is an unbiased estimator of Y_0.

(b) Since $Ee_0 = 0$, the var $\hat{Y}_0 = Ee_0^2$. Confirm. For the standard regression model $Y = \alpha + \beta X + \epsilon$, the variance of the forecast is rather complicated to derive since it involves cov $(\hat{\alpha}, \hat{\beta})$. (Why)? We can, however, avoid these complications by considering var $(\hat{Y}_0)$ from the constrained regression model $Y = \beta X + \epsilon^*$, $E\epsilon^* = 0$ of Problems 8-6 and 8-7. Recalling that the constrained least-squares estimator $\hat{\beta}_c = \sum XY/\sum X^2$ is unbiased and has variance $\sigma^2/\sum X^2$, show that for the constrained model

$$\text{Var }(\hat{Y}_0) = \sigma^2\left[\frac{X_0^2}{\sum X^2} + 1\right].$$

Why does the $\sigma^2(X_0^2/\sum X^2)$ component arise? Why does the σ^2 component arise?

(c) Use the results of (b) and Problem 8-7 to make a forecast of green pepper production for 1959 given that 43,400 acres were planted. Make your forecast in the form of a confidence interval statement with a degree of confidence ≥ 0.75. (Actual green pepper production amounted to 2.58 million hundred weight in 1959.)

8-9. Suppose we want to determine the relationship between consumption of bananas and income (an Engel curve). To merely regress consumption of bananas on income neglects an important derminant of banana consumption, namely the price of bananas. Surely price is a factor not of secondary importance and if we proceed by ignoring it, our results will embody the omitted variable bias. There is, however, a way to sidestep this problem and this is by obtaining an income–banana consumption sample over which price is a constant. That this will avoid the omitted variable bias is obvious since if price does not vary, it cannot account for any of the variation in consumption whose "explanation" is then attributed to income. A common method for obtaining a sample over which one important independent variable does not vary is to take a *cross section* sample of families at the same point in time. In this way we allow income and banana consumption to vary from family to family but all pay the same price.

(a) Using the following cross section data, estimate an Engel curve for banana consumption in Great Britain. Present your results in complete form.

(b) Using your results from (a), calculate the income elasticity of banana consumption, evaluated at the point of sample means $[= -(\Delta B/\bar{B}(/\Delta Y)/\bar{Y})]$. Give an interpretation to this number.

B = Average number of bananas consumed per week during the 4 weeks preceding the sample	Y = Annual income in thousands of pounds
1.626	0.250
1.743	0.625
2.695	0.875
3.046	1.125
2.889	1.375
3.317	1.375
3.158	1.625
2.969	1.625
4.209	2.000
3.839	2.000
4.130	2.625
4.845	3.375
$\sum B = 38.466$	$\sum Y = 18.875$
$\sum B^2 = 133.3443$	$\sum Y^2 = 37.8281$

$$\sum BY = 69.0595$$

Source: Compiled from three-person family averages in Prais and Houthakker, *Analysis of Family Budgets*, Cambridge at the University Press, 1955, Table F3.

8-10. A *Phillips curve* is a nonlinear relationship between the percentage change in wage rates (w) and the aggregate unemployment rate (u). A common form is

$$w = \alpha + \beta \log u + \epsilon.$$

Using the historical data below, fit a regression line to this semilog relation and then plot the corresponding Phillips curve (w on vertical axis, u on horizontal axis). At what level of u will $w = 0$? How would you interpret α?

Year	w = % change in wages of manufacturing workers	u	$\log_e u = X$
1950	3.73	5.3%	1.66771
1951	8.63	3.3	1.19392
1952	5.30	3.1	1.13140
1953	5.66	2.9	1.06471
1954	2.98	5.6	1.72277
1955	3.47	4.4	1.48160
1956	5.59	4.2	1.43508
1957	5.29	4.3	1.45862
1958	3.02	6.8	1.91692
1959	3.41	5.5	1.70745
1960	3.77	5.6	1.72277
1961	2.27	6.7	1.90211
1962	2.67	5.6	1.72277
1963	2.60	5.7	1.74047
1964	2.95	5.2	1.64866
	$\sum w = 61.34$		$\sum X = 23.51426$
	$\sum w^2 = 291.3746$		$\sum X^2 = 37.85244$
		$\sum Xw = 90.96346$	

Source: *Business Statistics*, 1965.

8-11. In Problem 8-1 we estimated a consumption function $C = \alpha + \beta Y + \epsilon$. In doing this, however, we omitted the relation $Y = C + N$ where N = nonconsumption expenditures on final goods and services (that is, the nonconsumption components of gross national product). We now know that this omitted relation leads to biased, inconsistent estimates of α and β. Re-estimate α and β by "solving back" from the equation

$$Y = \frac{\alpha}{1-\beta} + \frac{1}{1+\beta} N + \frac{\epsilon}{1-\beta}.$$

Derive the N observations from the data of Problem 1 and the identity $N = Y - C$.

8-12 Some economists would object to our formulation of the Phillips curve (see problem 8-10) and would maintain that the percentage change in wage rates during year t should depend on the unemployment rate of year (t-1).

(a) Interpret such an objection in terms of the assumed relation between the Y and X sets.

(b) Re-estimate the Phillips curve given that the unemployment rate in 1949 was $u = 5.9\%$ and $\log_e(5.9) = 1.77495$.

8-13. Suppose we want to estimate the demand curve for a certain commodity. We run a regression of quantity on price from a set of data based on historical statistics of quantities sold over a period of time and the prices at which these quantities were sold. We find that our estimated demand curve is upward sloping (that is, $\hat{\beta}$ from $Q = \alpha + \beta P + \epsilon$ is positive). In light of the discussion of elements of specification analysis in Section 8.6, how might we account for this result? (In more advanced econometric literature, this is known as the *identification problem.*)

9 FIRM DECISION-MAKING UNDER UNCERTAINTY

9.1 Introduction

The aim of this final chapter is to introduce the reader to two vitally important areas in which probability theory has recently started to contribute to the improvement of economic theory and business decision procedures.

From the viewpoint of a decision-maker, the contributions of quality control and econometrics are their abilities to provide reliable information about certain random phenomena which are crucial to the problem being considered. In all such cases, information is provided by means of sample evidence, and we have seen that such concepts as *operating characteristic curves* and *estimator efficiency* are of vital importance in judging the reliability of sample evidence. A general conclusion which has been reached is that a random sample is less likely to yield reliable parameter estimates and less likely to protect an investigator against false conclusions, the smaller the size of the sample. In Sections 9.2–9.3 we shall consider a technique — Bayesian analysis — which is frequently helpful when decision-makers have no choice but to settle for small sample sizes.

In the closing sections of the chapter, we shall turn to an area which has long been of central importance to economic analysis: the determination of optimal output. By recognizing that uncertainty may be an important element in the environment of a business firm, we can begin to consider some of the ways in which probability theory is contributing to the analytical apparatus of economic theory.

9.2 Bayes' Theorem

In the mid-18th century, Thomas Bayes derived the theorem which is the key element in modern Bayesian analysis. The theorem in question is actually a direct consequence of the basic definition of conditional probability and can be derived as follows.

Let $\mathcal{S}$ be a sample space partitioned by M events $A_1, A_2, \ldots, A_M$, and let H be another event; that is, $H \subset \mathcal{S}$. We illustrate with the Venn diagram of Figure 9.1. Note that the subsets $(A_1 \cap H)$, $(A_2 \cap H), \ldots,$

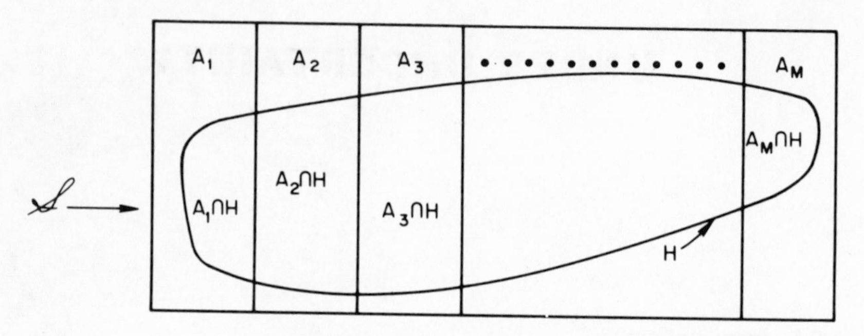

FIGURE 9.1. Venn Diagram for Bayes' Theorem.

$(A_M \cap H)$ are mutually disjoint and in fact partition H so that we may write

$$H = (A_1 \cap H) \cup (A_2 \cap H) \cup \ldots \cup (A_M \cap H). \tag{9.1}$$

Suppose that

(i) $P(A_i)$ is known for each $i = 1, 2, \ldots, M$.
(ii) $P(H) > 0$, and $P(H \mid A_i)$ is known for each $i = 1, 2, \ldots, M$.

It follows, from the definition of conditional probability, that

$$P(A_i \mid H) = \frac{P(A_i \cap H)}{P(H)}. \tag{9.2}$$

Equation (9.1) implies

$$P(H) = P(A_1 \cap H) + P(A_2 \cap H) + \cdots + P(A_M \cap H),$$

but

$$P(A_i \cap H) = P(A_i)\, P(H \mid A_i), \tag{9.3}$$

so that

$$\begin{aligned} P(H) &= P(A_1)\, P(H \mid A_1) + P(A_2)\, P(H \mid A_2) + \cdots + P(A_M)\, P(H \mid A_M) \\ &= \sum_{i=1}^{M} P(A_i)\, P(H \mid A_i). \end{aligned}$$

Substituting (9.3) and (9.4) into (9.2), we arrive at

$$P(A_i \mid H) = \frac{P(A_i)P(H \mid A_i)}{\sum_{i=1}^{M} P(A_i)P(H \mid A_i)}, \tag{9.5}$$

which is Bayes' theorem.

EXAMPLE 9.2.1. Table 9.1 gives information on college degrees granted in the United States during the academic year 1961–62. The numbers measure thousands of degrees granted; that is, a total of 517 thousand degrees were granted in 1961–62.

TABLE 9-1

Degrees	Men	Women	Total
Bachelor's and first professional* degree	252	158	410
Master's degree	59	26	85
Doctorate	20	2	22
Total	331	186	517

*This excludes doctorates in medicine and dentistry which are contained in the row labeled *Doctorate*.

If we think of drawing at random 1 of the 517 thousand individuals who received a degree and let

A_1 = bachelor's and first professional degree.

A_2 = master's degree.

A_3 = doctorate.

H = woman.

we can derive the following probabilities:

$$P(A_1) = \tfrac{410}{517} \cong 0.793,$$

$$P(A_2) = \tfrac{85}{517} \cong 0.164,$$

$$P(A_3) = \tfrac{22}{517} \cong 0.043,$$

$$P(H) = \tfrac{186}{517} \cong 0.360,$$

$$P(H \mid A_1) = \tfrac{158}{410} \cong 0.385,$$

$$P(H \mid A_2) = \tfrac{26}{85} \cong 0.306,$$

$$P(H \mid A_3) = \tfrac{2}{22} \cong 0.091,$$
$$P(A_1 \mid H) = \tfrac{158}{186} \cong 0.849,$$
$$P(A_2 \mid H) = \tfrac{26}{186} \cong 0.140,$$
$$P(A_3 \mid H) = \tfrac{2}{186} \cong 0.011.$$

Having all the information contained in the table, it is easy to determine that while among all degrees 4.3% are doctorates [$P(A_3) = 0.043$], among all degrees granted to women, only 1.1% are doctorates [$P(A_3 \mid H) = 0.011$].

To illustrate the use of Bayes' theorem, let us suppose that only the following information had been known at the start:

$$P(A_1) = 0.793,$$
$$P(A_2) = 0.164,$$
$$P(A_3) = 0.043,$$
$$P(H \mid A_1) = 0.385,$$
$$P(H \mid A_2) = 0.306,$$
$$P(H \mid A_3) = 0.091.$$

From the information above, determine the probability that a woman degree recipient chosen at random will have received a doctorate.

Solution: We seek $P(A_3 \mid H)$ which, by (9.5), is seen to be

$$P(A_3 \mid H) = \frac{P(A_3 \cap H)}{P(H)} = \frac{P(A_3)P(H \mid A_3)}{\sum_{i=1}^{3} P(A_i)P(H \mid A_i)}.$$

We find

$$P(A_1)\,P(H \mid A_1) = (0.793)(0.385) \cong 0.3053,$$
$$P(A_2)\,P(H \mid A_2) = (0.164)(0.306) \cong 0.0502,$$
$$P(A_3)\,P(H \mid A_3) = (0.043)(0.091) \cong 0.0039.$$

Thus,

$$P(H) = 0.3053 + 0.0502 + 0.0039$$
$$= 0.3594$$

and

$$P(A_3 \mid H) = \frac{0.0039}{0.3594} \cong 0.011.$$

The corresponding Venn diagram, drawn approximately to scale, would be

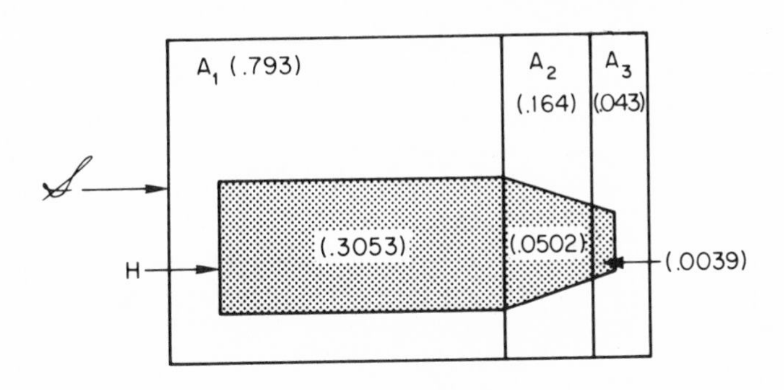

9.3 Elements of Bayesian Analysis

Suppose that a business firm is considering whether or not to market a new product. The appeal of the product would be limited to a particular class of customers and the firm has a large list of potential purchasers. An analysis of production costs and feasible selling prices has indicated that it would not be profitable to market the product unless at least 10% of the potential purchasers show a willingness to try the product. The firm's market research division has been instructed to estimate potential interest in the new product on the basis of past experience with similar products, an assessment of economic conditions over the next year, and so on. The research division has concluded that the potential interest in the product (that is, the proportion willing to try the product) will be between 5 and 20%. Their detailed report contains the following summary table:

Proportion interested (p)	Likelihood of each p
<0.05	0%
0.05	50%
0.10	25%
0.15	20%
0.20	5%
>0.20	0%

The table above indicates that the research division has ruled out interest in excess of 20% or interest below 5%. Further, the analysis led to the tentative conclusion that there is a 50% chance of 5% interest, a 25% chance of 10% interest, and so on.

Now the proportion interested in the new product is a particular characteristic of the class of potential purchasers, that is, a parameter. Since the value of this parameter is unknown, research has been undertaken both to narrow the range of possibilities (in this case cutting the range down from $0 \leq p \leq 1$ to $0.05 \leq p \leq 0.20$) and to evaluate points within the remaining range. In other words, the research division is making a statement such as

> "The degree of interest in the new product depends on a number of economic factors relating both to particular industries and the economy as a whole. Our reading of these economic conditions convinces us that 5% interest in the product is twice as likely as 10% interest, 10 times more likely than 20% interest . . . , etc."

which is precisely what it has been requested to do. If the firm has no other information, then it clearly makes sense for the firm to regard the proportion interested p as a random variable with the following probability distribution:

p	Prior Prob (p)
0.05	0.50
0.10	0.25
0.15	0.20
0.20	0.05
	1.00

The probabilities have been referred to as *prior probabilities* to indicate that these are not objective probabilities corresponding to some random experiment, but are rather *degrees of belief* based on a *prior economic analysis* of the conditions relevant to a particular problem.

The harnessing of economic analysis to provide a *prior probability distribution* for an unknown parameter is the distinguishing feature of the Bayesian approach to decision-making. It must be stressed, however, that the analysis *leading up* to the prior probability distribution remains a problem of economics;[1] the contribution of the Bayesian approach begins *after* the prior probability distribution has been determined as a consequence of the economic analysis.

At this point, the reader who has followed our previous discussion of parameter estimation will undoubtedly object on the grounds that the research division has failed to do the most obvious thing, namely, draw a

[1]Econometric and other statistical techniques might be employed to aid in the economic analysis, however.

random sample of potential purchasers and attempt to estimate the proportion who are interested in the new product. Indeed, such a criticism would be perfectly valid. Let us suppose that in fact n potential customers have been sampled at random and let the random variable $X =$ the number of customers willing to try the product. Since p is the proportion interested in the entire population of potential customers, the probability that an individual chosen at random will be interested (success) is p, while the probability that the individual will not be interested (failure) is $q = 1 - p$. Since n individuals are to be chosen at random, the total number interested, X, is a binomial random variable;[2] that is,

$$X \text{ is } B(n, p).$$

Consequently,

$$EX = np,$$

$$\sigma_X^2 = npq.$$

Now consider the random variable X/n, which is a simple transformation of the binomial variable. We find

$$E\left(\frac{X}{n}\right) = \frac{1}{n}(EX) = \frac{1}{n}(np) = p,$$

so that X/n, the proportion interested in the sample, is an unbiased estimator of p, the proportion interested in the population. Further,

$$\text{Var}\left(\frac{X}{n}\right) = \frac{1}{n^2}(\text{Var } X) = \frac{1}{n^2}(npq) = \frac{pq}{n}.$$

Clearly, the efficiency of X/n as an estimator of p increases as n increases. In fact,

$$\lim_{n \to \infty} \left(\frac{pq}{n}\right) = 0,$$

so that

$$\text{Var}\left(\frac{X}{n}\right) \to 0 \quad \text{as} \quad n \to \infty,$$

and X/n is not only unbiased but also consistent.

Now suppose that the research division is correct in its assessment that $0.05 \leq p \leq 0.20$. Then the variance of X/n is between

$$\text{Var}\left(\frac{X}{n}\right) = \frac{(0.05)(0.95)}{n} = \frac{0.0475}{n} \quad \text{and} \quad \text{Var}\left(\frac{X}{n}\right) = \frac{(0.20)(0.80)}{n} = \frac{0.16}{n}$$

[2]We assume either that the sampling is done with replacement, or n is small relative to the entire population so that the binomial approximates the hypergeometric satisfactorily (see Chapter 5, problems 5-19 and 5-20).

while the standard deviation of X/n is between

$$\sigma_{X/n} = \sqrt{\frac{0.0475}{n}} = \frac{0.218}{\sqrt{n}} \quad \text{and} \quad \sigma_{X/n} = \sqrt{\frac{0.16}{n}} = \frac{0.4}{\sqrt{n}}.$$

If $n = 100$, we have either

$$\sigma_{X/100} = \frac{0.218}{10} \cong 0.022 \quad \text{or} \quad \sigma_{X/100} = \frac{0.4}{10} = 0.040.$$

Thus if $p = 0.05$ so that the product should not be marketed, $X/100$ is unlikely to be as large as 0.10 since this would be nearly 2.3 standard deviations above the true $p = 0.05$. Similarly, if $p = 0.20$ so that the product should be marketed, $X/100$ is unlikely to be as low as 0.10, which is 2.5 standard deviations below the true $p = 0.20$[3] It appears, therefore, that basing the decision to market on whether or not $X/n > 0.10$ may not involve much risk if p is either close to 0.05 or close to 0.20 *and* if at least 100 potential customers can be sampled. If, on the other hand, it is not considered feasible to sample more than, say, 25 customers,[4] we find either

$$\sigma_{X/25} = \frac{0.218}{5} \cong 0.044 \quad \text{or} \quad \sigma_{X/25} = \frac{0.4}{5} = 0.08.$$

In this case a true p of 0.05 may easily lead to X/n as high as 0.10, while a true p of 0.20 may easily result in X/n even less than 0.10. It is clear, therefore, that even though X/n is an unbiased and consistent estimator of p, a small n exposes the company to considerable risk if the decision to market is based on X/n alone.

The optimal solution, certainly, is to obtain a large sample, in which case X/n is a highly efficient estimator. If a large sample simply is not feasible, we must then resort to another method. The Bayesian procedure observes that small samples are inefficient because they do not contain enough unequivocal information. An obvious source of information in addition to the sample is the prior probability distribution of p which, presumably, reflects the considered opinion of the research division. The logic behind the Bayesian procedure may now be stated as follows:

[3]Note, however, that if $p = 0.15$,

$$\sigma_{X/100} = \sqrt{\frac{(0.15)\,(0.85)}{100}} = 0.036,$$

so that $X/100$ may very well turn out less than 0.10, thus falsely indicating that the product should not be marketed.

[4]The sampling may involve a visit to each customer to explain the proposed new product and so on, and it may therefore be quite expensive.

All available evidence should be brought to bear on the estimation of a crucial parameter. When a random sample contains too little information to yield an estimator with a desirable level of efficiency, the parameter should be estimated by combining the sample evidence with that which yielded the prior probability distribution.

Bayes' theorem itself provides the key to "pooling" the two kinds of evidence. Essentially, we use the sample evidence to calculate an "improved" probability distribution for p. The prior probability distribution contains only the evidence available prior to the random sample; the new distribution to be calculated — known as the *posterior probability distribution* — incorporates also the evidence contained in the random sample.

Specifically, suppose we obtain a random sample of $n = 20$ and find three interested customers. In this case $X/n = 3/20 = 0.15$. According to the prior probability distribution, the possible values of p are 0.05, 0.10, 0.15, and 0.20. Let us calculate the probability that $X/n = 0.15$ for each of these possible p values. Since $n = 20$,

$$P\left(\frac{X}{20} = 0.15\right) = P(X = 3).$$

(i) If $p = 0.05$, X is $B(20, 0.05)$; hence

$$P(X = 3 \mid p = 0.05) = \binom{20}{3}(0.05)^3(0.95)^{17} \cong 0.059.$$

(ii) If $p = 0.01$, X is $B(20, 0.10)$; hence

$$P(X = 3 \mid p = 0.10) = \binom{20}{3}(0.10)^3(0.90)^{17} \cong 0.190.$$

(iii) If $p = 0.15$, X is $B(20, 0.15)$; hence

$$P(X = 3 \mid p = 0.15) = \binom{20}{3}(0.15)^3(0.85)^{17} \cong 0.243.$$

(iv) If $p = 0.20$, X is $B(20, 0.20)$; hence

$$P(X = 3 \mid p = 0.20) = \binom{20}{3}(0.20)^3(0.80)^{17} \cong 0.205.$$

We summarize in the following table:

p	Prior $P(p)$	$P(X = 3 \mid p)$
0.05	0.50	0.059
0.10	0.25	0.190
0.15	0.20	0.243
0.20	0.05	0.205
	1.00	

To the table above we wish to add a column of posterior probabilities, where we define

$$\text{Posterior } P(p) = P(p \mid X = 3).$$

In other words, $P(p = 0.05) = 0.50$ is the prior probability of 5% interest in the new product, while

$$\text{Posterior } P(p = 0.05) = P(p = 0.05 \mid X = 3)$$

is the conditional probability of 5% interest *given* that the sample of 20 revealed 3 interested customers. According to Bayes' theorem,

$$\begin{aligned} &P(p = 0.05 \mid X = 3) \\ &= \frac{P[(p = 0.05) \cap (X = 3)]}{P(X = 3)} \\ &= \frac{P(p = 0.05)P(X = 3 \mid p = 0.05)}{\{P(p = 0.05)P(X = 3 \mid p = 0.05) + P(p = 0.10)P(X = 3 \mid p = 0.10) + P(p = 0.15)P(X = 3 \mid p = 0.15) + P(p = 0.20)P(X = 3 \mid p = 0.20)\}}. \end{aligned}$$

A similar equation would be written for $P(p = 0.10 \mid X = 3)$, etc. The calculations are easily carried out in the following format:

p	$P(p)$	$P(X = 3 \mid p)$	$P(p)\,P(X = 3 \mid p)$	$P(p \mid X = 3) = \frac{P(p)\,P(X = 3 \mid p)}{P(X = 3)}$
0.05	0.50	0.059	0.02950	0.217
0.10	0.25	0.190	0.04750	0.350
0.15	0.20	0.243	0.04860	0.358
0.20	0.05	0.205	0.01025	0.075
	1.00		$P(X = 3) = 0.13585$	1.000

In the table above,

$$P(p = 0.05 \mid X = 3) = \frac{0.02950}{0.13585} \cong 0.217,$$

and so on. We see, then, that while the initial evidence indicated a 50% chance of only 5% interest [$P(p = 0.05) = 0.50$], the additional evidence of 3 favorable responses out of 20 results in a revised view of the likelihood of only 5% interest; that is, given 3 favorable responses out of 20, the likelihood of only 5% interest is reduced to 21.7% [$P(p = 0.05 \mid X = 3) = 0.217$]. Similarly, the probability of 15% interest has been revised from an initial level of 0.20 to a new level of 0.358, etc. We can also calculate

p	$P(p)$	$p \cdot P(p)$	$P(p \mid X = 3)$	$p \cdot P(p \mid X = 3)$
0.05	0.50	0.025	0.217	0.0109
0.10	0.25	0.025	0.350	0.0350
0.15	0.20	0.030	0.358	0.0537
0.20	0.05	0.010	0.075	0.0150
	1.00	Prior $E(p) = 0.090$	1.000	Posterior $E(p) = 0.1146$

Note that prior to the sample evidence we had

$$\text{Prior } E(p) = 0.090,$$

the sample evidence indicated

$$\frac{X}{n} = 0.15,$$

and the two pieces of evidence together resulted in

$$\text{Posterior } E(p) = 0.1146.$$

This illustrates the perfectly general result that the Bayesian procedure is simply a logical method for mediating between, or combining, the two sources of information: prior evidence and sample evidence. The relative weight given to the sample evidence can be calculated by[5]

$$\frac{[\text{Posterior } E(p) - \text{prior } E(p)]}{\left[\frac{X}{n} - \text{prior } E(p)\right]} = \frac{(0.1146) - (0.090)}{(0.15) - (0.090)} = 0.41.$$

Thus in calculating the posterior $E(p)$, the Bayesian procedure assigned a weight of 0.41 to the sample evidence and therefore 0.59 (1 − 0.41) to the prior evidence. In Example 9.3.1 we shall find that if a larger sample had indicated 15% interest, then the Bayesian procedure would have given a larger relative weight to the sample evidence. This indicates the general proposition that

The larger the sample size, the less weight the Bayesian procedure places on the prior evidence.

[5]Determine α such that

$$\alpha\left(\frac{X}{n}\right) + (1 - \alpha) \text{ prior } E(p) = [\text{posterior } E(p)];$$

hence

$$\alpha = \frac{[\text{posterior } E(p) - \text{prior } E(p)]}{\left[\frac{X}{n} - \text{prior } E(p)\right]}.$$

This is a desirable result since larger sample sizes provide more efficient estimators. This result justifies one in regarding the Bayesian procedure as essentially a small-sample estimation technique.

There are many ways to use the posterior probability distribution to aid in the decision regarding the new product. One might choose to market the new product if

$$\text{Posterior } E(p) > 0.10.$$

Alternatively, one might require

$$P(p > 0.10 \mid X = 3) \geq k,$$

where k is some value chosen by the decision-maker. If k is chosen as 0.80, then the decision-maker has said

"The product will be marketed if prior and sample evidence combined indicate at least an 80% chance that the product will be a success."

Several other methods of using the posterior probability distribution exist and are the focus of the area known as *Bayesian decision theory.*

EXAMPLE 9.3.1. Suppose that in the previous marketing problem a sample of size $n = 40$ had produced $X = 6$ favorable responses; thus again

$$\frac{X}{n} = \frac{6}{40} = 0.15.$$

Using the original prior distribution, calculate the posterior probability distribution corresponding to the sample evidence above. Calculate posterior $E(p)$ and determine the relative weights assigned to prior and sample evidence.

Solution: First we note that

$$X \text{ is } B(40, p)$$

so that

$$P\left(\frac{X}{40} = 0.15\right) = P(X = 6),$$

Thus (a) if $p = 0.05$, X is $B(40, 0.05)$;

therefore

$$P(X = 6 \mid p = 0.05) = \binom{40}{6}(0.05)^6(0.95)^{34} \cong 0.0055.^{6}$$

[6]This has been obtained using the normal approximation to $B(40, 0.05)$ and can easily be checked by the reader.

(b) If $p = 0.10$, X is $B(40, 0.10)$;

therefore

$$P(X = 6 \mid p = 0.10) = \binom{40}{6}(0.10)^6(0.90)^{34} \cong 0.1214.$$

(c) If $p = 0.15$, X is $B(40, 0.15)$;

therefore

$$P(X = 6 \mid p = 0.15) = \binom{40}{6}(0.15)^6(0.85)^{34} = 0.1742.$$

(d) If $p = 0.20$, X is $B(40, 0.20)$;

therefore

$$P(X = 6 \mid p = 0.20) = \binom{40}{6}(0.20)^6(0.80)^{34} \cong 0.1165.$$

Hence,

p	$P(p)$	$P(X = 6 \mid p)$	$P(p) \cdot P(X = 6 \mid p)$	$P(p \mid X = 6) = \frac{P(p)\,P(X = 6 \mid p)}{P(X = 3)}$
0.05	0.50	0.0055	0.002750	0.0373
0.10	0.25	0.1214	0.030350	0.4114
0.15	0.20	0.1742	0.034840	0.4723
0.20	0.05	0.1165	0.005825	0.0790
	1.00		$P(X = 6) = 0.073765$	1.0000

In comparing this posterior distribution with that obtained for $X = 3$, $n = 20$, it is clear that much greater weight is assigned to the sample evidence — for the same ratio X/n — the more reliable is the sample evidence. The following table aids the comparison:

p	Prior $P(p)$	Posterior $P(p)$ given $n = 20$, $X/n = 0.15$	Posterior $P(p)$ given $n = 40$, $X/n = 0.15$
0.05	0.50	0.217	0.0373
0.10	0.25	0.350	0.4114
0.15	0.20	0.358	0.4723
0.20	0.05	0.075	0.0790
	1.00	1.000	1.0000

Thus a small-sample indication of 15% interest reduced $P(p = 0.05)$ from the initial 0.50 to 0.217, while the same degree of interest based on a larger sample reduced $P(p = 0.05)$ from 0.50 to 0.0373. While $n = 20$, $X/n = 0.15$ yielded

$$\text{Posterior } E(p) = 0.1146,$$

we now find

p	Posterior $P(p)$ given $n = 40$, $X/n = 0.15$	$p \cdot$Posterior $P(p)$
0.05	0.0373	0.00187
0.10	0.4114	0.04114
0.15	0.4723	0.06410
0.20	0.0793	0.01586
	1.0000	Posterior $E(p) = 0.12297$

Having begun with prior $E(p) = 0.090$, the relative weight assigned to the sample evidence is calculated as

$$\frac{[\text{Posterior } E(p) - \text{prior } E(p)]}{\left[\dfrac{X}{n} - \text{prior } E(p)\right]} = \frac{(0.12297) - (0.090)}{(0.15) - (0.090)} = 0.55,$$

instead of the 0.41 which was obtained for the smaller sample. It should be clear to the reader that asymptotically we would have

p	Posterior $P(p)$ given $n \to \infty$, $X/n = 0.15$
0.05	0
0.10	0
0.15	1.0
0.20	0
	1.0

so that

$$\text{if } \frac{X}{n} \text{ remains fixed at 0.15 as } n \to \infty,$$

$$\text{posterior } E(p) \to 0.15 = \frac{X}{n}$$

and, in the limit, all weight is assigned to the sample evidence and none to the prior distribution.[7]

9.4 Output and Uncertainty

In this and the following two sections we shall be concerned with questions such as

(i) How much should a firm produce (or stock) if the demand for its output cannot be predicted with certainty?
(ii) How much will a firm offer for sale at each possible selling price, again under conditions of uncertainty with respect to the demand for its output?

As is well known in economics, there is no unique answer to either of these questions. Rather, the questions themselves would suggest additional questions which would have to be answered before one could attempt any useful analysis:

(i) What is the market environment of the firm: many producers of equivalent products?[8] a relatively small number of firms producing nearly equivalent products?[9] a relatively small number of firms producing products which are regarded as

[7]The limit need not be approached monotonically; that is, we may have the following:

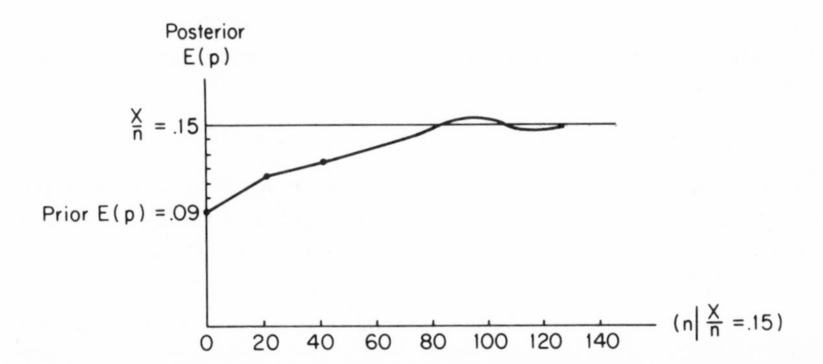

In fact, the reader can show that if $X/n = 0.15$ and $n = 100$, posterior $E(p) \cong 0.153$.

[8]Wheat farmers would be an example.

[9]Producers of flat glass would be an example.

"different" by consumers, even though they serve exactly the same purposes?[10] and so on.

(ii) *Can* the firm exercise any degree of control over its selling price?

(iii) If the firm has the ability to exercise some degree of control over its selling price, does it generally choose to exercise this control aggressively, or does it rather tend to maintain an established price which is considered "normal" in its industry, or does it tend to follow a "price leader" in order to maintain an established price structure and so on?

(iv) Does the firm produce one main product, or must it engage in joint determination of the output of a whole "line" of products?

(v) What economic (and other) goals are of importance in the firm's decision-making process?

It should be clear that the subject of output determination is not only important, but also sufficiently complex so that no definitive answers can be given to our original questions, which are now seen to have been far too general in scope. We can, however, make a useful beginning by restricting the context in which we wish to pose the questions. We therefore assume that

(i) Only one product is being produced.

(ii) The firm exercises no control over selling price,[11] but chooses how much to produce for sale at the given price.

(iii) Subject to the given price and its corresponding sales possibilities, the firm attempts to maximize its profits — at least on the average.

For purposes of defining terms and providing a useful benchmark for the main analysis we shall add one further assumption which will be dropped once it has served these ends:

(iv) The firm is able to sell all it wishes at the going price.

Under assumptions (i)–(iv), determination of optimal output is perfectly straightforward. If the firm finds it profitable to produce five units of output, then a sixth unit should be produced (that is, will increase the

[10]Automobile producers would be an example. In economic literature, products which serve nearly identical purposes but for which "brand differences" are of importance to the consumer are known as "differentiated" products.

[11]Two interpretations are possible. The firm may be unable to exercise much control by virtue of its small size relative to the total market. Alternatively, the firm may *choose* not to exercise control over price because the established "normal" price (or price structure) has served the industry well in the sense of providing satisfactory profits and there is consequently no desire to disturb a stable situation by unilateral action. The analysis to follow is more consistent with the second interpretation.

firm's profits) if the sale of the sixth unit of output adds at least as much to the firm's revenue as its production adds to the firm's cost. If the sixth unit passes this test, then a seventh unit should be produced if its sale adds at least as much to the firm's revenue as its production adds to the firm's cost, and so on. The addition to the firm's revenue resulting from the sale of one more unit of output is referred to as the *marginal revenue* (MR) of that additional unit of output. The addition to the firm's cost resulting from the production of one more unit of output is referred to as the *marginal cost* (MC) of that additional unit of output. Let

$$R(q) = \text{marginal revenue of the } q\text{th unit of output,}$$
$$C(q) = \text{marginal cost of the } q\text{th unit of output,}$$
$$r = \text{the price at which output is sold.}$$

Then if it is profitable to produce and sell $(q - 1)$ units of output, the qth unit should be produced and sold if

$$R(q) \geq C(q).^{12} \qquad (9.6)$$

Under the assumption that the firm can sell all it wishes at the given price, it is clear that

$$R(q) = r \quad (q = 1, 2, 3, \ldots),$$

for each additional unit sold increases the firm's revenue by precisely the selling price r. If we assume

$$C(q) > C(q - 1); \qquad (9.7)$$

that is, the second unit adds more to cost than the first,[13] the third unit adds more to cost than the second, etc., then we can represent the optimal output solution geometrically as in Figure 9.2.

[12]If $R(q) = C(q)$, then the qth unit leaves profit unaltered. We shall assume, by convention, that such a unit *would* be produced.

[13]This is not merely saying that it costs more to produce two units than it does to produce one unit. Consider the following two situations:

	A		B	
Units of output q	Total cost of q units	$C(q)$	Total cost of q units	$C(q)$
1	$12		$12	
2	14	$2	13	$1
3	16	2	15	2
4	18	2	18	3
5	20	2	22	4

In situation A, each additional unit of output adds $2 to the firm's cost, $C(q) = 2$ for all $q > 1$; this is referred to as constant marginal cost. In situation B, the second unit increases the firm's cost by $1, the third by $2, the fourth by $3, etc. In this case we have increasing marginal cost; that is, $C(q)$ itself increases as q increases.

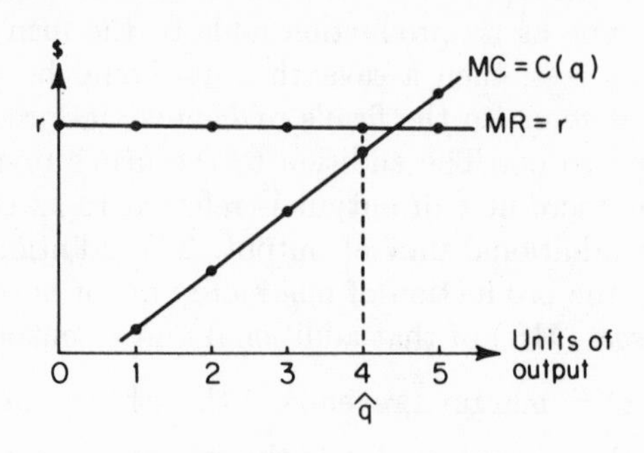

FIGURE 9.2

Each point lying on the curve labeled MR represents the marginal revenue of the output unit directly below it. All these points lie on a horizontal line which crosses the vertical axis at the given price r. The line connecting the marginal revenue points is known as the *marginal revenue curve.* The *marginal cost curve* is defined in a similar manner and must be upward sloping since for each q,

$$C(q) > C(q - 1).$$

It is clear that the firm will choose to produce at least four units of output for

$$r > C(1)$$

$$r > C(2)$$

$$r > C(3)$$

$$r > C(4).$$

Suppose the total profit on four units of output is \$100. For the fifth unit,

$$r < C(5),$$

so that total profits on five units must be less than \$100. If $r = \$50$ and $C(5) = \$60$, then the fifth unit is increasing revenue by \$50 while increasing cost by \$60; hence profit must decline to \$90. Thus the firm may be making profits by producing and selling five units, but it will *maximize* its profits by producing and selling only four units (denoted by $\hat{q}$ in Figure 9.2). We can summarize by saying that assumptions (i)–(iv), along with a rising marginal cost curve, imply that the firm wishing to maximize its profit should produce and sell

$$\boxed{\text{the largest } q \text{ such that } r \geq C(q).}^{14} \tag{9.8}$$

EXAMPLE 9.4.1. A tobacco farmer owns 100 acres of land. Fifty of these acres are extremely well suited to the growing of tobacco; the other 50 are progressively less well suited to tobacco growing and therefore require greater expenditures during the planting, growing, and harvesting operations to yield an acre of high quality tobacco. The farmer expects to be able to sell all he produces at a price of $1,150 per acre of output. With total production costs as given below, how many acres should he plant and harvest?

No. of acres planted and harvested	Total cost
40	$38,000
50	47,500
60	57,500
70	68,000
80	79,250
90	91,750
100	105,750

Solution: We assume that the cost figures refer to a situation in which the best 50 acres are used first, then the next 10 best, and so on. Further, we assume that the farmer faces the choice of planting tobacco or leaving land idle, so that there are no important alternative uses to consider. Using the data above, we construct the following table:

No. of acres planted and harvested	Total cost	Additional acres	Marginal cost of additional acres
40	$38,000	—	—
50	47,500	10	$9,500
60	57,500	10	10,000
70	68,000	10	10,500
→ *80*	79,250	10	*11,250* ←
90	91,750	10	12,500
100	105,750	10	14,000

[14]In situation B of Footnote 13, p. 277, if price $= r =$ $2.50, the largest q such that

$$r \geq C(q)$$

is $q = 3$, which therefore yields the maximum possible profit. Note, however, that total revenue would be $3 \times \$2.50 = \$7.50$ so that even the maximum profit is negative. The profit maximizing "rule" cannot, by itself, distinguish whether or not the maximum profit is a positive amount. We shall always assume that a positive profit is being earned at the point of profit maximization.

Here we have marginal cost given in terms of 10 acre units, so that the price of \$1,150 per acre becomes — in comparable terms — a marginal revenue of \$11,500 per 10 acre unit. Comparing this with the cost figures, it is clear that 80 acres should be utilized. The marginal cost of going from 70 to 80 acres is \$11,250, which is less than the marginal revenue of those 10 acres. The next 10 acres, however, involve a marginal cost of \$12,500 which is clearly not justified by the marginal revenue of \$11,500.
The following table is also useful:

No. of acres planted and harvested	Additional acres	MC	MR	Marginal profit = MR − MC	Cumulated marginal profit
40	—	—	—	—	—
50	10	\$9,500	\$11,500	\$2,000	\$2,000
60	10	10,500	11,500	1,500	3,500
70	10	10,500	11,500	1,000	4,500
80	10	*11,250*	*11,500*	*250*	*4,750*
90	10	12,500	11,500	−1,000	3,750
100	10	14,000	11,500	−2,500	1,250

The table above makes it clear that marginal profit (the addition to profit for each additional unit of output) is positive through the first 80 acres; that is, up to and including 80 acres, profits continue to rise. Note that the marginal profit is itself diminishing so that each additional 10 acres increases profits by a smaller amount than the previous 10 acres. Beyond 80 acres, each additional 10 acres actually decreases total profits. The last column indicates that total profit for 50 acres is \$2,000 greater than for 40 acres; total profit for 60 acres is \$3,500 greater than for 40 acres, and so on. On the first 40 acres, profits total

$$40(\$1{,}150) - \$38{,}000 = \$8{,}000,$$

so that maximum attainable profits amount to

$$\$8{,}000 + (\$2{,}000 + \$1{,}500 + \$1{,}000 + \$250) = \$8{,}000 + (\$4{,}750)$$
$$= \$12{,}750.$$

Figure 9.3 summarizes all the results.

Assumption (iv) having served its purpose, let us abandon it in favor of

(iv*) The firm cannot sell all it wishes at the price r; in fact the amount which can be sold at the price r is a random variable X, with probability distribution $D_{X|r}$.

The notation $D_{X|r}$ used in assumption (iv*) indicates that D represents the probability distribution of the random variable X, but that the distribution D is valid only if the price at which output sells is r.

Let us suppose that, somehow, the decision has been made to produce $(q - 1)$ units and the firm now wishes to decide whether it is worthwhile to produce the qth unit. Under assumption (iv), the decision would be made on the basis of whether the marginal revenue of the qth unit were at least as great as its marginal cost; that is, produce the qth unit if

$$R(q) \geq C(q).$$

Assumption (iv*) has no effect on the marginal cost, but it does affect the marginal revenue. The marginal revenue of the qth unit is now a random variable, the realization of which depends on whether or not the

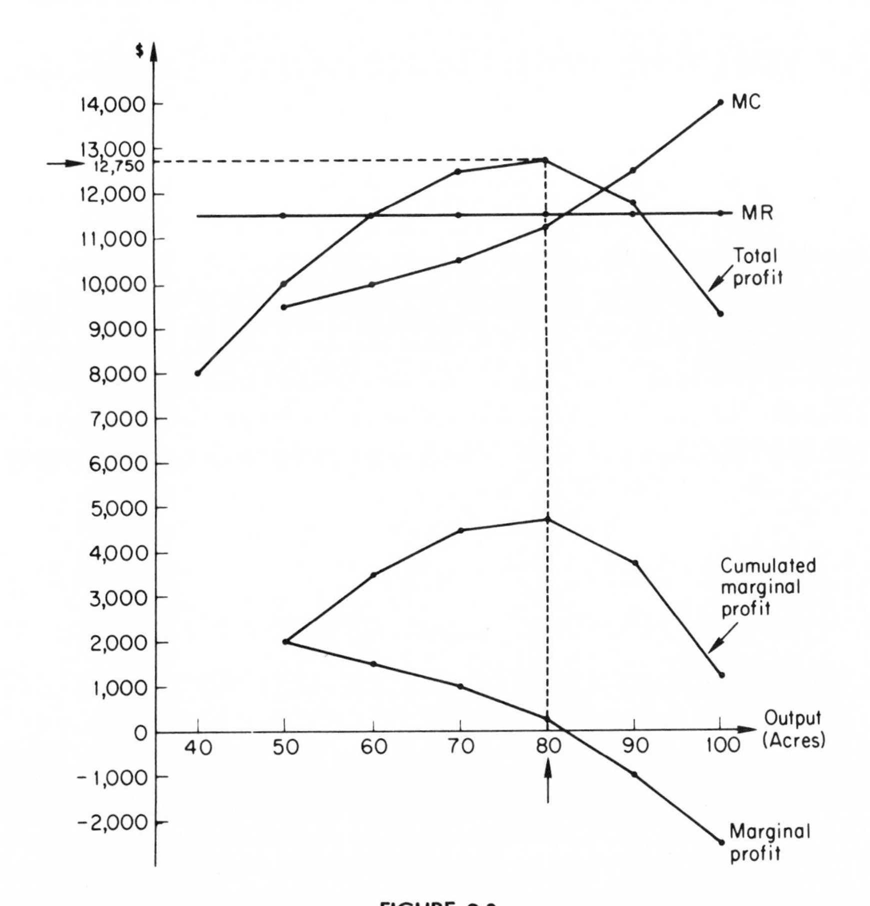

FIGURE 9.3

qth unit can be sold. If the qth unit is produced and sold, then the firm's revenue will rise by the per unit selling price r. If the qth unit is produced but cannot be sold,[15] then the firm's revenue will not rise at all. Table 9-2 summarizes the discussion above.

TABLE 9-2

Consequences of Producing qth Unit

Assumption: It has been decided that at least $(q - 1)$ units are to be produced.

Marginal cost of qth unit	Marginal revenue of qth unit
$C(q)$	r, if qth unit can be sold 0, if qth unit cannot be sold.

We now wish to determine the probability distribution of the random variable $R(q)$ = marginal revenue of the qth unit.
First,

$$R(q) \in \{r, 0\}; \tag{9.9}$$

that is, the only possible values of $R(q)$ are the selling price r and zero. The only way in which $R(q) = r$ can occur is if the total demand is large enough for the qth unit to be sold. Now the qth unit can be sold only under the condition that

$$X \geq q;$$

that is, total demand X must amount to at least q units if the qth unit is to be sold. We therefore find that

$$R(q) = r \quad \text{if and only if} \quad X \geq q;$$

hence

$$P[R(q) = r] = P(X \geq q).$$

Further if the total demand is for fewer than q units, then the qth unit will not be sold[16] and its marginal revenue will be zero:

$$R(q) = 0 \quad \text{if and only if} \quad X < q;$$

[15]We assume, *for the time being*, that if the unit is not sold, it cannot be stored for later sale; that is, if not sold during the period being considered, it simply perishes.

[16]Indeed, if total demand is for fewer than q units, then even the $(q - 1)$st unit may not be sold. That contingency, however, is of importance with respect only to the marginal revenue of the $(q - 1)$st unit, not the qth.

hence

$$P[R(q) = 0] = P(X < q) = 1 - P(X \geq q).$$

The probability distribution of $R(q)$ is thus given by, say, $D_{R(q)}$ where

$$D_{R(q)} = \{[r, P(X \geq q)], [0, 1 - P(X \geq q)]\}.$$

The expected value of $R(q)$, expected marginal revenue, is calculated as

$R(q)$	$P[R(q)]$	$R(q)\,P[R(q)]$
r	$P(X \geq q)$	$r\,P(X \geq q)$
0	$1 - P(X \geq q)$	$0[1 - P(X \geq q)]$
	1	$r\,P(X \geq q)$

Hence

$$E[R(q)] = r\,P(X \geq q). \tag{9.10}$$

It is easily seen that the expected marginal revenue of the $(q - 1)$st unit must be

$$E[R(q - 1)] = r\,P(X \geq q - 1),$$

and so on.

Before we introduced uncertainty through assumption (iv*), it was clear that if the firm wished to maximize its profits, it should produce the qth unit if the marginal profit of the qth unit were greater than (or equal to, see Footnote 12, p. 277) zero; that is, if

$$R(q) \geq C(q).$$

In the case of uncertainty, the criterion of maximizing profits is non-operational, for profits are now determined as a random variable. The profit to be earned on the production of, say, 10 units depends on the costs and revenues associated with an output of 10 units. The cost is assumed to be known with certainty. The revenue, however, cannot be determined until the demand is known, and the demand cannot be predicted with certainty since it is a random variable. In the case of uncertainty of demand, we shall interpret assumption (iii) to mean that the firm attempts to maximize *expected profit.*

Suppose now that the expected profit for $(q - 1)$ units is denoted by

$$E[\pi(q - 1)],$$

where, $\pi(q - 1)$ = profit on a *total* of $(q - 1)$ units of output, and $\pi(q - 1)$ is clearly a random variable. Using the same notation, $\pi(q)$ = profit on a *total* of q units of output, and the firm would want to produce the qth unit of output if

$$E[\pi(q)] \geq E[\pi(q - 1)], \tag{9.11}$$

that is, if the expected profit for a total of q units is at least as great as that for $(q - 1)$ units. Note, however, that the inequality above implies

$$E[\pi(q)] - E[\pi(q-1)] \geq 0,$$

$$E[\pi(q) - \pi(q-1)] \geq 0. \tag{9.12}$$

But $[\pi(q) - \pi(q-1)]$ is the marginal profit of the qth unit; hence the qth unit should be produced if the *expected marginal profit* of the qth unit is greater than or equal to zero. Now the marginal profit of the qth unit is

$$R(q) - C(q),$$

where $R(q)$ is the random marginal revenue of the qth unit and $C(q)$ is its known (nonrandom) marginal cost. The expected marginal profit of the qth unit is therefore

$$E[R(q) - C(q)] = E[R(q)] - C(q),$$

since $E[C(q)] = C(q)$. Then the qth unit should be produced if

$$E[R(q)] - C(q) \geq 0,$$

or

$$E[R(q)] \geq C(q). \tag{9.13}$$

Thus the condition

$$\text{MR} \geq \text{MC}$$

is transformed into

$$E(\text{MR}) \geq MC$$

in the case of random demand. But we have already calculated $E[R(q)]$ as $r\,P(X \geq q)$; hence the qth unit should be produced if

$$r\,P(X \geq q) \geq C(q). \tag{9.14}$$

We can now show that if the qth unit is profitable to produce (that is, it increases expected profit), then the $(q - 1)$st unit must also have been profitable to produce. First we make the assumption

$$C(q) \geq C(q-1); \tag{9.15}$$

that is, as output increases, marginal cost either rises or remains constant, but it does not fall. Now the expected marginal revenue of the $(q - 1)$st unit is $rP(X \geq q - 1)$ and clearly

$$r\,P(X \geq q-1) \geq r\,P(X \geq q) \tag{9.16}$$

for

$$P(X \geq q-1) - P(X = q-1) = P(X \geq q),$$

so that

$$P(X \geq q-1) \geq P(X \geq q).$$

If the qth unit is profitable to produce, then (9.14) must hold; whereupon (9.15) and (9.16) imply

$$r\,P(X \geq q-1) \geq r\,P(X \geq q) \geq C(q) \geq C(q-1).$$

Hence

$$r\,P(X \geq q-1) \geq C(q-1), \tag{9.17}$$

and the $(q-1)$st unit must also have been profitable to produce. In similar fashion it can be shown that if it is *not* profitable to produce the qth unit, then it will *not* be profitable to produce the $(q+1)$st unit.[17] This establishes the following result: Assumptions (i)–(iii) and (iv*), along with (9.15), imply that the firm wishing to maximize its *expected profit* should produce

$$\boxed{\begin{array}{c}\text{The largest } q \text{ such that}\\ r\,P(X \geq q) \geq C(q).\end{array}} \tag{9.18}$$

The highest output level which satisfies (9.18) is the output level which maximizes expected profit. Note that (9.18) generalizes (9.8) in two ways. First, it allows for random demand; second, the marginal cost curve need not be rising, but may in fact be at a constant level.

In Figure 9.4, we display the result above and compare it with the corresponding result in the case of unlimited demand. In the figure we assume r and MC are such that in the case of unlimited demand, the

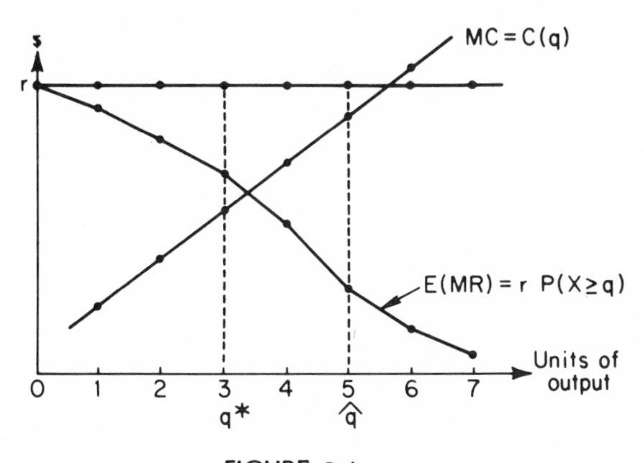

FIGURE 9.4

[17]That is, if the expected profit for a total of q units is less than the expected profit for a total of $(q-1)$ units, then the expected profit for a total of $(q+1)$ units must be less than the expected profit for $(q-1)$ units and less than or equal to that for q units.

profit-maximizing output would be five units, denoted by $\hat{q}$ in Figure 9.4. If demand is a random variable, the E(MR) curve must cross the vertical axis at r, since

$$P(X \geq 0) = 1;$$

therefore

$$r\,P(X \geq 0) = r.$$

As q increases, the expected marginal revenue curve must ultimately decline and approach the horizontal axis. This is easily seen. Inequality (9.16) implies that expected marginal revenue declines (or at least does not increase) with each increase in q. Further, as q approaches infinity, $P(X \geq q)$ approaches zero, so that

$$E\,(MR) = r\,P\,(X \geq q) \rightarrow 0$$

$$\text{as } q \rightarrow \infty\,.$$

The optimal output in the uncertainty case is assumed to be three units and is denoted by q^* in Figure 9.4. Note that the lower output in the uncertainty case is an illustration of the general rule that

> With given cost and price conditions,
> uncertainty of demand
> must result in[18]
>
> $$q^* \leq \hat{q}. \qquad (9.18)$$

Uncertainty has the effect of reducing output by virtue of the fact that it introduces a *risk of overproduction* which is absent in the case of unlimited demand.

EXAMPLE 9.4.2. A firm which produces a perishable product (sold at $20 per unit) is subject to the following probability distribution of demand:

[18]It is clear that $q^* = \hat{q}$ if

$$P(X \geq \hat{q}) \geq 1 - [r - C(q)].$$

Otherwise, $q^* < \hat{q}$. If $C(q)$ is constant and less than r, then $\hat{q}$ is indeterminate (infinitely large), while q^* must of course be finite.

X	$P(X)$
≤ 3	0
4	0.10
5	0.15
6	0.40
7	0.20
8	0.15
	1.00

Its costs of production are[19]

q	Total cost	$MC = C(q)$
1	$ 70.00	—
2	74.50	$4.50
3	80.00	5.50
4	85.50	5.50
5	91.00	5.50
6	97.50	6.50
7	104.00	6.50
8	112.00	8.00

What output level maximizes expected profit and what is the maximum expected profit?

Solution: We calculate the expected marginal revenue function as follows.

q	$P(X \geq q)$	$E(MR) = r\,P(X \geq q)$	$MC = C(q)$
1	1	$20.00	—
2	1	20.00	$4.50
3	1	20.00	5.50
4	1	20.00	5.50
5	0.90	18.00	5.50
6	0.75	15.00	6.50
7	0.35	*7.00*	*6.50*
8	0.15	3.00	8.00

[19]The marginal cost of the first unit is not shown since the problem does not specify how much of the $70 is due to production of the first unit and how much is due to fixed costs, such as rent, which would have to be paid regardless of the level of output. To be consistent with (9.15), we must assume

$$C(1) \leq \$4.50.$$

It is clear that the largest q such that

$$r\,P(X \geq q) \geq C(q)$$

is $q = 7$, which is therefore the optimal output level.

The expected profit corresponding to $q = 7$ can be calculated by noting

$$\begin{aligned} E(\text{profit} \mid q = 7) &= E(\text{revenue} - \text{cost} \mid q = 7) \\ &= E(\text{revenue} - \$104 \mid q = 7) \\ &= E(\text{revenue} \mid q = 7) - \$104, \end{aligned}$$

since $104 is the cost associated with $q = 7$. Then

$P(X)$	X	Sales	Revenue = $20(sales)	Revenue × P(revenue)
0	1	1	$20	0
0	2	2	40	0
0	3	3	60	0
0.10	4	4	80	$8.00
0.15	5	5	100	15.00
0.40	6	6	120	48.00
0.20	7	7	140	28.00
0.15	8	7[20]	140	21.00
1.00				$120.00

Hence

$$\begin{aligned} E(\text{profit} \mid q = 7) &= E(\text{revenue} \mid q = 7) - \$104 \\ &= \$120 - \$104 \\ &= \$16. \end{aligned}$$

An alternative calculation would make use of expected marginal profit as follows:

q	$E(MR) = r\,P(X \geq q)$	$MC = C(q)$	Expected marginal profit = $E(MR) - MC$	Cumulated expected marginal profit
1	$20.00	—	—	—
2	20.00	$4.50	$15.50	$15.50
3	20.00	5.50	14.50	30.00
4	20.00	5.50	14.50	44.50
5	18.00	5.50	12.50	57.00
6	15.00	6.50	8.50	65.50
7	7.00	6.50	0.50	66.00
8	3.00	8.00	−5.00	61.00

[20]Sales will be equal to seven even if demand equals eight, since only seven units are being produced.

One unit of output results in a profit of

$$\$20.00 - \$70.00 = -\$50.00;$$

therefore the expected profit for seven units of output is

$$\begin{aligned} E[\pi(7)] &= \$50.00 + (\$15.50 + \$14.50 + \$14.50 + \$12.50 + \$8.50 + \$0.50) \\ &= -\$50.00 + (\$66.00) \\ &= \$16. \end{aligned}$$

Figure 9.5 summarizes all the results of this example.

9.5 A Note on Inventories

The methodology and ideas presented in Section 9.4 have been of notable importance in the development of the field of inventory theory. The starting point in inventory theory is relaxation of the "perishable product" assumption. Instead, we recognize that the firm may begin its planning for the current period with a stock of goods left over from past periods. In this context the firm faces the problem of deciding how much to produce to add to its already existing stock of goods. Problems of this nature can quickly become rather complex, but the basic ideas can be illustrated through the analysis of what has come to be known as an *S-type* inventory problem. A problem is of S-type when there exists a critical number S, say $S = 15$, such that the firm will always want to have S units available for sale as long as the basic price, cost, and demand conditions remain constant.

When we recognize the possibility of holding inventories, at least two factors additional to those of Section 9.4 must be considered:

(1) There is a cost to holding inventories. Such costs are known as *storage* or *holding* costs.
(2) Stock in excess of current demand is not worthless, since it can be sold at a later date.

Along with assumptions (i)–(iii) and (iv*), we shall introduce further conditions as follows:

(v) Marginal production costs are constant at a level of C dollars.
(vi) Holding or storage costs amount to H dollars per unit of ending inventory, and $H < C$.

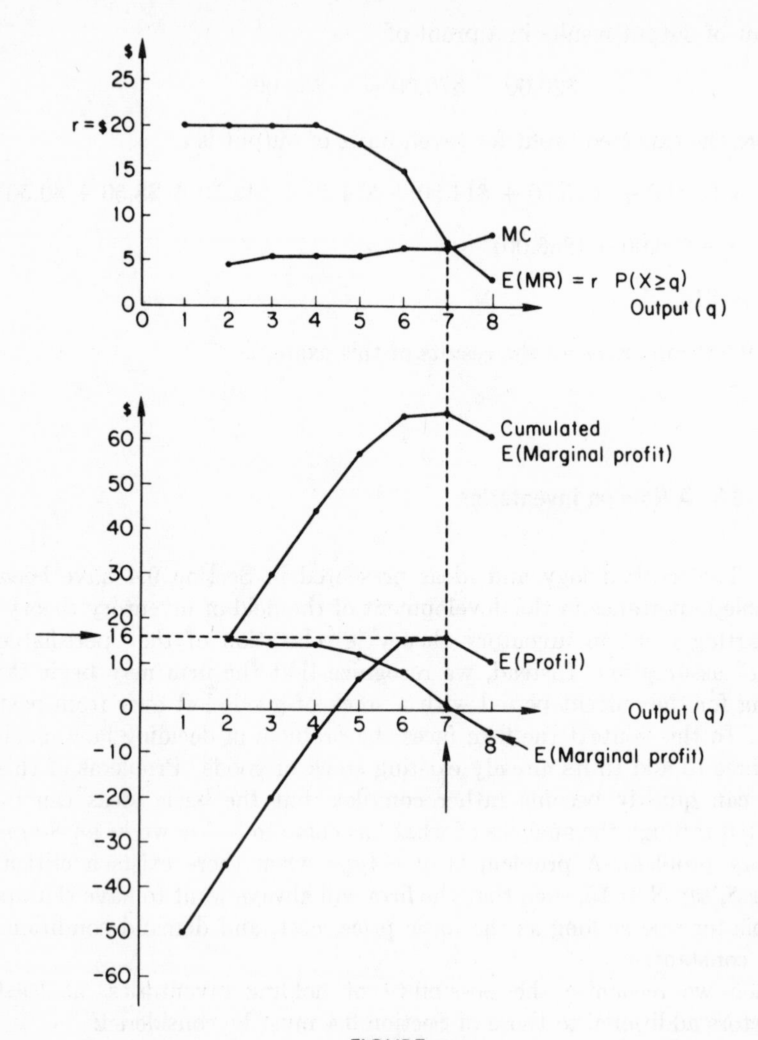

FIGURE 9.5

With these assumptions it is shown in more advanced treatments that the problem is of S-type.[21] Since this is the case, we can easily determine the value of a unit of ending inventory. Suppose that for our problem $S = 15$ and the firm begins a production period with 5 units of stock remaining from previous periods. For the current period the firm will produce 10 units in order to bring its stock available for sale up to 15. If the firm experiences

[21]The problem may also be of S-type under less stringent conditions; for example, marginal cost rises, but not *too* rapidly.

demand for only 13 units during the current period, it will have an ending inventory of 2 units. *The economic value of these 2 units is measured by what the firm would lose if it did not possess them.* Since for the next period the firm will again want 15 units available for sale, the possession of 2 units at the end of the current period will reduce the output of the following period by exactly 2 units. That is, if the firm had no ending inventory, it would have to produce 15 units; with 2 units of ending inventory it need only produce 13 units. The saving due to possession of the 2 units is therefore $2C$ dollars, where C is the constant marginal production cost.

With this background, suppose again that the decision has been made to produce $(q - 1)$ units and we wish to decide whether or not to produce an additional unit. Marginal cost now has two components: production cost and holding cost. The marginal production cost of the qth unit is C dollars, but the marginal holding cost is a random variable. If the qth unit is sold, then no holding costs are incurred for the qth unit; if the qth unit cannot be sold, then it will incur a holding cost of H dollars. The qth unit will be unsold if total demand X is less than $(q + I)$, where I is initial inventory. Thus,

Marginal holding cost for qth unit	Probability of holding cost	Holding cost × P(holding cost)
0	$1 - P(X < q + I)$	0
H	$P(X < q + I)$	$(H)P(X < q + I)$
	1	$(H)P(X < q + I)$

and

$$E(\text{marginal cost of } q\text{th unit}) = (\text{marginal production cost}) + E(\text{marginal holding cost})$$

$$= C + (H)P(X < q + I). \qquad (9.19)$$

The marginal revenue of the qth unit is also a random variable. If the qth unit can be sold, then its value is the selling price r dollars. If the qth unit cannot be sold, it becomes a unit of ending inventory with a value of C dollars.[22] For the qth unit to be sold, total demand X must be for at least $(q + I)$ units. Thus,

[22]Note that the firm's cash revenue will not be increased by C dollars; rather, its next period production costs will be reduced by C dollars. It is really of little consequence whether we consider the C dollars as a revenue or as a negative cost. Of greater importance is the question of whether C dollars saved *next* period is worth C dollars this period. This is a standard economic problem known as *discounting*. On the assumption of "short" periods, we can safely neglect this complication.

Marginal revenue for *q*th unit	Probability of marginal revenue	Marginal revenue × P(marginal revenue)
r	$P(X \geq q + I)$	$r\,P(X \geq q + I)$
C	$1 - P(X \geq q + I)$	$C[1 - P(X \geq q + I)]$
	1	$E(MR)$

and

$$E(\text{marginal revenue of } q\text{th unit}) = r\,P(X \geq q + I) + C[1 - P(X \geq q + I)]$$
$$= (r - C)\,P(X \geq q + I) + C. \tag{9.20}$$

Now the qth unit should be produced if its expected marginal revenue is at least as large as its expected marginal cost, that is, if

$$(r - C)\,P(X \geq q + I) + C \geq C + (H)\,P(X < q + I). \tag{9.21}$$

But the expression in (9.21) implies that the qth unit should be produced if

$$(r - C)\,P(X \geq q + I) \geq (H)\,P(X < q + I). \tag{9.22}$$

The geometric version of (9.21) is best approached in several steps. First, let us begin with (9.22) and the assumption that there is no initial inventory ($I = 0$). The upper half of Figure 9.6 displays the relations in (9.22) with the case ($r - C > H$) shown as Figure 9.6a and ($r - C < H$) shown as Figure 9.6b. The lower half of Figure 9.6 uses dashed curves to repeat the upper half. The solid curves represent the relations in (9.21) and are derived by "raising" each of the dashed curves by a vertical amount equal to C dollars.[23] The resulting curves are appropriately labeled E(MR) and E(MC). Since these curves are drawn on the assumption $I = 0$, the optimal output which results is in fact the value of S. If the curves had been drawn for $I > 0$ ($I \leq S$ since the firm never stocks more than S and can therefore never have an inventory in excess of S), the optimal output would have been $S - I$, that is, the output necessary to bring the stock available for sale up to S.

[23]The curves in Figure 9.6a correspond to the case r = \$10, C = \$6, and H = \$2. For Figure 9.6b we use r = \$10, C = \$6, and H = \$5. In both cases the probability distribution of demand is

X	0	1	2	3	4	5	6	7	8
$P(X)$	0	0.1	0.1	0.2	0.2	0.1	0.1	0.1	0.1

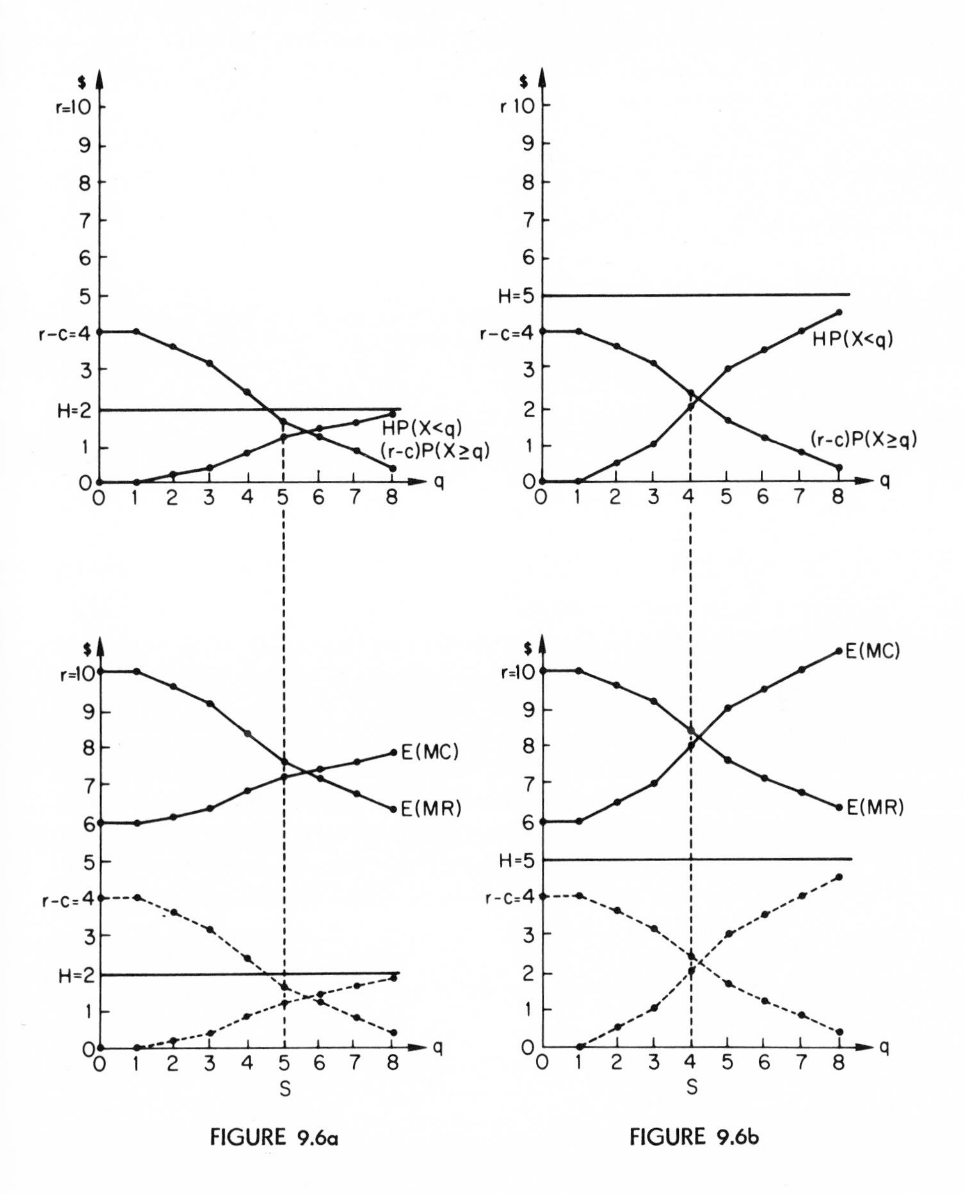

FIGURE 9.6a

FIGURE 9.6b

EXAMPLE 9.5.1. A retailer stocks a particular brand of soap powder (WOW!) which he sells for 40¢ per box. His cost is 30¢ per box, and he reorders once a week. At the end of each week, the unsold boxes of WOW! must be counted so that appropriate bookkeeping records can be kept. It is estimated that such costs of record keeping amount to 3¢ per unsold box. The weekly demand distribution is estimated to be

Demand = X	$P(X)$
100	0.02
101	0.02
102	0.03
103	0.04
104	0.05
105	0.07
106	0.10
107	0.15
108	0.12
109	0.10
110	0.08
111	0.07
112	0.07
113	0.05
114	0.02
115	0.01
	1.00

(a) To maximize the expected profit from the sale of WOW!, how many boxes should the retailer have available for sale each week?
(b) What is the retailer's maximum expected profit?
(c) How much can the cost of record keeping rise without changing the answer to (a)?

Solution to (a): The problem is clearly of S-type with

$$r = 0.40,$$

$$C = 0.30,$$

$$H = 0.03.$$

To determine S, we make use of (9.21) with I = 0; hence S is the largest q for which

$$(r - C)\,P(X \geq q) + C \geq C + (H)P(X < q),$$

where the expression on the left is expected marginal revenue and that on the right is expected marginal cost. For each q, expected marginal revenue and cost are calculated as follows (note that $r - C = 0.10$):

q	$P(X \geq q)$	$P(X < q)$	$E(MR) = 0.10\,P(X \geq q) + 0.30$	$E(MC) = 0.30 + 0.03\,P(X < q)$
100	1.00	0.00	0.400	0.300
101	0.98	0.02	0.398	0.301
102	0.96	0.04	0.396	0.301
103	0.93	0.07	0.393	0.302
104	0.89	0.11	0.389	0.303
105	0.84	0.16	0.384	0.305
106	0.77	0.23	0.377	0.307
107	0.67	0.33	0.367	0.310
108	0.52	0.48	0.352	0.314
109	0.40	0.60	0.340	0.318
→ *110*	0.30	0.70	*0.330*	*0.321* ←
111	0.22	0.78	0.322	0.323
112	0.15	0.85	0.315	0.326
113	0.08	0.92	0.308	0.328
114	0.03	0.97	0.303	0.329
115	0.01	0.99	0.301	0.330

From the table above it is clear that the highest q for which $E(\text{MR}) \geq E(\text{MC})$ is $q = 110$. Hence $S = 110$ and the retailer should reorder WOW! so as to bring his weekly stock available for sale to 110 boxes.

Solution to (b): By using the last two columns of the table above we find

q	E(marginal profit) $= E(\text{MR}) - E(\text{MC})$	Cumulated E(marginal profit)
100	0.100	0.100
101	0.097	0.197
102	0.095	0.292
103	0.091	0.383
104	0.086	0.469
105	0.079	0.548
106	0.070	0.618
107	0.057	0.675
108	0.038	0.713
109	0.022	0.735
→ 110	0.009	0.744 ←
111	−0.001	0.743
112	−0.011	0.732
113	−0.020	0.712
114	−0.026	0.686
115	−0.029	0.657

The first 99 boxes yield a profit of 99(\$0.40 − \$0.30) = \$9.90, so that the maximum expected profit per week on the sale of WOW! is[24]

$$\$9.90 + \$0.74 = \$10.64.$$

Solution to (c): The answer to (a) is 110 since 110 is the largest q which satisfies

$$(r - C)\,P(X \geq q) + C \geq C + (H)P(X < q).$$

With r and C fixed, 110 will still be the optimum stock level if H rises no further than, say, H^*, where

$$(r - C)\,P(X \geq 110) + C = C + (H^*)P(X < 110)$$

or

$$0.10\,P(X \geq 110) = (H^*)P(X < 110),$$

$$0.10\,(0.30) = (H^*)(0.70),$$

$$H^* = \frac{0.10(0.30)}{0.70} \cong 0.043.$$

Thus the cost of record keeping must rise above 4.3¢ per unsold box before it becomes profitable to stock fewer than 110 boxes per week.

9.6 A Note on Supply and Market Equilibrium

The previous two sections have centered attention on the determination of optimal output (or stock level) under the conditions of given price, cost, and demand relations. It is also of interest to know how the firm's supply — that is, quantity produced (or stocked) — responds to a change in the demand distribution and/or the price of output.

Consider the model which led to the geometric representation in Figure 9.4. If price remains constant and the demand distribution *shifts* in such a way that the probability of a total demand less than q^* diminishes, then the expected marginal revenue curve must shift upward in the neighborhood

[24]Note that the probabilistic calculations have revealed a policy which increases expected weekly profit by about 7.5%,

$$\left(\frac{0.74}{9.90} = 0.075\right).$$

Over a period of 1 year this can be expected to increase profits on the sale of WOW! from

$$52(\$9.90) = \$514.80 \quad \text{to} \quad 52(\$10.64) = \$553.28.$$

to the right of q^*. We shall refer to this as an *upward shift* of demand. It is clear that an upward shift of demand cannot decrease the firm's supply. A sufficiently large upward shift of demand will increase the firm's supply of output, even with marginal cost rising. There are several possible sources of such an upward shift of demand; among them,

(i) An increase in total income which causes an upward shift in the demand for most products.
(ii) A change in consumer tastes so that the demand for this particular product rises at the expense of the demand for other products.

Suppose now that the firms in a particular industry follow a price leader who attempts to set an equilibrium or market-clearing price. That is, a given price, say $10, calls forth a certain total output from all producers. If consumers wish to purchase — *at the price of* $10 — exactly that total amount which was produced for sale, then the $10 price is said to be an equilibrium or market-clearing price. The advantage of a market-clearing price is that it avoids two costly extremes:

(i) Too high a price would result in overproduction so that the industry as a whole would tend to build up excessive inventories and therefore incur substantial storage, maintenance, and spoilage costs.
(ii) Too low a price would result in underproduction so that the industry would be unable to satisfy its customers and would begin to lose customers, acquire a poor reputation, etc.

If we assume that, in the neighborhood of the equilibrium price, inventory levels are small relative to output and holding costs are negligible, then we can approach the problem of market equilibrium using Figure 9.4 once again.

Suppose that in Figure 9.4 the price is $r = \$2$. The firm depicted in the figure produces $q^* = 3$ units of output.[25] If the total output of all such firms amounts to 100 units, while the market demand at a price of $2 amounts to fewer than 100 units, the industry as a whole will discover that it is overproducing; that is, $2 is not an equilibrium price. If the price leader therefore "signals" a price reduction, it is clear that each firm will immediately experience a downward shift in its expected marginal revenue function.

[25]In this case we implicitly assume that the total market demand at each price is known. Uncertainty of demand at the firm level arises from uncertainty as to how the total market demand will be "divided" among the various firms.

This will of course lead to a reduction in supply for some firms (if not all) and for the industry as a whole. If total industry demand is invariant with respect to price,[26] all that is necessary to establish equilibrium is to reduce the industry price until total industry supply has fallen to the level of demand. It is more likely, however, that as the price of output declines, consumers will be willing to purchase a greater total amount of the product. The individual firms will then find that their expected marginal revenue curves undergo two separate changes. First a complete downward shift corresponding to the price decline alone, and second a partial upward shift corresponding to the fact that at the lower price a greater total demand is to be split among the producing firms. Some firms, then, will produce more following the price reduction than would have been the case if total demand had been invariant with respect to price. Some firms may even experience enough of an upward shift in E (MR) as a result of the greater total demand to produce an amount even greater than the original q^*. In the aggregate one would expect that total industry supply at the lower price would settle somewhere between the original level and that level which would have been obtained if total demand had been invariant with respect to price.[27] A reduction in price will therefore reduce (or at least not increase) quantity supplied, increase quantity demanded, and move the industry toward equilibrium.

EXAMPLE 9.6.1. We shall illustrate market equilibrium by means of a simplified example in which a product is produced by 10 identical firms. Suppose that the total industry demand relation is given by

Price	Total industry demand
$7	100
6	110
5	120
4	130
3	140

At a price of $5, each firm's probability distribution of demand is assumed to be the following.

[26]This is referred to as *totally inelastic* demand.

[27]Indeed, if this were not so, the stability of the market — that is, the existence of a tenable equilibrium price — might be seriously in doubt.

X	$P(X \mid r = 5)$
9	0.10
10	0.15
11	0.15
12	0.20
13	0.15
14	0.15
15	0.10
	1.00

so that $E(X \mid r = 5) = 12$, which is $\frac{1}{10}$ of the market demand. At a price of \$4, each firm's demand distribution would be

X	$P(X \mid r = 4)$
10	0.10
11	0.15
12	0.15
13	0.20
14	0.15
15	0.15
16	0.10
	1.00

so that $E(X \mid r = 4) = 13$, which is $\frac{1}{10}$ of the market demand at a price of \$4.

The marginal cost relation of each firm is given by

q	$C(q) = MC$
9	\$1.50
10	1.60
11	1.70
12	1.80
13	1.90
14	2.00
15	2.10
16	2.20

We shall show that a price of \$5 would result in overproduction, while a price of \$4 results in equilibrium.

Starting with a price of $5,

q	$P(X \geq q \mid r = 5)$	$E(MR) = 5\,P(X \geq q \mid r = 5)$	MC
9	1.00	$5.00	$1.50
10	0.90	4.50	1.60
11	0.75	3.75	1.70
12	0.60	3.00	1.80
→ *13*	0.40	*2.00*	*1.90* ←
14	0.25	1.25	2.00
15	0.10	0.50	2.10

Each firm would therefore maximize expected profit by producing 13 units of output per period. The total industry supply would be

$$10(13) = 130 \text{ units,}$$

which is 10 more than consumers will buy at a price of $5. If the product were perishable, the unsold units would cause no difficulty unless disposal were costly. If the product can remain in inventory, continued production of 13 units per firm would eventually result in inventory levels large enough to impose severe storage and/or maintenance costs on the firms, even if modest inventory levels involve negligible costs. In either the latter case or the perishable-product, costly disposal case, it is clear that a market-clearing price is advantageous.

At a price of $4 we find

q	$P(X \geq q \mid r = 4)$	$E(MR) = 4\,P(X \geq q \mid r = 4)$	MC
10	1.00	$4.00	$1.60
11	0.90	3.60	1.70
12	0.75	3.00	1.80
→ *13*	0.60	*2.40*	*1.90* ←
14	0.40	1.60	2.00
15	0.25	1.00	2.10
16	0.10	0.40	2.20

If the price reduction had not been accompanied by an increase in total quantity demanded, output would have declined to 12 units per firm. The upward shift of the $E(\text{MR})$ curve, however, served to keep output at 13 units despite the price reduction. Total industry supply is again 130 units, but at a price of $4 this is precisely the quantity demanded in the market.

PROBLEMS

9-1. The following table gives the age and sex of persons unemployed during the week including the 12th in March 1966. Units are in thousands of persons.

	Sex		
Age	Male	Female	Total
<20	445	304	749
20–25	284	193	477
>25	1,118	693	1,811
			3,037

Source: *Employment and Earnings and Monthly Report of the Labor Force, April 1966.*

Use Bayes' theorem to find the probability that an unemployed person selected at random is

(a) Less than 20 years of age given he is male.
(b) 25 years of age or younger given we select a female.

What is implied by this table concerning the relationship between age and the likelihood of being unemployed?

9-2. The 1962 *Survey of Consumer Finances* presents the results of a survey in which 2,523 families were interviewed twice — once in early 1960 and again in early 1961. The first interview revealed that 31 of the 596 families with incomes less than \$3,000 expressed intentions to purchase a new automobile during the next year. Of the 1,149 families with incomes in the interval \$3,000–7,499, 132 of these expressed intentions to purchase a new automobile. Finally, 160 of the families with incomes $\geq$ \$7,500 expressed intentions to buy a new automobile. The second survey was aimed at discovering how actual purchases conformed with buying intentions. In this second survey it was revealed that only 26% of the intenders in the low-income class actually had purchased new automobiles while 56% of the intenders in the middle-income class and 61% in the high-income class had actually made new car purchases. If we were to select from the sample a family which had intended to purchase a new automobile and did, with what probability could we say that this family had income in the interval \$3,000–7,499?

9-3. A salesman knows that the demand for his product in month t (X_t) is equal to the demand in the previous month (X_{t-1}) plus a random component u. That is, $X_t = X_{t-1} + u$, where $Eu = \alpha$ and var $u = \sigma^2$. The research department of the company for which the salesman works has found $\alpha = 9$ and has estimated σ^2 to have the following (prior) probability distribution:

σ^2	$P[\sigma^2]$
10	0.20
12	0.25
14	0.35
16	0.15
20	0.05
	1.00

Assuming that these estimates are correct and given that last month's sales were 50, use Chebyschev's inequality to find a minimum probability that this month's sales will lie in the interval 49–69, inclusive.

9-4. A prior probability distribution of the proportion of families with incomes below a poverty level in a certain area has been estimated by a government agency to be as follows:

p	Prior $P[p]$
0.10	0.30
0.12	0.50
0.15	0.15
0.18	0.05
	1.00

A random sample of 20 families in the area revealed 3 with incomes below the poverty level. Calculate the posterior probability distribution of p. Also calculate the expected value of p for both prior and posterior probability distributions and determine the weight given to the sample evidence in calculation of the latter.

9-5. The owner of a number of apartment buildings is contemplating the construction of a new 100-unit building. He calculates that the building will be profitable only if the expected number of vacancies is fewer than 20 units. On the basis of his past experience he estimates that the proportion of vacancies has the following prior probability distribution:

p	Prior $P(p)$
0.22	0.15
0.21	0.20
0.20	0.40
0.19	0.25
	1.00

On the basis of past experience the building would not be profitable to construct since $Ep = 0.2025 > 0.20$. But the prospective builder has supplemented his past experience estimates by sampling 50 apartments similar to those he proposes to construct. He found that 6 of these were vacant. Combine the prior evidence with the sample evidence to determine whether the apartment building should be constructed. What weight is given to the sample evidence?

9-6. A retailer will stock a certain new product only if the probability is at least 0.50 that 10% or more of the potential customers will try the new product. The retailer does not have a precise notion of the potential response but feels that the possible percentage responses are either 5%, 10%, 15%, or 20%. He also feels that a 10% response rate is as likely as a 5% response rate but only $\frac{2}{3}$ as likely as a 15% response rate. That is, his prior probability distribution is

p	Prior $P[p]$
0.05	X
0.10	X
0.15	$1.5X$
0.20	$1-3.5X$
	1.00

(a) What is the maximum value of X? At the maximum value, should the retailer stock the new product?

(b) A poll of 20 potential customers failed to reveal any who said he would purchase the new product. Calculate the implied posterior probability distribution (in terms of X). Should the retailer stock the product?

9-7. A college student is trying to decide whether to take a job selling encyclopedias door-to-door during his summer vacation. He would work on a commission basis and receive \$40 for every sale. He has calculated that the cost to him (including transportation, lodging, etc.) would be \$30 per week. The encyclopedia company's sales staff has told him that the proportion of house calls that will produce sales is between 0.01 and 0.04 with the following probability distribution:

p	$P[p]$
0.01	0.20
0.02	0.25
0.03	0.40
0.04	0.15
	1.00

Assume the college student would call on 100 houses every week.

(a) Find the probability that he will earn (in excess of costs) less than \$25 in a week.

(b) How would your answer to (a) change if, after 1 week (100 house calls), the college student had sold exactly one set of encyclopedias?

9-8. A firm which produces a perishable product is able to sell all it wishes at a price of \$4 per unit. Total cost of producing q units of the product is

$$TC(q) = \$10 + \$1q + \$0.10q^2.$$

Determine the optimal output ($\hat{q}$) and calculate the total profit earned at this output.

9-9. A firm which produces a perishable product is subject to the following probability distribution of demand and marginal cost structure:

q	$P[X \geq q]$	Marginal cost $= C(q)$
0	1.00	\$1.25
1	0.95	1.30
2	.90	1.45
3	.83	1.70
4	.70	2.00
5	.65	2.35
6	.55	2.80
7	.40	3.25
8	.26	4.00
9	.10	4.30
10	.05	4.95
≥11	0	—

The product sells at a price of $5 per unit. Compute the expected marginal revenue and plot the graph of both $E(\mathrm{MR})$ and $C(q)$. What is the optimum output?

9-10. A firm faces uncertain quantity demanded at a selling price of $1.50 per unit of perishable output. The table below gives the costs of producing various levels of output and the probabilities that exactly that much output will be sold.

q	$P[q]$	Total cost of q
≤20	0	$5.00
21	0.05	5.75
22	0.10	6.60
23	0.10	7.45
24	0.15	8.35
25	0.18	9.35
26	0.20	10.50
27	0.12	11.70
28	0.05	13.00
29	0.03	14.45
30	0.02	16.00
>30	0	—
	1.00	

What is the optimal output for the firm and what is its expected profit at this level?

9-11. A firm with the following probability distribution of demand produces a perishable product under conditions of increasing marginal costs. Total cost of producing q units is $\$0.02q^2$. The product sells for $6 per unit. Find the optimal output and its expected profit.

q	$P[X = q]$
≤45	0
46	0.08
47	0.12
48	0.15
49	0.15
50	0.20
51	0.12
52	0.08
53	0.06
54	0.04
≥55	0
	1.00

9-12. A secretary is contemplating baking cookies to sell in the office coffee lounge for 5¢ apiece. A friend of hers in another office with the same number of employees has been doing this for some time. Since cookies go stale after 3 days, this friend has been bringing a fresh batch of 11 dozen cookies to work every Monday and Thursday (people work on Saturdays in this city). This friend sells her cookies for 5¢ apiece and has found that she never sells fewer than 5 dozen before they go stale. She has sold all 11 dozen only 10% of the time and has sold 5–10 dozen with equal frequency. If it costs 35¢ per dozen to bake cookies, determine the optimum number of cookies (in dozens) our secretary should bring to her office every Monday and Thursday. How much profit can she expect to make on each optimal size batch of cookies?

9-13. A farmer sells grape juice at a roadside stand for 5¢ per ounce. The daily demand for his grape juice (in ounces) is a random variable distributed $\eta(160, 100)$. Having discovered that tending the roadside stand takes too much time away from his other duties, the farmer has decided to bottle his grape juice (in 8 ounce bottles to sell for 40¢ apiece) and leave the bottles unattended at the roadside with a basket in which purchasers can leave their money. The farmer has been warned by authorities that his grape juice ferments sufficiently in a day's time to be unsalable as grape juice. Since he is not licensed to produce wine, the farmer must regard his grape juice as a product which is perishable within 1 day. Bottling does not retard the fermentation process. Assuming all his customers are honest and that bottling does not affect their demand for his grape juice, compute the probability distribution of demand for $q = \leq 16, 17, 18, \ldots, 22, 23, \geq 24$ bottles per day. If it costs the farmer 30¢ per bottle to produce, how many should he make?

9-14. A firm is contemplating entering an industry which produces a durable product only on special order. The product sells at a price r and total cost of producing q units per year is $a + bq + q^c$, where $c = 0$ if $q \leq Z$, a constant, and $c = 2$ if $q > Z$. The number of orders received in any year is a random variable X with the following properties:

$$X > 1,$$

$$X = D + \epsilon,$$

where D is a constant and ϵ is a random variable with $E\epsilon = 0$ and $E\epsilon^2 = \sigma^2$. The firm will not enter the industry unless it can expect to make a certain minimum profit.

(a) What is this firm's expected profit?
(b) Use your answer to (a), along with Markov's inequality, to derive the following expression for minimum expected profits:

$$E\pi > (r - b)D - (a + 1) - \frac{D}{Z}(D^2 + \sigma^2).$$

9-15. A grocer purchases noodle soup for 11¢ a can and sells it for 18¢ a can. He reorders every week and estimates the costs of keeping informed on the status of his noodle soup inventory at 1¢ per unsold can per week. His weekly demand for noodle soup is a random variable with the following probability distribution:

X (in cans per week)	$P[X]$
195	0.01
196	0.09
197	0.14
198	0.16
199	0.18
200	0.14
201	0.10
202	0.08
203	0.07
204	0.03
	1.00

(a) How many cans of noodle soup should the grocer have on hand at the beginning of each week in order to maximize expected profits?
(b) What is his maximum expected profit?
(c) By how much can the cost (to him) of noodle soup rise and not change his optimal stock level?

9-16. The owner of a menswear shop reorders suits from his supplier every six months. Suits sell for $85 and cost the retailer $50 apiece. He has found that style changes make it impossible to sell the same number of six month old suits as new suits at a price of $85. He must lower the price by $5 for every six months the suit has been in stock in order to keep sales (in numbers of suits) at levels comparable to what he could sell if all suits in stock were new. The six month demand distribution for suits is estimated to be the following.

Demand X	$P[X]$
115	0.12
116	0.16
117	0.20
118	0.22
119	0.15
120	0.09
121	0.06
	1.00

(a) What is the optimum number of suits for the retailer to stock every six months?

Hint: Treat the \$5 cut in price for every six months a suit remains unsold as an inventory holding cost.

(b) What is the retailer's maximum expected profit?

(c) Suppose a haberdasher in another city offers to purchase all suits unsold after six months from our retailer at a price of \$43. Should this offer be accepted? Why?

9-17. An automobile dealer has found that he has probability $\frac{1}{2}$ of not selling a single automobile during any week. He has also found that selling any number of cars q is only half as probable as selling $q - 1$.

(a) Show that the dealer's probability distribution of demand is given by

$$P[X = q] = (\tfrac{1}{2})^{q+1}.$$

Use the algebraic relation

$$\sum_{i=0}^{\infty} a^i = \frac{1}{1-a} \quad \text{for} \quad (0 < a < 1)$$

to verify that $P[X \geq 0] = 1$.

(b) Using the relationship

$$\sum_{i=a}^{n} X^i = \sum_{j=0}^{n} X^{j+a}$$

prove that $P[X \geq q] = (\frac{1}{2})^q$.

(c) Use the results of (a) and (b) along with the information that

(i) The dealer reorders from the factory every week at a cost of \$2,000 per car.

(ii) He sells cars for \$2,350.

(iii) He incurs a holding cost of \$8 per unsold car per week to derive the optimum number of cars to have in stock every week.

9-18. A man is contemplating starting a kennel to breed and sell Labrador Retrievers. Labradors sell for r dollars per dog and the prospective breeder estimates that the cost of "producing" the qth dog is cq (c is a constant) regardless of whether the dog is sold. He estimates that the probability of selling any given dog during its tth year of life is p^t. To begin operations, the prospective breeder must borrow the amount of all costs and pay interest on borrowings at a rate of $100i$ percent per year. Ignore the fact that dogs do not live forever and verify that

(a) The expected cost of the qth dog is

$$\sum_{j=0}^{\infty} cq(1+i)^j p^{j+1} = \frac{(pcq)}{1-p(1+i)}.$$

(b) The expected revenue from the qth dog is

$$\sum_{i=0}^{\infty} rp^{j+1} = \frac{rp}{1-p}.$$

(c) The optimal number of dogs is the largest q which satisfies

$$q \leq \frac{r[1-p(1+i)]}{c(1-p)}.$$

9-19. A market which is fully supplied by only two firms is shared equally between them. That is, each firm has an equal probability of supplying any one purchaser. Suppose the probability distribution of total market demand at a price of \$100 per unit is

X = total market demand	$P[X]$
9	0.25
10	0.40
11	0.35
	1.00

(a) Derive the probability distribution of demand facing each firm.
(b) Assuming the product is perishable and production costs are \$60 per unit, what is the optimal production level of each firm?
(c) With both firms producing optimal output, will there be a tendency for average market demand to outstrip supply or vice versa?

(d) Suppose that a y dollar change in the market price has the following effect on demand:

X	$P[X]$
9	0.25
10	$0.40 + 0.2y$
11	$0.35 - 0.2y$

What price would equate expected demand and optimal market supply? Would the optimal supply change at this market-clearing price?

APPENDIX

This appendix contains the derivations of five results used elsewhere in the text. Each derivation is labeled with two Arabic numerals; the first numeral denotes the chapter and the second the section in which the result is first used.

1.4 THEOREM. If A is a finite set with n elements, it has 2^n subsets.

Proof: The proof is by induction. The theorem is clearly true for $n = 0$, 1, 2 and was proved for $n = 3$ in the text. Assume the theorem is true for $n = k$, where k is any positive integer greater than 3. We proceed to show that the theorem must hold for $n = k + 1$.

We begin with the set A_k which has k elements and 2^k subsets. We now add one additional element, say θ, to the set A_k to obtain A_{k+1}, a set with (k + 1) elements. Each subset of A_k is also a subset of A_{k+1}. From each of the original 2^k subsets, an additional subset of A_{k+1} can be created simply by adding on the element θ. We now have two times 2^k subsets of A_{k+1}. It is easy to see that there are no more subsets. Suppose $S \subset A_{k+1}$. If $S \subset A_k$, then it is one of the original 2^k subsets. If $S \not\subset A_k$, then it must be that $\theta \in S$, whereupon the set obtained by deleting θ from S must be a subset of A_k and S must be a subset created by appending θ to one of the subsets of A_k. The number of subsets of A_{k+1} must therefore be

$$2(2^k) = 2^{k+1}. \qquad \text{Q.E.D.}$$

4.4 The following rule is derived in the text: For x_i fixed,

$$\sum_y P(x_i \cap y) = P(X = x_i).$$

Let

$$A = \sum_y (x_1 + y)\, P(x_1 \cap y) + \sum_y (x_2 + y)\, P(x_2 \cap y) + \sum_y (x_3 + y)\, P(x_3 \cap y) + \sum_y (x_4 + y)\, P(x_4 \cap y).$$

If, say, $(x_1 + y_1) = (x_2 + y_3) = (x_4 + y_2) = t$, and no other $(x + y)$ sum is equal to t, then

$$P(X + Y = t) = P(x_1 \cap y_1) + P(x_2 \cap y_3) + P(x_4 \cap y_2).$$

Now bring these three terms together in the sum A to find

$$\begin{aligned}(x_1 + y_1)\, P(x_1 \cap y_1) + (x_2 + y_3)\, P(x_2 \cap y_3) + (x_4 + y_2)\, P(x_4 \cap y_2) \\ &= t\, P(x_1 \cap y_1) + t\, P(x_2 \cap y_3) + t\, P(x_4 \cap y_2) \\ &= t[P(x_1 \cap y_1) + P(x_2 \cap y_3) + P(x_4 \cap y_2)] \\ &= t\, P(X + Y = t),\end{aligned}$$

which is one of the terms in the sum which defines $E(X + Y)$. Suppose $(x_1 + y_2) = u$ and no other $(x + y)$ sum is equal to u, then $P(X + Y = u) = P(x_1 \cap y_2)$, and the term $(x_1 + y_2)\ P(x_1 \cap y_2)$ is equal to $uP(X + Y = u)$, which again is one of the terms in the sum defining $E(X + Y)$. The end result of such judicious rearranging of the terms in the sum A is clearly that $E(X + Y) = A$.

A typical term in the sum A is

$$\sum_y (x_i + y)\, P(x_i \cap y),$$

which we shall call A_i. But

$$\begin{aligned}A_i &= \sum_y (x_i + y)\, P(x_i \cap y) \\ &= \sum_y x_i\, P(x_i \cap y) + \sum_y y\, P(x_i \cap y) \\ &= x_i \sum_y P(x_i \cap y) + \sum_y y\, P(x_i \cap y) \\ &= x_i\, P(X = x_i) + \sum_y y\, P(x_i \cap y).\end{aligned}$$

We can now write A as

$$\begin{aligned}A = x_1\, P(X = x_1) + \sum_y y\, P(x_1 \cap y) + x_2\, P(X = x_2) + \sum_y y\, P(x_2 \cap y) \\ + x_3\, P(X = x_3) + \sum_y y\, P(x_3 \cap y) + x_4\, P(X = x_4) + \sum_y y\, P(x_4 \cap y)\end{aligned}$$

$$= \sum_x x\, P(X = x) + \sum_y [yP\,(x_1 \cap y)$$
$$+ y\, P(x_2 \cap y) + y\, P(x_3 \cap y) + y\, P(x_4 \cap y)]$$
$$= EX + \sum_y y[P(x_1 \cap y) + P(x_2 \cap y) + P(x_3 \cap y) + P(x_4 \cap y)].$$

The term in brackets is just

$$\sum_x P(x \cap y),$$

so that

$$A = EX + \sum_y y\Big[\sum_x P(x \cap y)\Big].$$

Doing the indicated summing over y,

$$A = EX + [y_1 \sum_x P(x \cap y_1) + y_2 \sum_x P(x \cap y_2) + y_3 \sum_x P(x \cap y_3)$$
$$+ y_4 \sum_x P(x \cap y_4) + \cdots],$$

which is the expression appearing in the text.

5.6 (a) If $p = q = \frac{1}{2}$,

$$\sum_x \binom{n}{x} p^x q^{n-x} = 1.$$

First, let

$$S_n = \sum_{x=0}^{n} \binom{n}{x} = 1 + n + \frac{n(n-1)}{2!} + \frac{n(n-1)(n-2)}{3!} + \cdots + 1.$$

Then,

$$S_1 = \sum_{x=0}^{1} \binom{1}{x} = 1 + 1 = 2,$$

$$S_2 = \sum_{x=0}^{2} \binom{2}{x} = 1 + 2 + 1 = 4 = 2^2,$$

$$S_3 = \sum_{x=0}^{3} \binom{3}{x} = 1 + 3 + 3 + 1 = 8 = 2^3,$$

$$S_4 = \sum_{x=0}^{4} \binom{4}{x} = 1 + 4 + 6 + 4 + 1 = 16 = 2^4,$$

.

.

.

$$S_n = \sum_{x=0}^{n} \binom{n}{x} = 2^n.$$

Now if $p = q = \frac{1}{2}$,

$$\begin{aligned}\sum_x \binom{n}{x}(0.5)^x(0.5)^{n-x} &= \sum_x \binom{n}{x}(0.5)^n \\ &= (0.5)^n \sum_x \binom{n}{x} \\ &= (0.5)^n S_n \\ &= (0.5)^n\,(2^n) \\ &= \frac{1}{2^n}\,(2^n) = 1.\end{aligned}$$

(b) THEOREM. If X is $B(n, p)$, $EX = np$.

Proof:

$$\begin{aligned}EX &= \sum_{x=0}^{n} x\binom{n}{x}p^x q^{n-x} \\ &= \sum_{x=0}^{n} x\,\frac{n!}{x!(n-x)!}\,p^x q^{n-x}.\end{aligned}$$

The first term in the sum corresponds to $x = 0$. Since x itself multiplies each term, the first term is zero and the sum can begin with $x = 1$:

$$\begin{aligned}EX &= \sum_{x=1}^{n} x\,\frac{n!}{x!(n-x)!}\,p^x q^{n-x} \\ &= \sum_{x=1}^{n} \frac{n!}{(x-1)!(n-x)!}\,p^x q^{n-x} \\ &= \sum_{x=1}^{n} \frac{n(n-1)!}{(x-1)!(n-x)!}\,(p)p^{x-1}q^{n-x} \\ &= np\sum_{x=1}^{n} \frac{(n-1)!}{(x-1)!(n-x)!}\,p^{x-1}q^{n-x}.\end{aligned}$$

Now let $y = x - 1$. When $x = 1$, $y = 0$; when $x = n$, $y = n - 1$. Thus

$$EX = np\sum_{y=0}^{n-1} \frac{(n-1)!}{y!(n-1-y)!}\,p^y q^{n-1-y}.$$

The latter sum is seen to be the sum over all possible values of the probabilities of a random variable Y, such that Y is $B(n - 1, p)$. The sum is therefore unity; hence

$$EX = np. \qquad \text{Q.E.D.}$$

8.5 THEOREM. Under the given assumptions concerning the linear stochastic equation $Y = \alpha + \beta X + \epsilon$, the variance of the least-squares estimator $\hat{\beta}$ is

$$\sigma_{\hat{\beta}}^2 = \frac{\sigma^2}{N-1} E\left[\frac{1}{s_X^2}\right].$$

Proof: By definition,

$$\begin{aligned}\sigma_{\hat{\beta}}^2 &= E[(\hat{\beta} - E\hat{\beta})^2] \\ &= E[(\hat{\beta} - \beta)^2],\end{aligned}$$

since $E\hat{\beta} = \beta$.

It was shown in the text that

$$\hat{\beta} = \beta + \sum_i f_i(X)\epsilon_i,$$

where

$$f_i(X) = \frac{(X_i - \bar{X})}{(N-1)s_X^2}.$$

Therefore

$$\begin{aligned}(\hat{\beta} - \beta)^2 &= [\sum_i f_i(X)\,\epsilon_i]^2 \\ &= \sum_i [f_i(X)]^2 \epsilon_i^2 + 2\sum_{i<j} f_i(X)f_j(X)\epsilon_i\,\epsilon_j.^*\end{aligned}$$

Hence,

$$\begin{aligned}\sigma_{\hat{\beta}}^2 = E[(\hat{\beta} - \beta)^2] &= E\sum_i [f_i(X)]^2\epsilon_i^2 + 2E\sum_{i<j} f_i(X)f_j(X)\epsilon_i\epsilon_j \\ &= \sum_i E[f_i(X)]^2 E\epsilon_i^2 + 2\sum_{i<j} E[f_i(X)f_j(X)]E(\epsilon_i\epsilon_j),\end{aligned}$$

the last line following from the independence of the ϵ's and X's. Further, $E(\epsilon_i\epsilon_j) = E(\epsilon_i)E(\epsilon_j) = 0$, since the ϵ's are independent by virtue of random sampling and have zero expected value. As a result, the variance of $\hat{\beta}$ becomes simply

$$\begin{aligned}\sigma_{\hat{\beta}}^2 &= \sum_i E[f_i(X)]^2\, E\epsilon_i^2 \\ &= \sum_i E[f_i(X)]^2\, \sigma^2\end{aligned}$$

*If, for example, $N = 3$,

$$(\hat{\beta} - \beta)^2 = \{[f_1(X)]^2\epsilon_1^2 + [f_2(X)]^2\epsilon_2^2 + [f_3(X)]^2\epsilon_3^2\} + 2\{f_1(X)f_2(X)\,\epsilon_1\epsilon_2 + f_1(X)f_3(X)\,\epsilon_1\epsilon_3 + f_2(X)f_3(X)\epsilon_2\epsilon_3\}.$$

$$= \sigma^2 \sum_i E[f_i(X)]^2$$
$$= \sigma^2 E \sum_i [f_i(X)]^2$$
$$= \sigma^2 E \sum_i \left[\frac{X_i - \overline{X}}{(N-1)s_X^2} \right]^2$$
$$= \sigma^2 E \sum_i \frac{(X_i - \overline{X})^2}{(N-1)^2 s_X^2 s_X^2}$$
$$\frac{\sigma^2}{N-1} E \sum_i \frac{(Xi - \overline{X})^2}{(N-1)\, s_X^2\, s_X^2}$$
$$= \frac{\sigma^2}{N-1} E \left\{ \frac{\sum_i (X_i - \overline{X})^2}{N-1} \frac{1}{s_X^2 s_X^2} \right\}$$
$$= \frac{\sigma^2}{N-1} E\left[\frac{1}{s_X^2}\right],$$

since

$$\frac{\sum_i (X_i - \overline{X})^2}{N-1} = s_X^2. \qquad \text{Q.E.D.}$$

Table A: Binomial Distribution Table

On the following pages a binomial distribution table is given. In the table,

$$X \text{ is } B(n, p)$$

and $\quad P[X = x] = \binom{n}{x} p^x (1-p)^{n-x} = \frac{n!}{x!(n-x)!} p^x (1-p)^{n-x},$

where $P[X = x]$ represents the probability of exactly x successes in n trials.

To find $P[X = x]$ for given n and p, locate the section of the table corresponding to the given n from the first column. Next, locate the desired value of x from the second column and read the value of $P[X = x]$ from the intersection of the row adjacent to x and the column below the relevant value of p. The probabilities in this table are rounded to the third decimal place and are, therefore, only approximations to the true values.

TABLE A

Individual Terms, X is $B(n, p)$

n	x	p 0.01	0.05	0.10	0.20	0.30	0.40	0.50	0.60	0.70	0.80	0.90	0.95	0.99	x
2	0	980	902	810	640	490	360	250	160	090	040	010	002	0+	0
	1	020	095	180	320	420	480	500	480	420	320	180	095	020	1
	2	0+	002	010	040	090	160	250	360	490	640	810	902	980	2
3	0	970	857	729	512	343	216	125	064	027	008	001	0+	0+	0
	1	029	135	243	384	441	432	375	288	189	096	027	007	0+	1
	2	0+	007	027	096	189	288	375	432	441	384	243	135	029	2
	3	0+	0+	001	008	027	064	125	216	343	512	729	857	970	3
4	0	961	815	656	410	240	130	062	026	008	002	0+	0+	0+	0
	1	039	171	292	410	412	346	250	154	076	026	004	0+	0+	1
	2	001	014	049	154	265	346	375	346	265	154	049	014	001	2
	3	0+	0+	004	026	076	154	250	346	412	410	292	171	039	3
	4	0+	0+	0+	002	008	026	062	130	240	410	656	815	961	4
5	0	951	774	590	328	168	078	031	010	002	0+	0+	0+	0+	0
	1	048	204	328	410	360	259	156	077	028	006	0+	0+	0+	1
	2	001	021	073	205	309	346	312	230	132	051	008	001	0+	2
	3	0+	001	008	051	132	230	312	346	309	205	073	021	001	3
	4	0+	0+	0+	006	028	077	156	259	360	410	328	204	048	4
	5	0+	0+	0+	0+	002	010	031	078	168	328	590	774	951	5
6	0	941	735	531	262	118	047	016	004	001	0+	0+	0+	0+	0
	1	057	232	354	393	303	187	094	037	010	002	0+	0+	0+	1
	2	001	031	098	246	324	311	234	138	060	015	001	0+	0+	2
	3	0+	002	015	082	185	276	312	276	185	082	015	002	0+	3
	4	0+	0+	001	015	060	138	234	311	324	246	098	031	001	4
	5	0+	0+	0+	002	010	037	094	187	303	393	354	232	057	5
	6	0+	0+	0+	0+	001	004	016	047	118	262	531	735	941	6
7	0	932	698	478	210	082	028	008	002	0+	0+	0+	0+	0+	0
	1	066	257	372	367	247	131	055	017	004	0+	0+	0+	0+	1
	2	002	041	124	275	318	261	164	077	025	004	0+	0+	0+	2
	3	0+	004	023	115	227	290	273	194	097	029	003	0+	0+	3
	4	0+	0+	003	029	097	194	273	290	227	115	023	004	0+	4
	5	0+	0+	0+	004	025	077	164	261	318	275	124	041	002	5
	6	0+	0+	0+	0+	004	017	055	131	247	367	372	257	066	6
	7	0+	0+	0+	0+	0+	002	008	028	082	210	478	698	932	7
8	0	923	663	430	168	058	017	004	001	0+	0+	0+	0+	0+	0
	1	075	279	383	336	198	090	031	008	001	0+	0+	0+	0+	1
	2	003	051	149	294	296	209	109	041	010	001	0+	0+	0+	2
	3	0+	005	033	147	254	279	219	124	047	009	0+	0+	0+	3
	4	0+	0+	005	046	136	232	273	232	136	046	005	0+	0+	4
	5	0+	0+	0+	009	047	124	219	279	254	147	033	005	0+	5
	6	0+	0+	0+	001	010	041	109	209	296	294	149	051	003	6

TABLE A (continued)

Individual Terms, X is $B(n, p)$

n	x	0.01	0.05	0.10	0.20	0.30	0.40	0.50	0.60	0.70	0.80	0.90	0.95	0.99	x
8	7	0+	0+	0+	0+	001	008	031	090	198	336	383	279	075	7
	8	0+	0+	0+	0+	0+	001	004	017	058	168	430	663	923	8
9	0	914	630	387	134	040	010	002	0+	0+	0+	0+	0+	0+	0
	1	083	299	387	302	156	060	018	004	0+	0+	0+	0+	0+	1
	2	003	063	172	302	267	161	070	021	004	0+	0+	0+	0+	2
	3	0+	008	045	176	267	251	164	074	021	003	0+	0+	0+	3
	4	0+	001	007	066	172	251	246	167	074	017	001	0+	0+	4
	5	0+	0+	001	017	074	167	246	251	172	066	007	001	0+	5
	6	0+	0+	0+	003	021	074	164	251	267	176	045	008	0+	6
	7	0+	0+	0+	0+	004	021	070	161	267	302	172	063	003	7
	8	0+	0+	0+	0+	0+	004	018	060	156	302	387	299	083	8
	9	0+	0+	0+	0+	0+	0+	002	010	040	134	387	630	914	9
10	0	904	599	349	107	028	006	001	0+	0+	0+	0+	0+	0+	0
	1	091	315	387	268	121	040	010	002	0+	0+	0+	0+	0+	1
	2	004	075	194	302	233	121	044	011	001	0+	0+	0+	0+	2
	3	0+	010	057	201	267	215	117	042	009	001	0+	0+	0+	3
	4	0+	001	011	088	200	251	205	111	037	006	0+	0+	0+	4
	5	0+	0+	001	026	103	201	246	201	103	026	001	0+	0+	5
	6	0+	0+	0+	006	037	111	205	251	200	088	011	001	0+	6
	7	0+	0+	0+	001	009	042	117	215	267	201	057	010	0+	7
	8	0+	0+	0+	0+	001	011	044	121	233	302	194	075	004	8
	9	0+	0+	0+	0+	0+	002	010	040	121	268	387	315	091	9
	10	0+	0+	0+	0+	0+	0+	001	006	028	107	349	599	904	10
11	0	895	569	314	086	020	004	0+	0+	0+	0+	0+	0+	0+	0
	1	099	329	384	236	093	027	005	001	0+	0+	0+	0+	0+	1
	2	005	087	213	295	200	089	027	005	001	0+	0+	0+	0+	2
	3	0+	014	071	221	257	177	081	023	004	0+	0+	0+	0+	3
	4	0+	001	016	111	220	236	161	070	017	002	0+	0+	0+	4
	5	0+	0+	002	039	132	221	226	147	057	010	0+	0+	0+	5
	6	0+	0+	0+	010	057	147	226	221	132	039	002	0+	0+	6
	7	0+	0+	0+	002	017	070	161	236	220	111	016	001	0+	7
	8	0+	0+	0+	0+	004	023	081	177	257	221	071	014	0+	8
	9	0+	0+	0+	0+	001	005	027	089	200	295	213	087	005	9
	10	0+	0+	0+	0+	0+	001	005	027	093	236	384	329	099	10
	11	0+	0+	0+	0+	0+	0+	0+	004	020	086	314	569	895	11
12	0	886	540	282	069	014	002	0+	0+	0+	0+	0+	0+	0+	0
	1	107	341	377	206	071	017	003	0+	0+	0+	0+	0+	0+	1
	2	006	099	230	283	168	064	016	002	0+	0+	0+	0+	0+	2
	3	0+	017	085	236	240	142	054	012	001	0+	0+	0+	0+	3
	4	0+	002	021	133	231	213	121	042	008	001	0+	0+	0+	4

TABLE A (continued)

Individual Terms, X is $B(n, p)$

n	x	0.01	0.05	0.10	0.20	0.30	0.40	0.50	0.60	0.70	0.80	0.90	0.95	0.99	x
12	5	0+	0+	004	053	158	227	193	101	029	003	0+	0+	0+	5
	6	0+	0+	0+	016	079	177	226	177	079	016	0+	0+	0+	6
	7	0+	0+	0+	003	029	101	193	227	158	053	004	0+	0+	7
	8	0+	0+	0+	001	008	042	121	213	231	133	021	002	0+	8
	9	0+	0+	0+	0+	001	012	054	142	240	236	085	017	0+	9
	10	0+	0+	0+	0+	0+	002	016	064	168	283	230	099	006	10
	11	0+	0+	0+	0+	0+	0+	003	017	071	206	377	341	107	11
	12	0+	0+	0+	0+	0+	0+	0+	002	014	069	282	540	886	12
13	0	878	513	254	055	010	001	0+	0+	0+	0+	0+	0+	0+	0
	1	115	351	367	179	054	011	002	0+	0+	0+	0+	0+	0+	1
	2	007	111	245	268	139	045	010	001	0+	0+	0+	0+	0+	2
	3	0+	021	100	246	218	111	035	006	001	0+	0+	0+	0+	3
	4	0+	003	028	154	234	184	087	024	003	0+	0+	0+	0+	4
	5	0+	0+	006	069	180	221	157	066	014	001	0+	0+	0+	5
	6	0+	0+	001	023	103	197	209	131	044	006	0+	0+	0+	6
	7	0+	0+	0+	006	044	131	209	197	103	023	001	0+	0+	7
	8	0+	0+	0+	001	014	066	157	221	180	069	006	0+	0+	8
	9	0+	0+	0+	0+	003	024	087	184	234	154	028	003	0+	9
	10	0+	0+	0+	0+	001	006	035	111	218	246	100	021	0+	10
	11	0+	0+	0+	0+	0+	001	010	045	139	268	245	111	007	11
	12	0+	0+	0+	0+	0+	0+	002	011	054	179	367	351	115	12
	13	0+	0+	0+	0+	0+	0+	0+	001	010	055	254	513	878	13
14	0	869	488	229	044	007	001	0+	0+	0+	0+	0+	0+	0+	0
	1	123	359	356	154	041	007	001	0+	0+	0+	0+	0+	0+	1
	2	008	123	257	250	113	032	006	001	0+	0+	0+	0+	0+	2
	3	0+	026	114	250	194	085	022	003	0+	0+	0+	0+	0+	3
	4	0+	004	035	172	229	155	061	014	001	0+	0+	0+	0+	4
	5	0+	0+	008	086	196	207	122	041	007	0+	0+	0+	0+	5
	6	0+	0+	001	032	126	207	183	092	023	002	0+	0+	0+	6
	7	0+	0+	0+	009	062	157	209	157	062	009	0+	0+	0+	7
	8	0+	0+	0+	002	023	092	183	207	126	032	001	0+	0+	8
	9	0+	0+	0+	0+	007	041	122	207	196	086	008	0+	0+	9
	10	0+	0+	0+	0+	001	014	061	155	229	172	035	004	0+	10
	11	0+	0+	0+	0+	0+	003	022	085	194	250	114	026	0+	11
	12	0+	0+	0+	0+	0+	001	006	032	113	250	257	123	008	12
	13	0+	0+	0+	0+	0+	0+	001	007	041	154	356	359	123	13
	14	0+	0+	0+	0+	0+	0+	0+	001	007	044	229	488	869	14
15	0	860	463	206	035	005	0+	0+	0+	0+	0+	0+	0+	0+	0
	1	130	366	343	132	031	005	0+	0+	0+	0+	0+	0+	0+	1
	2	009	135	267	231	092	022	003	0+	0+	0+	0+	0+	0+	2
	3	0+	031	129	250	170	063	014	002	0+	0+	0+	0+	0+	3
	4	0+	005	043	188	219	127	042	007	001	0+	0+	0+	0+	4

TABLE A (continued)

Individual Terms, *X is B (n, p)*

n	x	0.01	0.05	0.10	0.20	0.30	0.40	0.50	0.60	0.70	0.80	0.90	0.95	0.99	x
15	5	0+	001	010	103	206	186	092	024	003	0+	0+	0+	0+	5
	6	0+	0+	002	043	147	207	153	061	012	001	0+	0+	0+	6
	7	0+	0+	0+	014	081	177	196	118	035	003	0+	0+	0+	7
	8	0+	0+	0+	003	035	118	196	177	081	014	0+	0+	0+	8
	9	0+	0+	0+	001	012	061	153	207	147	043	002	0+	0+	9
	10	0+	0+	0+	0+	003	024	092	186	206	103	010	001	0+	10
	11	0+	0+	0+	0+	001	007	042	127	219	188	043	005	0+	11
	12	0+	0+	0+	0+	0+	002	014	063	170	250	129	031	0+	12
	13	0+	0+	0+	0+	0+	0+	003	022	092	231	267	135	009	13
	14	0+	0+	0+	0+	0+	0+	0+	005	031	132	343	366	130	14
	15	0+	0+	0+	0+	0+	0+	0+	0+	005	035	206	463	860	15
16	0	851	440	185	028	003	0+	0+	0+	0+	0+	0+	0+	0+	0
	1	138	371	329	113	023	003	0+	0+	0+	0+	0+	0+	0+	1
	2	010	146	275	211	073	015	002	0+	0+	0+	0+	0+	0+	2
	3	0+	036	142	246	146	047	009	001	0+	0+	0+	0+	0+	3
	4	0+	006	051	200	204	101	028	004	0+	0+	0+	0+	0+	4
	5	0+	001	014	120	210	162	067	014	001	0+	0+	0+	0+	5
	6	0+	0+	003	055	165	198	122	039	006	0+	0+	0+	0+	6
	7	0+	0+	0+	020	101	189	175	084	019	001	0+	0+	0+	7
	8	0+	0+	0+	006	049	142	196	142	049	006	0+	0+	0+	8
	9	0+	0+	0+	001	019	084	175	189	101	020	0+	0+	0+	9
	10	0+	0+	0+	0+	006	039	122	198	165	055	003	0+	0+	10
	11	0+	0+	0+	0+	001	014	067	162	210	120	014	001	0+	11
	12	0+	0+	0+	0+	0+	004	028	101	204	200	051	006	0+	12
	13	0+	0+	0+	0+	0+	001	009	047	146	246	142	036	0+	13
	14	0+	0+	0+	0+	0+	0+	002	015	073	211	275	146	010	14
	15	0+	0+	0+	0+	0+	0+	0+	003	023	113	329	371	138	15
	16	0+	0+	0+	0+	0+	0+	0+	0+	003	028	185	440	851	16
17	0	843	418	167	023	002	0+	0+	0+	0+	0+	0+	0+	0+	0
	1	145	374	315	096	017	002	0+	0+	0+	0+	0+	0+	0+	1
	2	012	158	280	191	058	010	001	0+	0+	0+	0+	0+	0+	2
	3	001	041	156	239	125	034	005	0+	0+	0+	0+	0+	0+	3
	4	0+	008	060	209	187	080	018	002	0+	0+	0+	0+	0+	4
	5	0+	001	017	136	208	138	047	008	001	0+	0+	0+	0+	5
	6	0+	0+	004	068	178	184	094	024	003	0+	0+	0+	0+	6
	7	0+	0+	001	027	120	193	148	057	009	0+	0+	0+	0+	7
	8	0+	0+	0+	008	064	161	185	107	028	002	0+	0+	0+	8
	9	0+	0+	0+	002	028	107	185	161	064	008	0+	0+	0+	9
	10	0+	0+	0+	0+	009	057	148	193	120	027	001	0+	0+	10
	11	0+	0+	0+	0+	003	024	094	184	178	068	004	0+	0+	11
	12	0+	0+	0+	0+	001	008	047	138	208	136	017	001	0+	12

TABLE A (continued)

Individual Terms, *X is B (n, p)*

n	x	0.01	0.05	0.10	0.20	0.30	0.40	0.50	0.60	0.70	0.80	0.90	0.95	0.99	x
17	13	0+	0+	0+	0+	0+	002	018	080	187	209	060	008	0+	13
	14	0+	0+	0+	0+	0+	0+	005	034	125	239	156	041	001	14
	15	0+	0+	0+	0+	0+	0+	001	010	058	191	280	158	012	15
	16	0+	0+	0+	0+	0+	0+	0+	002	017	096	315	374	145	16
	17	0+	0+	0+	0+	0+	0+	0+	0+	002	023	167	418	843	17
18	0	835	397	150	018	002	0+	0+	0+	0+	0+	0+	0+	0+	0
	1	152	376	300	081	013	001	0+	0+	0+	0+	0+	0+	0+	1
	2	013	168	284	172	046	007	001	0+	0+	0+	0+	0+	0+	2
	3	001	047	168	230	105	025	003	0+	0+	0+	0+	0+	0+	3
	4	0+	009	070	215	168	061	012	001	0+	0+	0+	0+	0+	4
	5	0+	001	022	151	202	115	033	004	0+	0+	0+	0+	0+	5
	6	0+	0+	005	082	187	166	071	015	001	0+	0+	0+	0+	6
	7	0+	0+	001	035	138	189	121	037	005	0+	0+	0+	0+	7
	8	0+	0+	0+	012	081	173	167	077	015	001	0+	0+	0+	8
	9	0+	0+	0+	003	039	128	185	128	039	003	0+	0+	0+	9
	10	0+	0+	0+	001	015	077	167	173	081	012	0+	0+	0+	10
	11	0+	0+	0+	0+	005	037	121	189	138	035	001	0+	0+	11
	12	0+	0+	0+	0+	001	015	071	166	187	082	005	0+	0+	12
	13	0+	0+	0+	0+	0+	004	033	115	202	151	022	001	0+	13
	14	0+	0+	0+	0+	0+	001	012	061	168	215	070	009	0+	14
	15	0+	0+	0+	0+	0+	0+	003	025	105	230	168	047	001	15
	16	0+	0+	0+	0+	0+	0+	001	007	046	172	284	168	013	16
	17	0+	0+	0+	0+	0+	0+	0+	001	013	081	300	376	152	17
	18	0+	0+	0+	0+	0+	0+	0+	0+	002	018	150	397	835	18
19	0	826	377	135	014	001	0+	0+	0+	0+	0+	0+	0+	0+	0
	1	159	377	285	068	009	001	0+	0+	0+	0+	0+	0+	0+	1
	2	014	179	285	154	036	005	0+	0+	0+	0+	0+	0+	0+	2
	3	001	053	180	218	087	017	002	0+	0+	0+	0+	0+	0+	3
	4	0+	011	080	218	149	047	007	001	0+	0+	0+	0+	0+	4
	5	0+	002	027	164	192	093	022	002	0+	0+	0+	0+	0+	5
	6	0+	0+	007	095	192	145	052	008	001	0+	0+	0+	0+	6
	7	0+	0+	001	044	153	180	096	024	002	0+	0+	0+	0+	7
	8	0+	0+	0+	017	098	180	144	053	008	0+	0+	0+	0+	8
	9	0+	0+	0+	005	051	146	176	098	022	001	0+	0+	0+	9
	10	0+	0+	0+	001	022	098	176	146	051	005	0+	0+	0+	10
	11	0+	0+	0+	0+	008	053	144	180	098	017	0+	0+	0+	11
	12	0+	0+	0+	0+	002	024	096	180	153	044	001	0+	0+	12
	13	0+	0+	0+	0+	001	008	052	145	192	095	007	0+	0+	13
	14	0+	0+	0+	0+	0+	002	022	093	192	164	027	002	0+	14
	15	0+	0+	0+	0+	0+	001	007	047	149	218	080	011	0+	15
	16	0+	0+	0+	0+	0+	0+	002	017	087	218	180	053	001	16

TABLE A (continued)

Individual Terms, *X is B (n, p)*

n	x	0.01	0.05	0.10	0.20	0.30	0.40	0.50	0.60	0.70	0.80	0.90	0.95	0.99	x
19	17	0+	0+	0+	0+	0+	0+	0+	005	036	154	285	179	014	17
	18	0+	0+	0+	0+	0+	0+	0+	001	009	068	285	377	159	18
	19	0+	0+	0+	0+	0+	0+	0+	0+	001	014	135	377	826	19
20	0	818	358	122	012	001	0+	0+	0+	0+	0+	0+	0+	0+	0
	1	165	377	270	058	007	0+	0+	0+	0+	0+	0+	0+	0+	1
	2	016	189	285	137	028	003	0+	0+	0+	0+	0+	0+	0+	2
	3	001	060	190	205	072	012	001	0+	0+	0+	0+	0+	0+	3
	4	0+	013	090	218	130	035	005	0+	0+	0+	0+	0+	0+	4
	5	0+	002	032	175	179	075	015	001	0+	0+	0+	0+	0+	5
	6	0+	0+	009	109	192	124	037	005	0+	0+	0+	0+	0+	6
	7	0+	0+	002	055	164	166	074	015	001	0+	0+	0+	0+	7
	8	0+	0+	0+	022	114	180	120	035	004	0+	0+	0+	0+	8
	9	0+	0+	0+	007	065	160	160	071	012	0+	0+	0+	0+	9
	10	0+	0+	0+	002	031	117	176	117	031	002	0+	0+	0+	10
	11	0+	0+	0+	0+	012	071	160	160	065	007	0+	0+	0+	11
	12	0+	0+	0+	0+	004	035	120	180	114	022	0+	0+	0+	12
	13	0+	0+	0+	0+	001	015	074	166	164	055	002	0+	0+	13
	14	0+	0+	0+	0+	0+	005	037	124	192	109	009	0+	0+	14
	15	0+	0+	0+	0+	0+	001	015	075	179	175	032	002	0+	15
	16	0+	0+	0+	0+	0+	0+	005	035	130	218	090	013	0+	16
	17	0+	0+	0+	0+	0+	0+	001	012	072	205	190	060	001	17
	18	0+	0+	0+	0+	0+	0+	0+	003	028	137	285	189	016	18
	19	0+	0+	0+	0+	0+	0+	0+	0+	007	058	270	377	165	19
	20	0+	0+	0+	0+	0+	0+	0+	0+	001	012	122	358	818	20
21	0	810	341	109	009	001	0+	0+	0+	0+	0+	0+	0+	0+	0
	1	172	376	255	048	005	0+	0+	0+	0+	0+	0+	0+	0+	1
	2	017	198	284	121	022	002	0+	0+	0+	0+	0+	0+	0+	2
	3	001	066	200	192	058	009	001	0+	0+	0+	0+	0+	0+	3
	4	0+	016	100	216	113	026	003	0+	0+	0+	0+	0+	0+	4
	5	0+	003	038	183	164	059	010	001	0+	0+	0+	0+	0+	5
	6	0+	0+	011	122	188	105	026	003	0+	0+	0+	0+	0+	6
	7	0+	0+	003	065	172	149	055	009	0+	0+	0+	0+	0+	7
	8	0+	0+	001	029	129	174	097	023	002	0+	0+	0+	0+	8
	9	0+	0+	0+	010	080	168	140	050	006	0+	0+	0+	0+	9
	10	0+	0+	0+	003	041	134	168	089	018	001	0+	0+	0+	10
	11	0+	0+	0+	001	018	089	168	134	041	003	0+	0+	0+	11
	12	0+	0+	0+	0+	006	050	140	168	080	010	0+	0+	0+	12
	13	0+	0+	0+	0+	002	023	097	174	129	029	001	0+	0+	13
	14	0+	0+	0+	0+	0+	009	055	149	172	065	003	0+	0+	14
	15	0+	0+	0+	0+	0+	003	026	105	188	122	011	0+	0+	15
	16	0+	0+	0+	0+	0+	001	010	059	164	183	038	003	0+	16

TABLE A (continued)

Individual Terms, *X is B (n, p)*

n	x	0.01	0.05	0.10	0.20	0.30	0.40	0.50	0.60	0.70	0.80	0.90	0.95	0.99	x
21	17	0+	0+	0+	0+	0+	0+	003	026	113	216	100	016	0+	17
	18	0+	0+	0+	0+	0+	0+	001	009	058	192	200	066	001	18
	19	0+	0+	0+	0+	0+	0+	0+	002	022	121	284	198	017	19
	20	0+	0+	0+	0+	0+	0+	0+	0+	005	048	255	376	172	20
	21	0+	0+	0+	0+	0+	0+	0+	0+	001	009	109	341	810	21
22	0	802	324	098	007	0+	0+	0+	0+	0+	0+	0+	0+	0+	0
	1	178	375	241	041	004	0+	0+	0+	0+	0+	0+	0+	0+	1
	2	019	207	281	107	017	001	0+	0+	0+	0+	0+	0+	0+	2
	3	001	073	208	178	047	006	0+	0+	0+	0+	0+	0+	0+	3
	4	0+	018	110	211	096	019	002	0+	0+	0+	0+	0+	0+	4
	5	0+	003	044	190	149	046	006	0+	0+	0+	0+	0+	0+	5
	6	0+	001	014	134	181	086	018	001	0+	0+	0+	0+	0+	6
	7	0+	0+	004	077	177	131	041	005	0+	0+	0+	0+	0+	7
	8	0+	0+	001	036	142	164	076	014	001	0+	0+	0+	0+	8
	9	0+	0+	0+	014	095	170	119	034	003	0+	0+	0+	0+	9
	10	0+	0+	0+	005	053	148	154	066	010	0+	0+	0+	0+	10
	11	0+	0+	0+	001	025	107	168	107	025	001	0+	0+	0+	11
	12	0+	0+	0+	0+	010	066	154	148	053	005	0+	0+	0+	12
	13	0+	0+	0+	0+	003	034	119	170	095	014	0+	0+	0+	13
	14	0+	0+	0+	0+	001	014	076	164	142	036	001	0+	0+	14
	15	0+	0+	0+	0+	0+	005	041	131	177	077	004	0+	0+	15
	16	0+	0+	0+	0+	0+	001	018	086	181	134	014	001	0+	16
	17	0+	0+	0+	0+	0+	0+	006	046	149	190	044	003	0+	17
	18	0+	0+	0+	0+	0+	0+	002	019	096	211	110	018	0+	18
	19	0+	0+	0+	0+	0+	0+	0+	006	047	178	208	073	001	19
	20	0+	0+	0+	0+	0+	0+	0+	001	017	107	281	207	019	20
	21	0+	0+	0+	0+	0+	0+	0+	0+	004	041	241	375	178	21
	22	0+	0+	0+	0+	0+	0+	0+	0+	0+	007	098	324	802	22
23	0	794	307	089	006	0+	0+	0+	0+	0+	0+	0+	0+	0+	0
	1	184	372	226	034	003	0+	0+	0+	0+	0+	0+	0+	0+	1
	2	020	215	277	093	013	001	0+	0+	0+	0+	0+	0+	0+	2
	3	001	079	215	163	038	004	0+	0+	0+	0+	0+	0+	0+	3
	4	0+	021	120	204	082	014	001	0+	0+	0+	0+	0+	0+	4
	5	0+	004	051	194	133	035	004	0+	0+	0+	0+	0+	0+	5
	6	0+	001	017	145	171	070	012	001	0+	0+	0+	0+	0+	6
	7	0+	0+	005	088	178	113	029	003	0+	0+	0+	0+	0+	7
	8	0+	0+	001	044	153	151	058	009	0+	0+	0+	0+	0+	8
	9	0+	0+	0+	018	109	168	097	022	002	0+	0+	0+	0+	9
	10	0+	0+	0+	006	065	157	136	046	005	0+	0+	0+	0+	10
	11	0+	0+	0+	002	033	123	161	082	014	0+	0+	0+	0+	11
	12	0+	0+	0+	0+	014	082	161	123	033	002	0+	0+	0+	12

TABLE A (continued)

Individual Terms, *X is B (n, p)*

n	x	0.01	0.05	0.10	0.20	0.30	0.40	0.50	0.60	0.70	0.80	0.90	0.95	0.99	x
23	13	0+	0+	0+	0+	005	046	136	157	065	006	0+	0+	0+	13
	14	0+	0+	0+	0+	002	022	097	168	109	018	0+	0+	0+	14
	15	0+	0+	0+	0+	0+	009	058	151	153	044	001	0+	0+	15
	16	0+	0+	0+	0+	0+	003	029	113	178	088	005	0+	0+	16
	17	0+	0+	0+	0+	0+	001	012	070	171	145	017	001	0+	17
	18	0+	0+	0+	0+	0+	0+	004	035	133	194	051	004	0+	18
	19	0+	0+	0+	0+	0+	0+	001	014	082	204	120	021	0+	19
	20	0+	0+	0+	0+	0+	0+	0+	004	038	163	215	079	001	20
	21	0+	0+	0+	0+	0+	0+	0+	001	013	093	277	215	020	21
	22	0+	0+	0+	0+	0+	0+	0+	0+	003	034	226	372	184	22
	23	0+	0+	0+	0+	0+	0+	0+	0+	0+	006	089	307	794	23
24	0	786	292	080	005	0+	0+	0+	0+	0+	0+	0+	0+	0+	0
	1	190	369	213	028	002	0+	0+	0+	0+	0+	0+	0+	0+	1
	2	022	223	272	081	010	001	0+	0+	0+	0+	0+	0+	0+	2
	3	002	086	221	149	031	003	0+	0+	0+	0+	0+	0+	0+	3
	4	0+	024	129	196	069	010	001	0+	0+	0+	0+	0+	0+	4
	5	0+	005	057	196	118	027	003	0+	0+	0+	0+	0+	0+	5
	6	0+	001	020	155	160	056	008	0+	0+	0+	0+	0+	0+	6
	7	0+	0+	006	100	176	096	021	002	0+	0+	0+	0+	0+	7
	8	0+	0+	001	053	160	136	044	005	0+	0+	0+	0+	0+	8
	9	0+	0+	0+	024	122	161	078	014	001	0+	0+	0+	0+	9
	10	0+	0+	0+	009	079	161	117	032	003	0+	0+	0+	0+	10
	11	0+	0+	0+	003	043	137	149	061	008	0+	0+	0+	0+	11
	12	0+	0+	0+	001	020	099	161	099	020	001	0+	0+	0+	12
	13	0+	0+	0+	0+	008	061	149	137	043	003	0+	0+	0+	13
	14	0+	0+	0+	0+	003	032	117	161	079	009	0+	0+	0+	14
	15	0+	0+	0+	0+	001	014	078	161	122	024	0+	0+	0+	15
	16	0+	0+	0+	0+	0+	005	044	136	160	053	001	0+	0+	16
	17	0+	0+	0+	0+	0+	002	021	096	176	100	006	0+	0+	17
	18	0+	0+	0+	0+	0+	0+	008	056	160	155	020	001	0+	18
	19	0+	0+	0+	0+	0+	0+	003	027	118	196	057	005	0+	19
	20	0+	0+	0+	0+	0+	0+	001	010	069	196	129	024	0+	20
	21	0+	0+	0+	0+	0+	0+	0+	003	031	149	221	086	002	21
	22	0+	0+	0+	0+	0+	0+	0+	001	010	081	272	223	022	22
	23	0+	0+	0+	0+	0+	0+	0+	0+	002	028	213	369	190	23
	24	0+	0+	0+	0+	0+	0+	0+	0+	0+	005	080	292	786	24
25	0	778	277	072	004	0+	0+	0+	0+	0+	0+	0+	0+	0+	0
	1	196	365	199	024	001	0+	0+	0+	0+	0+	0+	0+	0+	1
	2	024	231	266	071	007	0+	0+	0+	0+	0+	0+	0+	0+	2
	3	002	093	226	136	024	002	0+	0+	0+	0+	0+	0+	0+	3
	4	0+	027	138	187	057	007	0+	0+	0+	0+	0+	0+	0+	4
	5	0+	006	065	196	103	020	002	0+	0+	0+	0+	0+	0+	5
	6	0+	001	024	163	147	044	005	0+	0+	0+	0+	0+	0+	6

TABLE A (continued)

Individual Terms, X *is* $B(n, p)$

n	x	0.01	0.05	0.10	0.20	0.30	0.40	0.50	0.60	0.70	0.80	0.90	0.95	0.99	x
25	7	0+	0+	007	111	171	080	014	001	0+	0+	0+	0+	0+	7
	8	0+	0+	002	062	165	120	032	003	0+	0+	0+	0+	0+	8
	9	0+	0+	0+	029	134	151	061	009	0+	0+	0+	0+	0+	9
	10	0+	0+	0+	012	092	161	097	021	001	0+	0+	0+	0+	10
	11	0+	0+	0+	004	054	147	133	043	004	0+	0+	0+	0+	11
	12	0+	0+	0+	001	027	114	155	076	011	0+	0+	0+	0+	12
	13	0+	0+	0+	0+	011	076	155	114	027	001	0+	0+	0+	13
	14	0+	0+	0+	0+	004	043	133	147	054	004	0+	0+	0+	14
	15	0+	0+	0+	0+	001	021	097	161	092	012	0+	0+	0+	15
	16	0+	0+	0+	0+	0+	009	061	151	134	029	0+	0+	0+	16
	17	0+	0+	0+	0+	0+	003	032	120	165	062	002	0+	0+	17
	18	0+	0+	0+	0+	0+	001	014	080	171	111	007	0+	0+	18
	19	0+	0+	0+	0+	0+	0+	005	044	147	163	024	001	0+	19
	20	0+	0+	0+	0+	0+	0+	002	020	103	196	065	006	0+	20
	21	0+	0+	0+	0+	0+	0+	0+	007	057	187	138	027	0+	21
	22	0+	0+	0+	0+	0+	0+	0+	002	024	136	226	093	002	22
	23	0+	0+	0+	0+	0+	0+	0+	0+	007	071	266	231	024	23
	24	0+	0+	0+	0+	0+	0+	0+	0+	001	024	199	365	196	24
	25	0+	0+	0+	0+	0+	0+	0+	0+	0+	004	072	277	778	25

TABLE B

2500 Random Digits

00	49487	52802	28667	62058	87822	14704	18519	17889	45869	14454
01	29480	91539	46317	84803	86056	62812	33584	70391	77749	64906
02	25252	97738	23901	11106	86864	55808	22557	23214	15021	54268
03	02431	42193	96960	19620	29188	05863	92900	06836	13433	21709
04	69414	89353	70724	67893	23218	72452	03095	68333	13751	37260
05	77285	35179	92042	67581	67673	68374	71115	98166	43352	06414
06	52852	11444	71868	34534	69124	02760	06406	95234	87995	78560
07	98740	98054	30195	09891	18453	79464	01156	95522	06884	55073
08	85022	58736	12138	35146	62085	36170	25433	80787	96496	40579
09	17778	03840	21636	56269	08149	19001	67367	13138	02400	89515
10	81833	93449	57781	94621	90998	37561	59688	93299	27726	82167
11	63789	54958	33167	10909	40343	81023	61590	44474	39810	10305
12	61840	81740	60986	12498	71546	42249	13812	59902	27864	21809
13	42243	10153	20891	90883	15782	98167	86837	99166	92143	82441
14	45236	09129	53031	12260	01278	14404	40969	33419	14188	69557
15	40338	42477	78804	36272	72053	07958	67158	60979	79891	92409
16	54040	71253	88789	98203	54999	96564	00789	68879	47134	83941
17	49158	20908	44859	29089	76130	51442	34453	98590	37353	61137
18	80958	03808	83655	18415	96563	43582	82207	53322	30419	64435
19	07636	04876	61063	57571	69434	14965	20911	73162	33576	52839
20	37227	80750	08261	97048	60438	75053	05939	34414	16685	32103
21	99460	45915	45637	41353	35335	69087	57536	68418	10247	93253
22	60248	75845	37296	33783	42393	28185	31880	00241	31642	37526
23	95076	79089	87380	28982	97750	82221	35584	27444	85793	69755
24	20944	97852	26586	32796	51513	47475	48621	20067	88975	39506
25	30458	49207	62358	41532	30057	53017	10375	97204	98675	77634
26	38905	91282	79309	49022	17405	18830	09186	07629	01785	78317
27	96545	15638	90114	93730	13741	70177	49175	42113	21600	69625
28	21944	28328	00692	89164	96025	01383	50252	67044	70596	58266
29	36910	71928	63327	00980	32154	46006	62289	28079	03076	15619
30	48745	47626	28856	28382	60639	51370	70091	58261	70135	88259
31	32519	91993	59374	83994	59873	51217	62806	20028	26545	16820
32	75757	12965	29285	11481	31744	41754	24428	81819	02354	37895
33	07911	97756	89561	27464	25133	50026	16436	75846	83718	08533
34	89887	03328	76911	93168	56236	39056	67905	94933	05456	52347
35	30543	99488	75363	94187	32885	23887	10872	22793	26232	87356
36	68442	55201	33946	42495	28384	89889	50278	91985	58185	19124
37	22403	56698	88524	13692	55012	25343	76391	48029	72278	58586
38	70701	36907	51242	52083	43126	90379	60380	98513	85596	16528
39	69804	96122	42342	28467	79037	13218	63510	09071	52438	25840

TABLE B ***(continued)***

2500 Random Digits

40	65806	22398	19470	63653	27055	02606	43347	65384	02613	81668
41	43902	53070	54319	19347	59506	75440	90826	53652	92382	67623
42	49145	71587	14273	62440	15770	03281	58124	09533	43722	03856
43	47363	36295	62126	42358	20322	82000	52830	93540	13284	96496
44	26244	87033	90247	79131	38773	67687	45541	54976	17508	18367
45	72875	39496	06385	48458	30545	74383	22814	36752	10707	48774
46	09065	16283	61398	08288	00708	21816	39615	03102	02834	04116
47	68256	51225	92645	77747	33104	81206	00112	53445	04212	58476
48	38744	81018	41909	70458	72459	66136	97266	26490	10877	45022
49	44375	19619	35750	59924	82429	90288	61064	26489	87001	84273

INDEX